TECHNICAL REPORTS SERIES No. 442

REMEDIATION OF SITES WITH MIXED CONTAMINATION OF RADIOACTIVE AND OTHER HAZARDOUS SUBSTANCES

INTERNATIONAL ATOMIC ENERGY AGENCY
VIENNA, 2006

COPYRIGHT NOTICE

IAEA Library Cataloguing in Publication Data

Remediation of sites with mixed contamination of radioactive and other
    hazardous substances. — Vienna: International Atomic Energy
    Agency, 2006.
        p. ; 24 cm. – (Technical reports series, ISSN 0074–1914 ; 442)
    STI/DOC/010/442
    ISBN 92–0–104705–3
    Includes bibliographical references.

    1. Hazardous waste site remediation. — I. International Atomic
Energy Agency. II. Technical reports series (International Atomic
Energy Agency) ; 442.

IAEAL   05–00422

FOREWORD

The IAEA attaches great importance to the dissemination of information that can assist Member States with the development, implementation, maintenance and improvement of systems, programmes and activities that support the nuclear fuel cycle and nuclear applications, including the legacy of past practices and accidents. Consequently, the IAEA has initiated a comprehensive programme of work covering all aspects of environmental remediation:

— Technical and non-technical factors influencing decisions on environmental remediation;
— Site characterization techniques and strategies;
— The assessment of remediation technologies;
— The assessment of technical options for cleanup of contaminated media;
— Post-restoration compliance monitoring;
— The assessment of the costs of remediation measures;
— 'Mixed' contamination, i.e. the co-occurrence of radionuclides and heavy metals or (toxic) organic compounds, which poses a particular challenge to those charged with its remediation.

Mixed contamination poses a particular challenge because of the combination of different types of hazards and potential exposures. These challenges concern inter alia worker health and safety, environmental impacts, selection of remediation technologies and waste management options. While radionuclides and toxic (heavy) metals pose similar and mostly compatible challenges, organic contaminants often require different approaches that may not be compatible with the former. Additional complexity is introduced by different and sometimes conflicting regulatory frameworks for radiological and non-radiological contamination, including the prescribed waste management routes.

In consideration of the added complexities of remediating mixed contamination, the IAEA determined that this subject warranted the development of a specialized report for assisting Member States.

This report outlines applicable remediation technologies and strategies, with their advantages and limitations being discussed. The need for a holistic design of the remedial action is stressed. An extensive body of references, including relevant web sites, will help the reader to find more detailed or more up to date information.

The technical officer responsible for this publication was W.E. Falck of the Division of Nuclear Fuel Cycle and Waste Technology.

CONTENTS

1. INTRODUCTION

1.1. BACKGROUND

Responding to the needs of its Member States, the International Atomic Energy Agency (IAEA) has initiated an environmental remediation project to address radioactive contamination found in soil and waters (i.e. groundwater and surface water). The term 'remediation' is defined in this report as those measures taken for contaminant removal, containment or monitored non-intervention at a contaminated site to reduce exposure to radiation, and to the improvement in the environmental and/or economic value of the contaminated site. Remediation of a site does not necessarily imply a restoration of the site to pristine condition.

As part of the remediation project, the IAEA has been charged by its Member States to develop publications that address various aspects of radioactive contamination (Table 1). A particularly challenging aspect of remediation of radioactive contamination within soil, groundwater and other media is that radioactive contamination is often found accompanied by non-radiological contaminants such as heavy metals, organic material, explosives and asbestos. The presence of these co-contaminants provides several remediation challenges beyond dealing solely with radioactive contamination, including:

— Additional public health and ecological concerns;
— Varying impacts on the nature and mobility of the contaminants (e.g. enhancement of radionuclide mobility in some cases);
— More complex characterization approaches (e.g. sampling and analysis methods);
— More complex worker health and safety issues;
— The choice of the correct remediation processes and technologies;
— More complex waste management and disposal processes;
— Complex regulatory issues related to ores.

Owing to the added complexities of remediating 'mixed' contamination, the IAEA has determined that this subject sufficiently warrants the development of a special report on the subject for assisting Member States.

TABLE 1. RELATIONSHIP BETWEEN RELEVANT TOPICAL PUBLICATIONS PRODUCED OR UNDER DEVELOPMENT

Safety	Management	Databases	Technology	Special topics
Management of Radioactive Waste from the Mining and Milling of Ores [1]	Factors for Formulating Strategies for Environmental Restoration [2]	A Directory of Information Resources on Radioactive Waste Management, Decontamination and Decommissioning, and Environmental Restoration [3]	Technologies for Remediation of Radioactively Contaminated Sites [4]	Environmental Contamination by Naturally Occurring Radioactive Material (NORM) and Technologies for Mitigation [5]
Monitoring and Surveillance of Residues from the Mining and Milling of Uranium and Thorium [6]	Characterization of Radioactively Contaminated Sites for Remediation Purposes [7]	Design Criteria for a Worldwide Directory of Radioactively Contaminated Sites (DRCS) [8]	Technical Options for the Remediation of Contaminated Groundwater [9]	The Long Term Stabilization of Uranium Mill Tailings [10]
Remediation of Areas Contaminated by Past Activities and Accidents [11]	Compliance Monitoring for Remediated Sites [12]	Directory of Radioactively Contaminated Sites (DRCS) [13]	Site Characterization Techniques Used in Environmental Restoration Activities [14]	

TABLE 1. RELATIONSHIP BETWEEN RELEVANT TOPICAL PUBLICATIONS PRODUCED OR UNDER DEVELOPMENT (cont.)

Safety	Management	Databases	Technology	Special topics
Removal of Sites and Buildings from Regulatory Control Upon the Termination of Practices [15]	Non-technical Factors Impacting on the Decision Making Processes in Environmental Remediation [16]		Remediation of Sites with Dispersed Radioactive Contamination [17]	
	Applicability and Limitations of Monitored Natural Attenuation at Radioactively Contaminated Sites [18]		This report	

1.2. SCOPE

This report addresses the remediation of co-mingled radioactive and other hazardous contaminants found within various media, including surface water, groundwater and soil (including geological media). In part, the report is designed to provide Member States with an overview of some of the added challenges that are encountered in the remediation of such sites, beyond working at sites solely contaminated with radionuclides. In addition, the report provides an overview of the technologies that can be applied to remediate such sites.

The IAEA has already prepared several reports related to the remediation of radiological contamination, each dedicated to a particular technical or conceptual area (Table 1). These subjects include: characterization of contaminated sites [7, 14], technical and non-technical factors relevant for the selection of the preferred remediation strategy and technology [2, 16], an overview of applicable technologies for environmental remediation [4], options for cleanup of contaminated groundwater [9], and planning and management issues [19, 20]. In addition, a number of other IAEA publications dealing with related aspects have been compiled under different IAEA projects. These include reports on the remediation of uranium mill tailings [10], remediation of dispersed contamination [17], decontamination of buildings and roads, and the characterization of decommissioned sites.

This report is intended for individuals interested in the design, selection, review or approval of projects to remediate sites containing mixed contamination. The report provides a basic overview of the current state of knowledge for decision makers in governments and at community level, and for consultants.

1.3. STRUCTURE

This report will highlight the main issues and problems in instances of mixed contamination, followed by a discussion of the general remediation approach and descriptions of the technologies used to remediate such sites. The report is divided into sections as follows.

Section 1 provides an introduction to the subject. Section 2 discusses the types of sites and hazards at which mixed contamination might occur and the respective contaminant behaviour in the environment. The regulatory implications, in particular competing regulatory regimes and waste acceptance problems are outlined in Section 3. The remediation of sites with mixed contamination requires special consideration for worker health and safety,

4

which are discussed in Section 4. As is elucidated in Section 5, mixed contamination also has special implications for sampling and monitoring techniques and programmes. Generic planning procedures and the influencing factors are outlined in Section 6, while Section 7 is concerned with the criteria for evaluation and selection of remediation technology. Detailed discussions on the concepts and applicability of most applicable technologies are the subject of Sections 8–11. The report is completed in Section 12 with a summary and conclusions, followed by a glossary of terms and abbreviations. Annexes provide a selection of illustrative examples of instances of mixed contamination and related remediation activities.

2. TYPES OF SITES, HAZARDS AND CONTAMINANT BEHAVIOUR

2.1. TYPES OF SITES WITH MIXED CONTAMINATION

Mixed contamination sites generally result from waste disposal practices, unintentional releases from waste or material storage facilities, accidental spills during transportation or operations at facilities that manage hazardous and radioactive materials, and mining. They can also derive from smelting operations and incineration of radioactive and hazardous wastes when air emissions are deposited on land. Releases of hazardous and radioactive contamination to the environment can have an impact on surface soil and the vadose zone, groundwater, surface water and sediments.

Historically, the following practices have created sites that now require remediation:

— Disposal of radioactive and hazardous wastes in landfills, abandoned quarries or other depressions where leaching of waste materials has contaminated the vadose zone and the groundwater;
— Discharges of wastewater containing radioactive and hazardous contaminants onto land (e.g. surface impoundments, drainage cribs or lagoons) that have contaminated the soil and the groundwater;
— Discharges of wastewater into water bodies, such as rivers, lakes, estuaries or the ocean, that have contaminated the surface water and sediments;
— Discharges of wastewater by direct injection into an aquifer or permeable layer in the vadose zone that has contaminated the groundwater;

— Leakage from storage tanks and associated piping containing radioactive and hazardous liquids that has contaminated the surface soil, vadose zone and/or groundwater;
— Accidental spills of hazardous and radioactive materials that have contaminated the surface soil, sediments and/or surface water;
— Smelting and waste incineration that have contaminated the soil from air deposition of contaminants;.
— Mining and the residues resulting that have contaminated the surface water, groundwater and soil.

Table 2 lists a number of types of industrial and military activities under which the above practices may have occurred, together with relevant contaminants and some example sites.

2.2. TYPES OF HAZARDS AT SITES WITH MIXED CONTAMINATION

2.2.1. Overview

The diversity of contaminants results in a greater complexity of process and hazards unknown in instances of purely radioactive contamination, such as toxic and corrosive gases or biohazards. The mixture of contaminants may also result in new or accelerated pathways for migration, for example multiphase flow. There are a number of reasons why sites may first be identified as of potential concern:

— Known contamination problems, for example, radiation or chemical contamination detected outside controlled process area boundaries, high radiation levels, contamination of surface or groundwater sources or areas of atmospheric deposition;
— Experience from sites where similar processes and materials were used or with similar histories or geologies, etc.;
— General review and screening of potential future liabilities, etc.

Contaminants at sites with mixed contamination include radioactive material and toxic substances, heavy metals and certain organic compounds. Other contaminants and hazards that could be present at mixed contaminant sites include nitrates, biohazardous agents, asbestos and materials that pose a physical hazard – i.e. substances that are flammable, corrosive, reactive or explosive. Typically, the actual quantity of radioactive material at sites with

TABLE 2. SOURCES OF MIXED CONTAMINATION

Type of activity		Candidate contaminants	Example sites
Weapons production	Reactor operations	^{3}H, ^{60}Co, ^{90}Sr, Cr^{6+}, SO$_4^{2-}$	*Russian Federation*: Mayak Nuclear Complex, Tomsk-7 Site at Severk, Krasnoyarsk-26 Mining and Chemical Combine *United Sates of America (USA)*: Hanford Site, Rocky Flats Plant, Savannah River Site
	Irradiated fuel processing	^{3}H, ^{90}Sr, ^{99}Tc, ^{129}I, ^{137}Cs, Pu, U, CN$^-$, Cl, F$^-$, NO$_3^-$	*Russian Federation*: Mayak Nuclear Complex, Tomsk-7 Site at Severk, Krasnoyarsk-26 Mining and Chemical Combine *USA*: Hanford Site, Rocky Flats Plant
	Plutonium purification	Pu, ^{241}Am, carbon tetrachloride, chloroform, NO$_3^-$	*Russian Federation*: Mayak Nuclear Complex, Tomsk-7 Site at Severk, Krasnoyarsk-26 Mining and Chemical Combine *USA*: Hanford Site, Rocky Flats Plant, Savannah River Site
	Fuel fabrication	^{99}Tc, U, Cr^{6+}, Cu, Be, TCE[a]	*Russian Federation*: Mayak Nuclear Complex, Tomsk-7 Site at Severk, Krasnoyarsk-26 Mining and Chemical Combine *USA*: Hanford Site, Rocky Flats Plant
	Fuel enrichment	F, U	*USA*: Paducah Site, K-25 Plant at Oak Ridge Reservation, Gaseous Diffusion Plant at Portsmouth, Ohio

For footnotes see p. 11.

TABLE 2. SOURCES OF MIXED CONTAMINATION (cont.)

Type of activity		Candidate contaminants	Example sites
Weapons production (cont.)	Waste storage: landfills, tanks	(a) *Landfills*: organic solvents, high levels of radioactive liquids, including transuranic elements, oils, cellulosics and contaminated clothing. Mixed with asbestos (b) *Tanks*: sodium nitrate solutions, PCBs[b]	*Russian Federation*: Mayak Nuclear Complex, Tomsk-7 Site at Severk, Krasnoyarsk-26 Mining and Chemical Combine *USA*: Hanford Site, Rocky Flats Plant, Savannah River Site, Idaho National Engineering and Environmental Laboratory
Weapons assembly		High explosives, barium, VOCs[c], radionuclides, other metals	*USA*: Pantex plant
	Machining	U and Pu mixed with machine oils, mercury	*USA*: Rocky Flats Plant, Y-12 Plant at Oak Ridge Reservation
	Warhead development, temperature testing	α emitting material with chlorinated solvents (used as a heat transfer medium)	*USA*: Los Alamos National Laboratory, Sandia National Laboratory
	Depleted uranium penetrators and armour	Uranium with machining oil, degreasing solvents	*USA*: Fernald Environmental Management Project
Weapons testing	Safety testing of weapons	Partially exploded weapon fragments, Be, Pb, Ba, explosive residues, Pu, depleted and natural uranium	*Australia*: Maralinga site *Kazakhstan*: Semipalatinsk Test Site *USA*: Nevada Test Site
	Underground test sites	NA[d]	*USA*: Nevada Test Site

TABLE 2. SOURCES OF MIXED CONTAMINATION (cont.)

Type of activity		Candidate contaminants	Example sites
Weapons testing (cont.)	Above ground test sites	U, Pu, Hg, NO_3, other metals from laboratories, $NaNO_3$, HNO_3, TBP[e], UNO_3, Al, kerosene, HCl, CrO_4, heating oil, Zr, HF, TCE[a], acetone, petroleum hydrocarbons, ordnance, depleted uranium	*USA*: Tonopah Test Range
	Radiological warfare agent testing	^{60}Co, ^{90}Sr, ^{137}Cs, ^{154}Eu, ^{155}Eu, ^{241}Am, Pu isotopes, corrosive substances	*Kazakhstan*: Semipalatinsk Test Site
Peaceful nuclear explosions	Oil and gas reservoir enhancement	Radioactive soil and debris	*Russian Federation*: Takhta-Kugulta (Stravropol territory), Orenburg region, Komi Republic
Military bases	Nuclear submarine decommissioning	Fission and activation products, PCBs[b], asbestos	*Russian Federation*: dockyards
	Army/Air force	Depleted uranium	*USA*: Twin Cities Army Ammunition Plant
Prototype reactors	Test reactors	Fission and activation products, heavy metals	*USA*: Idaho National Engineering and Environmental Laboratory
Prototype engines	Test nuclear engines	Mercury, lead, asbestos, radionuclides	*USA*: Idaho National Engineering and Environmental Laboratory

For footnotes see p. 11.

TABLE 2. SOURCES OF MIXED CONTAMINATION (cont.)

Type of activity		Candidate contaminants	Example sites
Research reactors		Residues in cooling ponds, landfilled chromium solutions, oils in pumps that has become tritiated, waste lubricants and PCBs[b] with activation products	USA: Idaho National Engineering and Environmental Laboratory, Brookhaven National Laboratory
Commercial reactors	Fuel fabrication		
	Operations	Gas cooled reactors, oils contaminated with fission products	
Mining	Uranium mill tailings		Germany: various Wismut sites USA: Belfield, North Dakota; Monticello Mill Tailings Site, Utah
	General mining residues		Worldwide
	Explosives and mines		Worldwide
Hospitals	In vivo testing	^{3}H, ^{14}C, biological materials	Worldwide
	Medical laboratories	Liquid scintillation cocktails with radioactive tracers and hazardous materials such as toluene and xylene	Worldwide
	Pharmaceutical testing	Labelled tracers	Worldwide
Research facilities	Radioecological and biology studies	^{90}Sr, ^{137}Cs with animal remains, chlorinated solvents and mercury	USA: University of Georgia, Lawrence Berkley National Laboratory
	Incinerator wastes	Heavy metals, fission products	
Industrial (naturally occurring radioactive material)	Oil and gas	Ra, scales	North Sea, Syrian oil fields
	Mining industry	Base and heavy metals	Worldwide

10

TABLE 2. SOURCES OF MIXED CONTAMINATION (cont.)

Type of activity		Candidate contaminants	Example sites
Industrial (cont.)	Rare earth production	Radionuclides with rare earth metals and alloys, sometimes mixed with chlorinated solvents	*USA*: Teledyne Wah Chang, zirconium production
	Welding rods	Thorium, degreasing material	
	Instrument manufacturing and maintenance, including luminising dials	Ra, ^{3}H, ^{90}Sr and other β-emitters in paint phosphors, chlorinated solvents, etching solutions, mercury switches	*United Kingdom (UK)*: Ditton Manor Park, Stirling Army Site
	Colouring agents for glazing	Zirconium, uranium, heavy metals	
Accident sites	Tank explosions		*Russian Federation*: Tomsk, Chelyabinsk
	Pipe breakage		
	Tank leakage		*USA*: Hanford Reservation
	Aircraft crashes	U, Pu fissile material, aviation fuel, depleted uranium counterweights, Th engine components	Greenland, Spain

[a] TCE: trichloroethylene.
[b] PCBs: polychlorinated biphenyls.
[c] VOCs: volatile organic compounds.
[d] NA: not applicable.
[e] TBP: tributylphosphate.

mixed contamination is small relative to the total quantity of hazardous material, and the cumulative risk from the hazardous components often exceeds the total risk from the radioactive component. In addition, many non-radioactive hazardous compounds are more mobile in the environment and have greater potential to contaminate groundwater.

2.2.2. Radionuclides

Exposure to radionuclides can occur in the form of direct exposure, through ingestion or through inhalation. Targets for radiation induced effects in humans can include the thyroid, breast, lungs, blood (bone marrow), stomach, liver, small and large intestines, brain, bone, oesophagus, bladder, pancreas, lymphatic tissue, skin, pharynx, uterus, ovaries and kidneys. Alpha emitters and low energy beta particles are generally considered ingestion and inhalation hazards but not significant external exposure concerns. Conversely, radionuclides can generate significant exposures by inhalation, ingestion and external exposure. For more information the reader is referred to the Basic Safety Standards [21] and its derivative publications.

2.2.3. Toxic and heavy metals

Heavy metals are notable for their wide dispersion in the environment; their tendency to accumulate in biological tissue and their toxicity potential even at low levels of exposure. While some metals, such as copper and iron, are essential to life, other metals apparently have no useful role in human or animal physiology and can even be toxic at trace levels (i.e. lead and mercury). It may be noted that various radionuclides, for example uranium and plutonium, in addition to inducing radiation effects, are also toxic. Furthermore, even metals essential to life can have adverse effects at high levels of exposure.

Exposure to toxic metals can occur through inhalation as dust or fumes (tiny particulate matter) and ingestion through food and drink. The amount actually absorbed into the body will vary depending on the chemical form of the metal and the age and nutritional status of the state of the exposed individual. Once absorbed, heavy metals are distributed into tissues and organs and tend to accumulate and persist in the liver, bones and kidneys for many years.

Most commonly the brain and kidneys are damaged by exposure to heavy metals. Some metals, such as arsenic, can even cause cancer. Diagnosis of the toxicity of metals is difficult since only general symptoms such as weakness and headache are typically manifest. In addition, no symptoms can be associated with chronic high level exposure to metals such as lead and cadmium, which can affect blood pressure and the retina, respectively.

Those toxic heavy metals that are of greatest concern to human health are also most prevalent at mixed waste sites, such as those containing lead, mercury, arsenic and cadmium. Specific toxic effects from exposure to these heavy metals are summarized in Annex I.

2.2.4. Toxic organic compounds

A wide variety of organic compounds are considered to be damaging to human health upon exposure. These chemicals are often persistent in the environment, they can bioaccumulate in organisms [22], are often highly mobile and after release to the environment rapidly migrate through the vadose zone causing groundwater contamination.

Aromatic hydrocarbons and halogenated hydrocarbons are frequently detected at sites with mixed contamination; quantities at many sites can be quite substantial. The aromatic hydrocarbons (e.g. benzene, xylenes and toluene) are mobile in the environment and many are considered to be carcinogens. The halogenated hydrocarbons (e.g. carbon tetrachloride, trichloroethylene (TCE), tetrachloroethylene and polychlorinated biphenyls (PCBs)) are highly persistent and mobile in the environment. They bioaccumulate and persist in organisms for long periods of time. Exposure generally affects the central nervous system, and at higher concentrations and/or exposures the resulting damage can be irreversible. Many halogenated hydrocarbons are known or suspected to be carcinogens.

Common toxic organic compounds at sites with mixed contamination include carbon tetrachloride, methylene chloride, tetrachloroethylene and polychlorinated biphenyls PCBs. The toxic effects of these organic chemicals are summarized in Annex I.

Metal–organic compounds, such as methyl mercury and tributyl tin (TBT), form a special group [23]. Methylated metals are actually formed in the environment.

2.2.5. Nitrates

Nitrates in the environment are of concern because they can reduce to nitrites in biological systems. Nitrites act in the blood to oxidize haemoglobin to methaemoglobin, which cannot conduct oxygen to the tissues. This condition, known as methaemoglobinaemia, is caused in humans by high levels of nitrites or, indirectly, by excessive levels of nitrates. Nitrate toxicity can result from ingestion of water and vegetables high in nitrates [24, 25]. Newborns (0–3 months) are more susceptible to nitrate toxicity than adults. Other effects associated with the ingestion of nitrates can include hypotension, relatively rapid heartbeat, respiratory dysfunction (from methaemoglobinaemia), headache, nausea, vomiting and diarrhoea.

2.2.6. Biohazardous agents

Biohazardous agents are biological in nature, capable of self-replication and possess the capacity to produce deleterious effects upon organisms. Biohazardous agents include viruses, bacteria and other pathogens. It should be noted that dormant viruses and spores, such as those from anthrax, can survive for very long periods in the ground, in some instances for centuries.

A biohazardous material is any material that contains or has been contaminated by a biohazardous agent. Examples of biohazardous wastes that may be present at contaminated sites are:

— Human and animal body parts;
— Organisms with recombinant DNA;
— Potentially infectious bacteria, viruses and spores;
— Live and attenuated vaccines;
— Toxins;
— Cultures and stocks of infectious agents;
— Primary human cell lines and tissue cultures;
— Blood and blood products;
— Biohazard contaminated laboratory items.

Biohazardous wastes may also be contaminated with radioactive and/or chemical materials and be constituents of mixed contaminant wastes. The principle threat from biohazardous wastes is from exposure to infectious agents or tissues.

2.2.7. Asbestos and other inhalable fibres

Asbestos is a mineral fibre that had been used widely alone and as a component in a variety of building construction materials for insulation and as a fire-retardant. Although the use of asbestos is now limited, wastes containing asbestos can be present at sites with mixed contamination, in particular those resulting from decommissioning activities.

Intact material containing asbestos is a low level hazard. The major risk occurs when the material is disturbed or has deteriorated, so that loose fibres become airborne and respirable. Inhalation of asbestos fibres increases the risk of developing lung cancer or mesothelioma, a cancer of the lining of the lungs and abdominal area. It may also cause a condition known as asbestosis.

2.2.8. Flammable and combustible materials

Flammable and combustible materials include solids, liquids or gases that will ignite, if exposed to a source of ignition, and continue to burn in ambient air. Flammable and combustible chemicals include certain gases and liquids, such as organic solvents, oils, greases, tars, oil based paints, lacquers and varnishes. As a general rule, the lower the flash point of a liquid, the greater the fire and explosion hazard. The flash point of a liquid is the minimum temperature at which it gives off sufficient vapour to form an ignitable mixture with the air near its surface or within its containment vessel.

Flammable materials could be present at sites with mixed contamination in the form of containers containing flammable liquids and of compressed gases in cylinders.

2.2.9. Corrosive chemicals

Corrosive chemicals are solids, liquids, or gases capable of irreparably harming living tissues or damaging material on contact. Representative corrosive chemicals are grouped into their classes as follows:

— Acids;
— Dehydrating agents such as phosphorus pentoxide and calcium oxide;
— Organic halides and organic acid halides such as acetyl chloride and benzyl chloroformate;
— Bases ('caustics' or 'alkalis');
— Halogens and halogen salts such as bromine, iodine, zinc chloride and sodium hypochlorite;
— Some organic compounds such as phenols (carbolic acid);
— Acid anhydrides.

Use of corrosive chemicals is common in the processing of nuclear materials and other industrial processes. Current waste management practices generally dictate that corrosive chemicals and wastes be neutralized before disposal. However, it is possible that corrosive chemicals can be present at inactive waste disposal sites with mixed contamination and at sites where accidental spills have occurred. Corrosive chemicals can burn, irritate or destructively attack living tissue. When inhaled or ingested, the lung and stomach tissues are affected respectively. Corrosive chemicals are also incompatible with many other chemicals; interaction of incompatible chemicals can result in generation of toxic gases, fire and/or explosion.

2.2.10. Reactive chemicals

Reactive chemicals include those that are inherently unstable and susceptible to rapid decomposition as well as chemicals, which, under specific conditions, can react alone, or with other substances in a violent uncontrolled manner, liberating heat and toxic gases or leading to fire or explosion. Because reaction rates increase dramatically as the temperature increases, if heat evolved from a reaction is not dissipated, the reaction can accelerate out of control and cause serious injury or death.

There are three general categories of reactive chemicals:

(1) *Explosives*: Explosive chemicals cause sudden, nearly instantaneous, releases of pressure, gas and heat when subjected to sudden shock, pressure or high temperature. Examples include acetylene, hydrogen and nitrogen containing compounds, ammonia, halogens, oxygen and perchlorates.

(2) *Oxidizers*: Oxidizing agents provide oxygen for chemical reactions. Oxidizers spontaneously evolve oxygen at ambient temperature and can explode violently when exposed to shock or heat. Because their chemical stability varies, oxidizing agents are very unpredictable and therefore particularly dangerous. Examples include peroxides, hyperperoxides and peroxyesters.

(3) *Peroxide formers*: Peroxide formers are organic compounds that react with oxygen from the air to form unstable peroxides. Peroxide formation can occur under normal storage conditions, when compounds become concentrated by evaporation, or when mixed with other chemicals. The accumulated peroxides can violently explode when exposed to shock, friction or heat. Examples include cyclohexane, tetrahydrofuran, ethyl ether, isopropyl ether, aldehydes and ketones.

Common laboratory chemicals include peroxide formers such as tetrahydrofuran and ethyl ether. Because of chemical instability, there are storage limits for these chemicals and if such a chemical is not utilized within this limit it is discarded. Therefore, when these chemicals are used in a laboratory that also performs research with radioactive materials, peroxide formers may become part of a mixed waste stream.

2.2.11. Pyrophoric metals

Pyrophoric chemicals oxidize rapidly and ignite spontaneously upon contact with air or water vapour. Many metals, including the radioactive metals plutonium, uranium and thorium, are pyrophoric when they have a high specific area ratio (thin sections, fine particles or molten states). However, the same metals in massive solid form are difficult to ignite.

Hot or burning metals may react violently upon contact with other materials, such as oxidizing agents and extinguishing agents used on fires involving ordinary combustible or flammable liquids. Temperatures produced by burning metals can be significantly higher than temperatures generated by burning flammable liquids. Some metals can continue to burn in carbon dioxide, nitrogen, water or steam atmospheres in which ordinary combustible substances or flammable liquids would be incapable of burning.

2.2.12. Ordnance and explosives

Ordnance and explosives may also be present at sites with mixed contaminants. The major hazards from ordnance are personal injury and property damage, and the wider distribution of contaminants, caused by heat, blast, noise, fumes and flying debris or projectiles from unintentional or inadequately controlled ignition or explosion of such materials. Explosives are especially vulnerable to elevated temperature, with possible consequences ranging from mild decomposition to vigorous deflagration or detonation. Explosives can also be ignited by mechanical action through friction or impact.

Explosives may be toxic, with exposure pathways being inhalation of dust or vapour, ingestion or contact with skin. While explosives are not acutely toxic, improper handling can result in systemic poisoning affecting the bone marrow and the liver.

2.3. ENVIRONMENTAL BEHAVIOUR OF CONTAMINANTS

2.3.1. Overview

The behaviour of inorganic contaminants has been reviewed in detail in the companion report on natural attenuation [18]; the following sections give a brief overview but focus also on the behaviour of organic contaminants. The same geochemical and mineralogical processes control the transport mechanisms of radionuclides and heavy metals. However, solubilities and mobilities can be quite different for different metals or their species. Thus, for instance, adsorption onto soil particles, chemical precipitation and ion exchange retard the movement of U, Pu, Cs and Sr; other radionuclides, such as I, Tc or tritium are not readily retarded by the soil and may migrate at a rate nearly equal to that of the infiltrating water.

Transport processes of organic compounds are affected by the polarity and corresponding solubility in water of the chemicals (Fig. 1). The literature on the properties and behaviour of organic contaminants is extensive. In the following sections, basic environmental processes are presented and the reader is referred to the relevant textbooks, for example Ref. [26].

The transport and fate of contaminants in the vadose zone is affected by the nature of the contaminants, the characteristics of the site and the subsurface processes. Given specific conditions at a mixed contaminant site, the

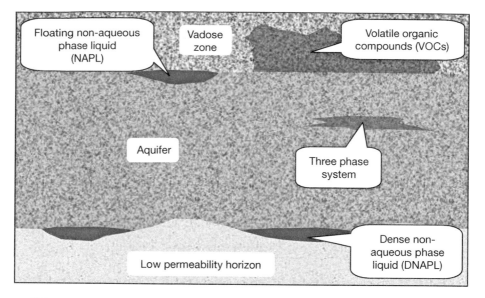

FIG. 1. *Behaviour of non-miscible organic contaminants in groundwater systems.*

investigator may be interested in the behaviour of these constituents individually or when commingled with other contaminants.

The functional groups on certain organic molecules, such as carboxylic or phenolic groups and amines, will dissociate when the substance is dissolved in groundwater. Because these functional groups are ionic, giving the molecules a negative charge, attenuation by negatively charged hydrolysed mineral surfaces is not favoured. The interaction between non-polar organic molecules and solid mineral surfaces is more complex. For example, such molecules may form surface coatings on clays and become immobile.

At many sites, the releases of large quantities of non-miscible organic compounds, for example, chlorinated solvents and oils (also known as non-aqueous phase liquids (NAPLs)) has resulted in the formation of a three phase system with the solid substrate and the groundwater. In cases where the vapour pressure of the contaminant at ambient temperature is high, a four phase system that includes a gas phase may develop.

Where a separate phase of non-miscible organic compounds exists, two cases can be distinguished:

(1) One in which the density of the organic liquid is lower than the density of water (a light non-aqueous phase liquid (LNAPL)), where the contaminant floats on the aquifer (Fig. 1);

(2) One in which the organic liquid has a higher density than water (a dense non-aqueous phase liquid (DNAPL)), where the organic liquids collect on the bottom of the aquifer (Fig. 1).

A large number of processes can contribute to the migration behaviour of inorganic and organic contaminants. These are outlined in the following sections. A more detailed presentation on physical, chemical and biological processes for radionuclides can be found in Ref. [18].

2.3.2. Physical environmental processes

2.3.2.1. Fluid flow and dispersion

The two basic contaminant transport processes are advection and dispersion; Advection is the transport of dissolved and suspended contaminants in flowing water or groundwater. Dispersion is the mixing and spreading of contaminants within the flow system. The dispersion process has two components: mixing and molecular diffusion.

The mixing component, also known as mechanical dispersion, is caused by velocity variations in porous media. Velocity variations may occur at the microscopic level due to the friction between soil particles and the fluid and also to the curvatures in the flow path. These velocity variations result in concentration variations. When the concentration variations are averaged over a given volume, the contaminants have essentially dispersed.

Molecular diffusion results in the spreading of contamination due to concentration gradients. This process occurs even when the seepage velocity is zero. Molecular diffusion is dependent on the degree of saturation or volumetric water content of the porous medium.

2.3.2.2. Dilution

Dilution is the process in which a contaminant becomes less concentrated. It is similar for both organic and inorganic contaminants, including radionuclides. It reduces risk because resulting exposures will be lower. By itself, however, dilution does not reduce contaminant mass; rather it spreads the area of potential exposure. Some contaminants are also believed to be hazardous even at levels too dilute to be detected by standard field characterization techniques.

The most common cause of dilution in groundwater is infiltration or recharging of precipitation to the aquifer. Infiltration of precipitation causes a reduction in contaminant concentration by mixing with the contaminant plume and thus dilution.

2.3.2.3. *Filtration — physical blocking of pore spaces*

Resistate minerals (e.g. monazite, zircon and baryte), other insoluble materials, for example cement, or particulate matter onto which contaminants have become bound, including bacteria and other microorganisms, may be retarded by filtration. This will depend on the relative size of the particles and the pore distribution of the host medium. However, fine-grained clay matrices or fibrous peat may remove even small colloids. In the case of aquifer transport, adequate characterization of the hydrogeological flow regime (requiring knowledge of permeability, hydraulic conductivity, heterogeneity and fracture distribution) is a prerequisite for quantitative assessment. With surface deposits, variably saturated conditions and geotechnical issues also have to be taken into account.

2.3.2.4. *Volatilization*

Volatilization is the process by which chemicals dissolved in groundwater are transferred from the aqueous phase to the vapour phase. The chemical then migrates through the capillary fringe and into the vadose zone. In general, the higher the vapour pressure of the contaminant, the more likely the contaminant will be released from the soil or groundwater to the soil gas.

The contaminants most liable to gas phase dispersion are volatile organic compounds (VOCs). Weather conditions, such as changing ambient air pressure and heating of soil due to solar irradiation, will control inter alia the movement of gases in the vadose zone. Another source of heat and gases (CH_4, H_2 and H_3) is degrading organic matter, such as in domestic landfills.

2.3.2.5. *Radioactive decay*

As radioactive isotopes decay, they are transformed into other, often less radioactive, isotopes of the same element or sometimes even other elements. While radionuclides degrade naturally, the degradation process itself is hazardous to living organisms. As some radioactive isotopes decay to form more hazardous radionuclides, however, it is important to consider the hazard posed by the progeny as well as radiation from the original hazard when evaluating the effects of natural radioactive decay.

The half-lives of radionuclides now present in the environment range from seconds to many millions of years. For higher members of the natural series (^{234,235,238}U and ^{232}Th), together with some transuranic elements (e.g. ^{239}Pu) and fission products (e.g. ^{99}Tc and ^{129}I), no substantial decay will have occurred even on the longest assessment time frames. However, many other isotopes produced by nuclear fission (e.g. ^{60}Co, ^{90}Sr and ^{137}Cs) or contained in industrial naturally occurring radioactive materials (NORMs) (e.g. ^{210}Po and ^{210}Pb) will not persist beyond a few hundred years. Clearly, therefore it is important that a detailed radionuclide inventory is compiled before deciding on a remediation strategy at any given site. The extreme fractionation between members of a decay series, which can be caused by chemical processing, precludes the assumption of secular equilibrium in the majority of cases [27].

2.3.3. Chemical environmental processes

2.3.3.1. Precipitation

Precipitation of an element due to its high concentration can take place in soil solutions. This reaction takes place when the solution becomes supersaturated with respect to that element. A supersaturated solution is a solution containing more solute (such as the dissolved element) than allowed at equilibrium. This type of solution is unstable and any further addition of solute will cause the precipitation of an insoluble solid.

Precipitation from soil solutions is common for abundant elements in soil such as aluminium, iron, silica, manganese, calcium and magnesium. Relatively few natural radionuclides, except for uranium, lead and thorium, and no artificial isotopes will exist in sufficient concentrations to precipitate as pure phase from surface, pore or groundwaters.

The concentrations of most heavy metals would also be too low to precipitate unless pollution at a site greatly increases the metal concentration. When this occurs, precipitation can control the mobility and toxicity of that element in the soil because the solid is often immobile and thus less toxic to organisms.

2.3.3.2. Co-precipitation

Often the solubility of an element is lower in the soil solution than predicted by the solubility product because ion solubility is lower in mixed ionic solutions than in pure ionic solutions. One possible reason for reduced solubility is co-precipitation. Co-precipitation is the incorporation of trace elements into mineral structures during solid solution formation and recrystallization of minerals. This process reduces the mobility and toxicity of metals that are incorporated into the mineral.

Minerals only incorporate elements into their structure that have similar ionic radii to the elements composing the mineral. For example, during the formation of calcite, Ra^{2+}, Mn^{2+}, Cd^{2+} and Fe^{2+} can possibly be incorporated into the mineral structure. Co-precipitation reactions are also controlled by the rate of soil mineral dissolution.

An important example from both a nuclear and a NORM perspective is the high selectivity shown by radium for baryte, a system that has been very well characterized and is also exploited in a remediation context (see, for example, Refs [28–30], and also Sections 9.1 and 11.2.5). It is probable that transuranic isotopes would be similarly incorporated in uranium and lanthanide bearing minerals.

Co-precipitation on ferric oxyhydroxide flocs is an extremely efficient removal mechanism for a large number of radioelements and heavy metals in solution. As the contaminants tend to be released upon crystallization to goethite, the process is often classified under the more general heading 'sorption'.

2.3.3.3. Adsorption

In its strictest sense, adsorption refers to the non-specific and reversible uptake of ionic species at charged surface sites. Used loosely, it has come to encompass aspects of co-precipitation, ion exchange and a number of ion-specific interactions that are more appropriately termed complexation. The distinction is not made here other than in the case of co-precipitation, described above, as the latter clearly extends beyond the surface, resulting in the formation of a defined mineral phase [31].

Clay minerals typically show a strong affinity for radionuclides in the cationic form. Geological media with high clay mineral content are more likely, therefore, to bring about attenuation. Adsorption and ion exchange would be expected to play an important role in retarding the migration of soluble monovalent and divalent ions. Examples include the pronounced retention of caesium on zeolites (e.g. clinoptilolite) and the substitution of strontium for interlayer cations in smectites. Surface sorption is an important transient for multivalent ions in the formation of new mineral phases.

The organic matter content in soil governs adsorption of organic molecules. Since water is the major carrier in soil, advective transport is dependent on partitioning between the water phase and the soil organic phase. The extent to which organic chemicals are adsorbed onto soil surfaces is affected by the chemical's structure and molecular properties as follows:

(a) *Molecular size*: In general, the larger the molecular size the greater the propensity to remain in the adsorbed state.

(b) *Hydrophobicity (repulsion from water)*: Organic chemicals preferentially accumulate in water-insoluble solvents and organic matter in soil that have hydrophobic surfaces.

(c) *Molecular charge*: Some organic molecules have an intrinsic positive or negative charge that causes the molecule to become adsorbed onto cation or anion exchange sites on soil surfaces. In general, soils possess a higher number of negative surface charges than positive surface charges, which can lead to decreased adsorption or organic anions on soil surfaces because of charge repulsion between the contaminant and the soil surface.

(d) *Spatial structure*: The molecular structure of organic molecules can affect the degree of adsorption. For example, adsorption studies show that two isomeric forms of a common pesticide lindane exhibit significantly different partition coefficients due to differences in the spatial arrangement of chlorine atoms between the molecules.

(e) *Competition*: Other (major) ions compete for sorption places (Example 1).

Example 1. Competition for sorption places between contaminants and major ions.

Mixed solutions of inorganic contaminants that leak into the ground may also facilitate the migration of certain radionuclides. For example, the Hanford nuclear reservation in Washington State, United States of America (USA) is the home of several single shell tanks (SSTs) that were used to store self-boiling, caustic and saline radioactive and hazardous wastes. Approximately 204 000 m^3 of these liquid wastes leaked into the underlying vadose zone. This zone is comprised of sediments with a large ion-exchange capacity that are normally saturated with calcium and magnesium. The principal variables influencing the degree of adsorption of the liquid waste constituents are the concentrations of competing cations of similar size, for example potassium and ammonium, pH, the ion-exchange capacity of the soil, and the total concentration of caesium (natural + ^{137}Cs). In this case, the high sodium concentrations probably swamped the available exchange sites in the near field, lowering the caesium distribution coefficient to nearly zero. This enhances the migration of the caesium. This trend has been noted in groundwater samples beneath some tank farms [32, 33]. The elevated temperature is likely to be important mainly through its effect on dissolution and precipitation. Caesium mobility in the saturated zone is less uncertain in the Hanford Site sediments beneath the waste tanks [34], and caesium would probably not move more than a few metres. This is also supported by observations of the caesium distribution around an injection well [35].

2.3.3.4. Complexation by organic compounds

A typical soil solution will easily contain several hundred different soluble species, many of them involving metal cations and organic ligands. A complex is said to form whenever a molecular unit, such as an ion, acts as a central group to attract and form a close association with other atoms or molecules. Most complexes that form in groundwater are metal–ligand complexes. The most common complexing anions present in groundwater are HCO_3^-/CO_3^{2-}, Cl^-, SO_4^{2-} and humic substances (i.e. organic materials). There can be a large number of dissolved, small chain humic substances present in groundwater and their complexation properties are not well understood. Complexes with humic substances are likely to be very important in systems containing appreciable amounts of humic substances (>1 mg/L). In shallow aquifers, organic ligands from humic materials can be present in significant concentrations and dominate the chemistry.

Complexation usually results in reducing the concentration of the central molecule — the uncomplexed free species. Possible outcomes of this include lowering the potential for adsorption and increasing its solubility, which enhance migration potential (Example 2). On the other hand, some humic acids readily bond to soil and thus retard migration of complexed metals.

Example 2. Potential effect of ferrocyanide.

As part of the procedure for separating plutonium from uranium and fission products during reprocessing, chelating agents were added to ensure that all constituents remained in solution. The most common organic chelating agents were glycolate, citrate, HEDTA (hydroxyethyl ethylene diamine triacetic acid) and EDTA (ethylene diamine triacetic acid) (for multivalent ions such as uranium and plutonium) [40] as well as ferrocyanide (for caesium). The fate of ferrocyanide under tank conditions is probably similar to that of the organic ligands, with carbon eventually becoming oxidized to carbonate and nitrogen becoming oxidized to nitrate or nitrite. Thus, this important complexer of caesium would also have probably contributed to the caesium mobility during early leaks. The groundwater below the 'BY' tank farms at Hanford showed extensive and relatively continuous ^{60}Co plumes, which are used as an indicator of other radioactive contamination, such as caesium. Cobalt-60 was detected in all but a few of the boreholes, which is not surprising, as the BY tanks were used for in-tank ferrocyanide scavenging operations. The ^{60}Co has been shown to form a chemical complex with the ferrocyanide, increasing the mobility of an element that was already relatively mobile.

A number of radionuclides and heavy metals exhibit significant migration potential in the presence of aqueous, low molecular weight organic compounds. Equally, however, immobile organic matter in the form of peat [36] or organic-rich horizons in soils and sediments may provide an excellent substrate [37] for radionuclide retention. These phenomena have been studied extensively in the context of 'natural analogue' studies for the performance assessment of radioactive waste repositories [38, 39]. Uranium at concentrations approaching percentage levels has been reported in peat from Canada and northern Europe whereas iodine, often considered to be a conservative tracer in such assessments, has been shown to be fixed in organic-rich lacustrine deposits.

2.3.4. Biological environmental processes

Microbes in the vadose zone may have a significant influence on metal transport by either increasing or decreasing sorption of metals or radionuclides to soil particles. The manner by which microbes can influence metal solubility and transport are as follows:

— Changing the pH of the solution;
— Causing redox reactions that affect metal valence states and solubility;
— Chelation, solubilization and leaching by microbial metabolites and decomposition products;
— Biomethylation and production of volatile and or toxic alkylated metal compounds;
— Biodegradation of organic complexes with metals [41].

Microbes are also capable of sorbing metals, which could lead to increased proportions of metals in the solid phase or to increased colloidal transport of the metals. The presence of microbes may also result in increased availability of metals and radionuclides to plants and other organisms in the soil. Although microorganisms may use some metals in solution, increased concentrations of toxic metals may cause decreased growth and increased mortality. These effects are important when predicting the fate and transport of heavy metals and radionuclides in the vadose zone and when considering remediation efforts. The influence of microbes on contaminants in the vadose zone is particularly important because most contaminant releases are to the vadose zone.

Studies have shown microbes can decrease sorption of metals to soils and many metal tolerant microbes produce metabolites that complex with heavy metals and increase transport through soil. For example, Chanmugathas and Bollag determined that mobilization of strongly bound cadmium is a microbially mediated process [42], in a study by Gerringa [43], many metals increased in mobility concomitant with aerobic degradation of organic matter, and Burke et al. [44] determined that sediments containing microbes sorbed less cadmium than sediments that were autoclaved.

Processes affecting organic contaminants, such as biodegradation, are discussed in more detail in Section 10.4.5.

3. REGULATORY IMPLICATIONS

3.1. REGULATORY REGIMES

Strategies for the remediation of sites with mixed contamination have to satisfy current regulations applicable in the respective IAEA Member State. National laws and regulations on, for example, environmental protection, human health, radiation safety and occupational safety will need to be considered and complied with. It is unlikely that any remediation strategy that does not fit within the regulatory framework will be acceptable to either the regulatory bodies or the general public, even if all other assessment factors, for example, health impact assessment, technical feasibility, waste acceptance criteria and disposal routes, are acceptable.

Most countries do not have specific regulatory regimes to deal with mixed radioactive and non-radioactive contamination. In many cases, separate regulatory regimes operate for the two types of contaminant. The lead regulator is either the one responsible for radioactive materials or is selected on the basis of the judged or perceived dominant source of risk or hazard. Thus the regulatory approach is often to assess and deal separately with the two types of constituent within any mixed contamination on any site. One of the two classes of contaminant may, in practice, dominate, dependent upon the controlling acceptable limits on soil, water and air from releases. However, the regulatory problems can sometimes be simplified by subdividing the site into areas where one or the other type of contaminant dominates the risks and hence controls the remedial strategy.

The degree of regulation, regulatory control and guidance for environmental remediation projects for sites with mixed contamination varies markedly from country to country. The variations frequently reflect the status and scale of any nuclear power and weapons development, the significance of radioactivity issues, the size of the country and the degree of autonomy exercised by regional governments over environmental issues. Protection of the public, operational safety and environmental protection are key areas for regulation. In some countries, such as the USA (Example 3) and many European Union (EU) countries, there are regulatory bodies, for example, the

US Nuclear Regulatory Commission (USNRC) and the Nuclear Installations Inspectorate (NII/NSD) in the United Kingdom (UK), with specific responsibilities for overseeing the operational safety of all works, including remediation activities, at major commercial nuclear sites, for example, power reactors and nuclear fuel fabrication and reprocessing facilities. Their remit may extend to nuclear weapons development and production facilities, as in the UK, whereas in others, for example the USA, there is a separate internal regulator, for example, the US Department of Energy (USDOE). For other facilities, which are not primarily nuclear facilities and where the use of radioactive materials is secondary to that of chemicals or other hazardous substances, the prime regulatory authority for safety in all operational works is frequently the one with responsibility for general workplace safety, for example, the Occupational Safety and Health Administration (OSHA) in the USA or the Health and Safety Executive (HSE) in the UK. For protection of the environment, which includes any discharges from sites to the air, water or land, waste disposals, etc. with potential impacts on the off-site public, flora and fauna, other regulatory bodies may be involved in environmental remediation. Examples are the US Environmental Protection Agency (USEPA) and the Environment Agency (EA/SEPA) in the UK. Local regulatory authorities, for example individual state or district environmental protection departments or agencies, may also have significant roles (see also Example 3).

The boundaries between the responsibilities of the different regulators may not always be clear where environmental remediation projects involving mixed waste sites are involved. In addition, the level of input and the importance of the different regulators may often vary over the project life. These issues may frequently be resolved by agreements between the different regulators to work in unison or delegate the lead at particular sites or projects to one another, dependent upon the nature of the problems prevailing at the specific site. However, it is often beneficial at the start of any project to have the full involvement of all potentially interested regulatory bodies to ensure a common understanding of the problems, the proposed solutions and the constraints from different regulators (Example 4).

3.2. ASSESSMENTS OF ENVIRONMENTAL IMPACTS

A degree of broader regulatory control may also be exercised over major projects, including remediation of sites, through national requirements for assessments of environmental impacts before any new project is undertaken. This is the case, for instance, in countries of the EU, where there are European Directive requirements for environmental impact assessments (EIAs). Such

EIAs may not only assess and quantify environmental impacts but may also justify the selection of the chosen remedial strategy through critical review of the potential options and quantification of their potential impacts. The EIAs can also identify measures to be taken to mitigate impacts and reduce them to the lowest practicable levels. Regulatory bodies are often statutory consultees to the EIAs and may, therefore, also influence the proposed remedial works through this route. In some countries, such as the UK, major remedial projects are treated as new developments on land and are also covered by land use planning regulations. The requirements for EIAs form part of these regulations, as do controls on potential public nuisances.

Example 3. Mixed waste regulations in the USA [45].

A dual regulatory framework exists for mixed waste with the USEPA or authorized states regulating the hazardous component of the waste and the USNRC, the USNRC agreement states or the USDOE regulating the radioactive component. The USNRC generally regulates commercial and non-USDOE Federal facilities. USDOE orders apply to USDOE sites and contractors.

Using the authority provided by the Atomic Energy Act (AEA), the USNRC and USDOE regulate mixed wastes with regard to radiation hazards. Using the authority provided by the Resources Control and Recovery Act (RCRA), the USEPA regulates mixed wastes with regard to chemical hazards. The USNRC is authorized by the AEA to issue licences to commercial users of radioactive materials. The RCRA gives the USEPA the authority to control hazardous waste from 'cradle to grave'. Once a waste is determined to be a mixed waste, the waste handlers must comply with both AEA and RCRA statutes and regulations. The requirements of the RCRA and AEA are generally consistent and compatible. However, the provisions in Section 1006(a) of the RCRA allow the AEA to take precedence in the event that provisions of requirements of the two acts are found to be inconsistent.

Under the 1984 Amendments to the RCRA, land disposal restriction regulations prohibit disposal of most mixed wastes until they meet specific treatment standards. While most of the commercial mixed wastes that are generated and stored can be treated by commercially available treatment technology to meet the land disposal restriction regulations by commercially available treatment technology, there still exist a small percentage of commercial mixed wastes for which no treatment or disposal capacity is available. Commercial mixed waste volumes are very small (approximately 2%) compared with the total volume of mixed wastes being generated or stored by the USDOE.

As mandated by the Federal Facilities Compliance Act, which was signed into law on 6 Oct. 1992, the USDOE has developed site treatment plans to handle its mixed wastes under the purview of the USEPA or its authorized states. These plans are being implemented by orders issued by the USEPA or the state regulatory authority.

Example 4. Dealing with biological, chemical and other hazards in the USA [45].

In the USA major environmental laws have been passed that fully take into account biological, chemical and other hazards. Operators of facilities must abide by these laws to protect workers, the public and the environment. Laws are enforced through operators implementing regulations, which are the responsibility of the USEPA, which in turn delegates some regulatory authority to Agreement States. One such law is the RCRA giving the USEPA the authority to control hazardous wastes from 'cradle to grave'. This includes the generation, transportation, treatment, storage and disposal of hazardous wastes. The RCRA also sets forth a framework for the management of non-hazardous wastes. The 1986 amendments to the RCRA enabled the USEPA to address the environmental problems that could result from underground tanks storing petroleum and other hazardous substances. The RCRA focuses only on active and future facilities and does not address abandoned or historical sites, which are covered by the Comprehensive Environmental Response, Compensation and Liability Act (CERCLA or Superfund), 42 U.S.C. 9601, which is also regulated by the USEPA. The Federal Hazardous and Solid Waste Amendments are the 1984 amendments to the RCRA that required phasing out land disposal of hazardous wastes. Some of the other mandates of this strict law include increased enforcement authority for the USEPA, more stringent hazardous waste management standards and a comprehensive underground storage tank programme.

As part of the environmental assessment process, impacts from chemical hazards are assessed. These assessments are required prior to construction of spent fuel and radioactive waste management facilities. For example, the Environmental Impact Statement prepared for Yucca Mountain examined the consequences for chemically toxic materials, which were found to be lower than the maximum contaminant level goals identified. Heavy metal elements were of particular interest, including chromium, molybdenum, nickel and vanadium contained in the metals proposed to package the wastes and support the packages. The USDOE concluded that there are no impacts on water quality or human health from toxic materials that would exceed USEPA standards applicable to the proposed repository.

3.3. CLEANUP TARGETS

In the remediation of sites with mixed contaminants, assessments are often necessary for regulatory approval of worker and public exposures during the period work is carried out and finally for acceptable residual levels of contamination. These are usually determined by safety and risk assessments that address in separate parts the impacts of the radioactive and non-radioactive hazardous components. Some regulators may also prescribe methodologies and computer codes for undertaking assessments of acceptable residual levels of chemical or radioactive contamination. The acceptable residual levels often depend on scenarios for future site use and are subject to optimization (see, e.g., Ref. [11]). In addition, in some cases regulators and site liability owners/operators have been working together to develop guidance on agreed best practice on the characterization, assessment and remediation of contaminated sites, for example the UK Safegrounds Learning Network [46]. Synergistic effects between radioactive and chemical contaminants are not generally considered in these assessments unless specific data are available. The risk assessment methodologies used for assessing operational safety during remedial work and environmental impacts before, during and after such work employ very similar exposure pathway models for both types of contaminant. They also use the same risk basis for acceptability, i.e. 10^{-4}–10^{-6} lifetime risk.

An IAEA Safety Requirements publication [11] provides radiological criteria for aiding decision making on the remediation of areas contaminated by past practices and accidents. In some Member States remediation objectives for contaminants in soils have been implemented (see, for example, Refs [47, 48]). There are international standards for acceptable levels of some radionuclides and toxic chemicals in drinking water [49]. Databases have been established for chemical and hazardous substances, which relate their toxicity to acceptable levels in soils and water [50].

3.4. LIMITS ON WORKER AND PUBLIC EXPOSURES

Remediation of sites contaminated with hazardous and radioactive substances can result in the exposure of workers and potentially the public to physiological and possibly physical harm. Radiological, chemical, biological and some hazardous materials, for example asbestos, can give rise to the former, while corrosive, flammable and explosive constituents can give rise to the latter. At sites with ongoing activities, the exposure of workers directly involved in the remediation work and elsewhere on the site is frequently controlled through workplace regulations. Relevant national regulations often cover chemical and toxic substances hazardous to health, ionizing radiation, environmental nuisances, for example odours, noise and traffic, and construction type risks. All of these factors need to be considered in operational safety and require full assessment as in a safety case. When planning and licensing a remediation strategy, reductions in public exposures may be balanced against the exposures incurred by workers as a result of the remediation action.

Information about safety and health risks and associated guidance can be obtained from standard reference sources, regulatory standards, medical surveillance, safety studies, toxicological data and epidemiological studies. Most of the guidance is national, with the exception perhaps of the EU, where an internationally agreed body of regulations is being developed. In a similar way, existing international standards and guidance are usually focused on either radioactive or hazardous materials.

For radiological risks the reader is referred to the Basic Safety Standards [21] and its derivative publications. The BSS reflect current scientific understanding and are in turn reflected in the regulations of many Member States. There are international recommendations on exposure limits for workers and the public to radioactive substances [51, 52].

There are also similar national standards in many countries controlling such exposures to toxic substances (e.g. by the National Institute for Occupational Health and Safety (NIOSH) [53] in the USA and the HSE [54] in the UK). Given similarities in the latter, these are effectively internationally accepted standards.

Section 4 discusses in more detail the organizational and technical aspects of this subject.

3.5. WASTE MANAGEMENT

Management of wastes arising from the remediation is another key issue at sites with mixed contamination. It will affect remedial approaches and has regulatory implications. Wastes will arise directly from the remediation activities, for example cleanup of contaminated soils, retrieval of buried wastes, treatment of groundwater and filtration of contaminated ventilation air.

Many countries have established regulatory frameworks for dealing with radioactive wastes, for example dose limits, clearance limits, acceptable levels of contamination at the different stages of waste management, specific activity limits and criteria regarding hazardous contents [55–69]. They may also have similar frameworks for chemical and hazardous wastes. Wastes with mixed contaminants, however, are generally considerably more difficult to condition, store and dispose of than radioactive or hazardous wastes alone. Their characteristics frequently do not comply with the waste acceptance criteria of disposal facilities managing radioactive wastes from more traditional origins, for example operational wastes from nuclear power plants, research reactors, fuel fabrication and reprocessing plants, R&D sources and small users of radioactive material. Conversely, many hazardous waste landfills are not normally licensed to accept radioactive materials and those that are may have very low limits. As a result, the remediation strategy needs to take account of the availability of disposal routes, including specific conditioning of mixed or separated wastes, in order to meet the waste acceptance criteria and long term safety of the disposal facilities.

The key additional issues in deciding on waste acceptance are frequently those of the impacts of the non-active hazardous components on the handling of the wastes prior to conditioning, on storage and on repository performance. The latter usually relates to enhancement of source mobilization and migration through leachate formation, then through the groundwater and gaseous pathways. This is particularly the case when organic contaminants are present. The gaseous pathway may be enhanced through significant gas generation by chemical or microbial degradation, radiolysis or chemical reaction. In circumstances where the residual level of the non-radioactive component is too high for acceptance, the wastes will require pretreatment to reduce it to acceptable levels. This pretreatment can involve incineration or biodegradation in the case of organic contaminants. Once contamination is removed from the ground and becomes a discrete package of waste, regulatory authorizations are often required to accumulate, store and ultimately dispose of these radioactive and hazardous materials.

3.6. MIXED WASTE TRANSPORTATION

Remediation strategies also need to meet requirements regarding regulations for transportation of radioactive materials and hazardous materials. Attention may need to be given to international shipments, where sites being remediated are close to national borders. There are separate international standards for the safe transport of radioactive materials [70] and hazardous materials by road, rail, air and water [71, 72]. There are also standards and guidance within the EU [55–69] for determining hazardous waste categories through assessment of levels at which residues contaminated with selected substances should be treated as hazardous. Thus, there is a body of international guidance and best practice that is useful, although by no means fully comprehensive, in the regulation of sites with mixed contaminants.

3.7. REGULATIONS AFFECTING THE IMPLEMENTATION OF A REMEDIATION OPERATION

Implementation of remediation projects can potentially result in environmental impacts additional to those associated with mixed contamination alone. As a result various other regulatory permits and authorizations may be required.

Thus, some techniques involving the re-injection of treated water into the geological formation may need a water disposal permit or licence. Any operation that typically can or will result in emission is likely to attract regulatory oversight. Permits, authorization or licences related to the remediation process could be needed for operations such as:

— Construction of wells.
— Extraction of water and also discharge of treated water.
— Re-injection of treated water into a geological formation.
— Introduction of materials to aid remediation. The materials may need to be of an approved standard, for example, food quality.
— Gaseous discharges. Supplementary assessments including air plume modelling, environmental impact assessments and the need for off-gas treatments.
— All types of excavations (checks for underground services in utility company records and physical surveys for underground services).
— On-site treatment of contaminated soil.
— For remediation operations in areas of historical interest, archaeological permits may be needed.

Remediation work normally would be organized and carried out according to locally or internationally recognized best practice. This will help to ensure that environmental impacts accord with the as low as reasonably practicable (ALARP) principle (see, for example, Refs [73, 74]).

3.8. INSTITUTIONAL CONTROL AND STEWARDSHIP ISSUES

For some sites, it may not be practicable to reduce the contamination, whether radioactive or hazardous, to such low levels that they are suitable for unrestricted use. This will result in the imposition of restrictions referred to as institutional controls [1, 6, 11]. These could involve surveillance of the site and control access systems. Regulatory authorities are typically responsible for approving the design of the programme, its implementation, and the evaluation of the results with respect to the residual impact on the public and the environment. Maintenance of institutional control over extended periods of time is a concern. The collection of processes and provisions for this are generally referred to as stewardship and will be discussed in detail in a forthcoming report [75].

4. IMPLICATIONS FOR WORKER HEALTH AND SAFETY

4.1. GENERAL CONSIDERATIONS

Workers involved with remediating a mixed contaminated site, in addition to encountering all of the usual risks encountered in hazardous waste work (i.e. conventional construction and operations hazards), may also come across radioactive material, toxic metals, organic compounds or biohazardous agents, respirable fibres, flammable and combustible materials, corrosive and reactive chemicals, and explosives. As an example, site workers who may be involved with conducting a drilling and sampling programme in soils contaminated with a mixture of radionuclides and an organic solvent (e.g. carbon tetrachloride) may not anticipate that they may be exposed to volatile toxic gases in their breathing space around the drilling operation; or that in handling soil samples, individuals may be subject to exposure via skin contact with the organic substance in its liquid form.

Remediating a mixed contaminated site requires a thorough and disciplined approach to evaluating the potential hazards to site workers, and taking the necessary steps to perform work in a safe manner. The following section describes the key elements for conducting a robust worker health and safety programme at a mixed contaminated site, which have been adapted from Ref. [76].

4.2. ESTABLISHMENT OF A PROPER ORGANIZATION

Establishment of a multidisciplinary team is the first step required to plan, organize, evaluate and conduct a remediation activity associated with a mixed contaminated site. This team should include health and safety specialists with expertise in more than just radiation protection, for example, specialists who can also assess chemical and biological hazards and develop safety procedures accordingly. The organization typically would also include a health and safety officer who has the responsibility for maintaining the health and safety of the site.

4.3. TRAINING

All workers involved in the various phases of remediation of a mixed contaminated site would ideally be appropriately trained, with the workers certified in both radiological and non-radiological hazardous worker safety. For example, at such sites in the USA, a minimum 40 hour special training course is required for workers at hazardous sites in addition to training in radiological work. This course typically includes training at various levels in the use of personal protective equipment (PPE) including, for example, the wearing of protective clothing designed to mitigate chemical exposure [77]. In addition to generalized training designed to support hazardous cleanup activities, more specific health and safety training may be required on the basis of specific site and contaminant characteristics, and the remediation approach.

Similarly, site managers need to be trained to a sufficient level of awareness for a variety of individual and synergistic risks.

4.4. HAZARD CHARACTERIZATION AND EXPOSURE ASSESSMENT

For a mixed contaminated site, the remediation team typically conducts a thorough safety analysis to assess potential impacts on site workers (and the public) such as a nuclear safety assessment and a criticality assessment, as well as evaluating the hazards associated with radioactive constituents. In addition, the team assesses exposure scenarios and pathways associated with non-radiological contaminants, such as biological contaminants, chemical contaminants and explosives. The results of the safety analysis are then incorporated into the site health and safety plan, along with remediation work plans and procedures. As new hazards are identified at the site, they become incorporated into an update of the assessment.

4.5. HEALTH AND SAFETY PLAN

Prior to initiating site remediation field activities, a health and safety plan is developed for conducting the various types of field or laboratory activities that typically integrates an existing site-wide health and safety programme with worker protection requirements specific to the worksite. The possible elements of a health and safety plan involve the following:

— Identification of key personnel;
— Determination of temperature extremes;
— Air monitoring requirements;
— Spill containment options;
— Required PPE;

— Emergency action plan;
— Results of hazard analysis;
— Medical surveillance schedules;
— Emergency response;
— Entry provisions for confined spaces;
— Decontamination (personnel and equipment);
— Training requirements.

4.6. SITE ACCESS AND HAZARD CONTROLS

An additional component of protecting worker health and safety during the conduct of mixed waste remediation is accomplished through the application of a hierarchy of access and hazard control methods. The first option to consider in implementing control of worker access to hazards is the use of engineering controls to remove or isolate the hazard (e.g. defining a support zone, contamination reduction zone, exclusion zone and control room). The next option is the use of administrative controls, and finally, PPE can be used as a supplement to the two preferred methods. Different levels of PPE may be required, beyond dealing with only the radiological component. For example, respiratory protection with specialized filters (e.g. designed to filter out certain toxic organic compounds) may be required.

4.7. SITE AND WORKER MONITORING

The health and safety officer and support technicians typically conduct appropriate monitoring of the worksite using, for example, hand-held monitoring instruments, to ensure protection of workers and the environment. There will also be a medical surveillance programme for site workers in order to minimize adverse health effects on the workforce. The medical surveillance programme would need to be broad enough to anticipate potential exposure to contaminants other than just radiological hazards.

4.8. WORKER AND EQUIPMENT DECONTAMINATION

Worker and equipment decontamination programmes are critical to expedite entry of workers, minimize the generation of costly hazardous wastes and minimize equipment replacement. Before work can begin, contamination control and decontamination programmes for workers and equipment are documented in the health and safety plan, communicated to site workers and implemented in areas where there is a possibility for exposure to chemical, biological or radiological hazards.

4.9. EMERGENCY PREPAREDNESS AND RESPONSE

On-site remediation activities also include an emergency preparedness and response plan to address potential uncontrolled hazardous substance releases causing a potential health, safety or environmental hazard, i.e. one that cannot be mitigated by personnel in the immediate work areas where the release occurs. For example, a fire at the site may come into contact with, and volatilize, certain chemical contaminants that could be released into the air. Such a plan can include the following items:

— Hazard evaluation;
— Emergency action plan (including evacuation plan);
— Emergency response plan;
— Emergency response organization;
— Emergency equipment and PPE;
— Emergency training;
— Medical surveillance;
— Emergency medical treatment, transport and first aid arrangements.

4.10. CONTINGENCY PLANNING

The remediation organization should anticipate possibilities in their plans to revise their health and safety planning in the light of new discoveries. Such 'contingency' planning allows a more efficient adaptation to necessary changes in the health and safety approach.

5. IMPLICATIONS FOR SAMPLING AND ANALYSIS

5.1. OVERVIEW

A remediation programme at a mixed contaminated site will typically require a comprehensive sampling and analysis programme for the different contaminated media, for example soils, lakes and stream sediments, surface and groundwaters and air. At such sites, both radioactive and non-radioactive contaminants are analysed for the following purposes:

(a) Characterizing the site to assess the nature and extent of contamination;
(b) Monitoring of worker health and safety;
(c) Monitoring of any potential emissions during remediation to ensure permit compliance;
(d) Monitoring of the performance and degree of success of remedial action;
(e) Taking decisions about waste streams.

The following information highlights selected considerations in conducting a sampling and analysis programme for such sites, with an emphasis on dealing with the additional complexity resulting from mixed contamination.

5.2. SAMPLING STRATEGIES

Conducting a proper sampling and analysis programme for mixed contaminated sites requires employing specialists who have expertise in both radiological and chemical sampling and analysis protocols, and in some cases microbiological sampling and analysis.

On the basis of the preliminary understanding of the site (e.g. through desk studies), the site investigator developes a thorough sampling and analysis plan that identifies the sampling and analysis protocols required for both radioactive and non-radioactive constituents. As the understanding of the site evolves (i.e. through a progression of investigative phases), the sampling and analysis programme becomes increasingly more focused. For example, the initial sampling and analysis phase may include analyses for a full suite of possible contaminants, while later analyses may be necessary for only a few key contaminants of concern.

The radioactive and non-radioactive contaminants at a site may exist in the field intermixed together, or in isolation. Furthermore, the physical phase of these contaminants may vary within the same area as well (Section 2). For example, in the subsurface a particular organic contaminant may occur in either a liquid or gas phase within the soils, or be dissolved in the groundwater. Thus the sampling and analysis programme needs to anticipate these possibilities.

In a sampling and analysis programme in soils or sediments, it is also worthwhile to consider making a full mineralogical and geochemical analysis of the soils affected by the contamination to better understand possible interactions between the soils and contaminants of concern. This understanding, in turn, may assist in the understanding of the specific contaminant forms present and contaminant migration rates.

Analysis of soils may be worthwhile for natural microbes that might be present in the contaminated soils, as these natural microbes may have an impact on contaminant migration and the degradation of certain contaminants (e.g. organic degradation of carbon tetrachloride). This requires a special sampling and testing methodology.

The key to analysing contaminants is an understanding of the physical characteristics, temperature, barometric pressure and other parameters in the contaminated media. For example, variations in barometric pressure can have an impact on the amount of volatile organic compounds (or even radon) measured in the soil at a specific time.

Non-intrusive characterization methods (e.g. involving georadar and geoelectrics) will help to identify those areas where special precautions may need to be taken.

5.3. SAMPLING TECHNIQUES

International and national standards [78] provide guidance for the choice of sampling methods for hazardous constituents depending on the media. In various Member States procedures are approved by regulatory authorities for measuring the presence and concentration of physical and chemical contaminants, within different types of media.

Among the typical media to be sampled relative to remediation of sites contaminated with radioactive and hazardous contaminants are:

— Soils and sediments;
— Groundwater;
— Surface water;
— Air.

Sampling techniques for media contaminated by both radioactive materials and hazardous materials are usually the same as those used for media contaminated by one or the other of these types of contaminant.

Tables 3–6 provide a comparison of the effectiveness of the sampling techniques widely used for soils and sediments [79].

The investigator may consider using 'field screening' analytical techniques that can address both radioactive and non-radioactive constituents. For example, a field gas chromatograph can be used to quickly identify certain contaminants while in the field, thus accelerating decision taking. Typically, these analyses would need to be corroborated by analyses made using qualified or standardized techniques conducted at a certified laboratory, to be accepted by certain regulatory agencies. Use of field screening technologies can reduce the costs of a sampling and analysis programme.

In the following some general remarks are made concerning special precautions taken during sampling and analysis at sites with mixed contamination.

TABLE 3. SHALLOW SOIL SAMPLING METHODS

	Subject of laboratory analysis								Sample type			Depth		
	Radionuclides	Volatiles	Semivolatiles	Metals	Pesticides	PCBs	TPH[a]	Geotechnical	Grab	Composite (vertical)	Composite (areal)	Surface (0.0–0.152 m)	Shallow (0.0–1.52 m)	Lithology description
Scoop	1	2	1	1	1	1	1		1		1	1		1
Hand auger	1		1	1	1	1	1			1	2	1	1	1
Slide hammer	1	1	1	1	1	1	1		1	1	2	1	1	2
Open tube									1			1	1	1
Split tube/ solid tube	1/1	1/1	1/1	1/1	1/1	1/1	1/1		1/1	1/2	2/2		1	1/2
Thin walled tube								1	1				1	

[a] TPH, total petroleum hydrocarbons.

TABLE 4. DEEP SOIL SAMPLING METHODS

	Subject of laboratory analysis								Sample type			Depth	
	Radionuclides	Volatiles	Semivolatiles	Metals	Pesticides	PCBs	TPH[a]	Geotechnical	Grab	Composite (vertical)	Composite (areal)	Deep (> 1.52 m)	Lithology description
Split tube/ solid tube	1/1	1/1	1/1	1/1	1/1	1/1	1/1		1/1	1/2	2/2	1/1	1/2
Thin walled tube								1	1			1	

[a] TPH, total petroleum hydrocarbons.

TABLE 5. SEDIMENT SAMPLING METHODS FOR STREAMS, RIVERS AND SURFACE WATER DRAINAGE

	Subject of laboratory analysis								Sample type			Depth		
	Radionuclides	Volatiles	Semivolatiles	Metals	Pesticides	PCBs	TPH[a]	Geotechnical	Grab	Composite (vertical)	Composite (areal)	Surface (0.0–0.152 m)	Shallow (0.0–1.52 m)	Lithology description
Scoop	2	2	2	2	2	2	2		2		2	2		2
Slide hammer	1	1	1	1	1	1	1		1	1	1	2	1	2
Box sampler	1	2	1	1	1	1	1		1		1	1		1

[a] TPH, total petroleum hydrocarbons.

TABLE 6. SEDIMENT SAMPLING METHODS FOR PONDS, LAKES AND RETENTION BASINS

	Subject of laboratory analysis								Sample type			Depth		
	Radionuclides	Volatiles	Semivolatiles	Metals	Pesticides	PCBs	TPH[a]	Geotechnical	Grab	Composite (vertical)	Composite (areal)	Surface (0.0–1.52 m)	Shallow (0.0–0.152 m)	Lithology description
Scoop or dipper	2	2	2	2	2	2	2		2		2	2		2
Slide hammer	1	1	1	1	1	1	1		1	1	1	2	1	2
Box sampler	1	2	1	1	1	1	1		1		1	1		1
Dredge sampler	1	2	1	1	1	1	1		1		1	1		1

[a] TPH, total petroleum hydrocarbons.

It is important to understand that certain constituents have transit times that must not be exceeded prior to analysis. The use of adequate containers with simple or double containment and cooling or freezing of samples is an example of common and best practice in sampling media contaminated with radioactive and hazardous substances. The scientific literature and national regulations provide relevant information.

The quantity required for the analysis of various non-radiological constituents varies dependent upon the analytical method and the required detection limit. This may place constraints on the sampling technique to be employed.

The investigator may need to contract more than one analytical laboratory since certain laboratories may, for example, not allow radioactively contaminated samples into their facilities. Other laboratories may only conduct analyses for radioactive contaminants.

Collecting samples and making analyses results in wastes for which adequate treatment and disposal routes have to be established. Depending on the type of contract and the regulations of the Member State they may fall into the responsibility of either the contracting analytical laboratory or the owner of the samples. In the latter case, the remaining samples and wastes are returned to the originator.

The complexities of conducting a sampling and analysis programme at a mixed contaminant site may give rise to significant additional costs that have to be adequately considered in the project budget.

During the actual remediation process, on-line monitoring of certain contaminants may be required, for instance, to:

— Control process performance, for example in the case of on-site treatment of contaminated material;
— Ensure compliance with health and safety requirements;
— Monitor emissions to the environment, such as air emissions;
— Decide on waste stream options.

Groundwater is typically sampled via monitoring wells using various types of pumps or bailers. It is critical to ensure that steps are taken to ensure that there is sufficient purging of wells such that the samples taken for analysis are representative of the actual formation water. Purging a well prior to taking a sample may potentially result in mixed contaminated wastewater for which an adequate disposal or discharge route has to be established. In addition, the purging may result in venting of hazardous volatile compounds so that adequate precautions have to be taken. There is an extensive body of literature and regulations at the national level on water sampling procedures and their respective applicabilities in given circumstances and for given groundwater constituents.

It should also be noted that establishing groundwater wells and the sampling process itself can introduce chemicals that may have an impact on the analysis, including petroleum products, solvents or grease. When selecting a drilling or sampling technique this potential source of confounding contamination has to be considered. The equipment to be used in sampling, including the well construction materials, needs to be thoroughly cleaned before being used in this environment. Again, there is a large body of scientific and technical literature on this subject, the review of which is beyond the scope of this report.

Special procedures are required for the sampling of volatile compounds from the groundwater and the soil air. These procedures prevent degassing of water samples or provide for sampling the headspace. Further details can be found in the specialized literature.

In recent years sampling techniques that result in little or no wastes have been developed, such as cone penetrometers that are also equipped to take samples from both the saturated and unsaturated zones. A penetrometer essentially consists of a hollow rod that is pushed into the ground, using as a counterweight the vehicle on which the equipment is mounted. Screened ports allow the abstraction of water or gas samples. The rod head may also be provided with geophysical logging tools, such as electrodes for geoelectrical measurements. These, together with the cone penetration resistance, provide stratigraphic information.

5.4. HEALTH AND SAFETY PRECAUTIONS

Sampling at sites with mixed contaminants may require additional health and safety measures for workers involved in the sampling programme, over and above radiation safety measures. There may be risks of fire, explosion, skin burns, ingestion of toxic substances, inhalation of volatile hazardous substances or contamination by biological agents.

Site workers may need to take precautions during the drilling and sampling of areas contaminated with volatile organic compounds, as toxic vapours may be present around the drilling rig or excavation pit. In this case, appropriate hand-held monitoring by a health and safety technician for both radioactivity and volatile organic compounds at the borehole would be suggested. Arrangements for safe handling and decontamination of field sampling equipment may need to be made.

Sampling in such areas might also have to be done cautiously because of the risk of creating sparks that could ignite any volatile vapours present. The equipment and machinery used may need to be protected from explosions. In addition, a sampling team may need to be properly attired in PPE, including respirators, have available a permanent vacuum cleaning system for dust and ensure that there is containment and ventilation in the sampling area.

In addition, precise and durable labelling of the samples and an indication of potential hazards from contaminants is particularly important. The various analytical laboratories may not otherwise be aware of the spectrum of hazards associated with a specific sample.

5.5. QUALITY CONTROL AND QUALITY ASSURANCE

Confidence in site characterization rests on the data provided by sampling and analysis being consistent and accurate. Therefore, the quality assurance of the analysis and sampling practices is of vital importance. The strategy employed is two pronged, involving both standardized sampling and analytical techniques as well as the associated quality management procedures.

As has been pointed out already, over the last few decades a comprehensive system of standards and procedures to control and assure quality during the collection and analysis of environmental samples has been developed, both in many Member States and on the international level. The actual methods and analytical techniques may differ from Member State to Member State, even though they may emulate ISO standards [78]. The overall concepts of quality management have been collated in the ISO 9000 family of standards [80, 81].

It is increasingly required, both by the public and private sectors, that companies undertaking field investigations and laboratories performing analyses be accredited with a relevant government body or be certified to comply with ISO 9000. Certified laboratories are audited periodically.

6. ELEMENTS OF THE REMEDIATION PROCESS

6.1. OVERVIEW

This section considers the overall remediation process for a site and in particular the factors governing the selection of the most suitable remediation option. The general procedures for site characterization and development of remediation strategies have been outlined in various IAEA reports [2, 7, 14, 16, 19, 20]. This section will focus on aspects pertinent to mixed contamination problems.

6.2. MANAGEMENT OPTIONS

The most suitable option will be the one that can be implemented with assurance of success and that provides the most benefits or results in the least damage to the environment as a whole, at acceptable cost, in the long term, as well as in the short term. It will usually be the outcome of a systematic consultative decision making procedure. A wide range of technical and management options will need to be considered and evaluated. Options are assessed against a wide range of criteria such as environmental and human health effects, regulatory acceptability, technical feasibility, effectiveness and cost. These criteria are considered in more detail in Ref. [16].

The option studies normally involve obtaining quantitative and qualitative information about the various options, initial screening of options on the basis of operational and regulatory constraints, proven risk reduction performance, environmental performance, etc. and a final analysis of the favoured options using a pragmatic application of decision support techniques. A quantitative decision making tool, such as multicriteria analysis, helps to make the process more transparent, traceable and better documented should any (legal) challenges arise later [16].

The remediation processes may need to be implemented in phases. For example, a technique used during the initial phase of cleanup may no longer be efficient or economical during later phases, and may need to be replaced with a different type of process.

The handling and disposal of any wastes arising from remediation need to be considered carefully. Otherwise a worse situation, including mixed waste that is more of a liability, may arise.

The process of making judgements on what might be the most suitable management option in environmental remediation projects has been considered in previous IAEA reports [2, 16]. The four main steps of a remedial action (see also Fig. 2) are:

(1) *Design of the most suitable management option* — including the design, construction, licensing and commissioning of any supporting technologies. This will also include preparation of necessary safety assessments/ cases for different stages of the process/plant design and operation and of a full environmental impact assessment for the management option.

(2) *Implementation of the most suitable management option* — through to achievement of the required remedial objectives and target levels for residual contamination.

(3) *Monitoring* — in order to (independently) verify and certify the achievement of the remediation goals.

(4) *Closeout* — of any remedial works, decommissioning of any remediation plant, installation of any long term monitoring systems and demobilization. At this stage any long term liability management (stewardship) plans [75] would also begin to be implemented.

Some of the above stages are often iterated, as additional data needs are identified requiring, for example, further characterization or refined assessments.

If active remediation is to be undertaken, this process will also involve the selection of suitable techniques to effect the most suitable management option.

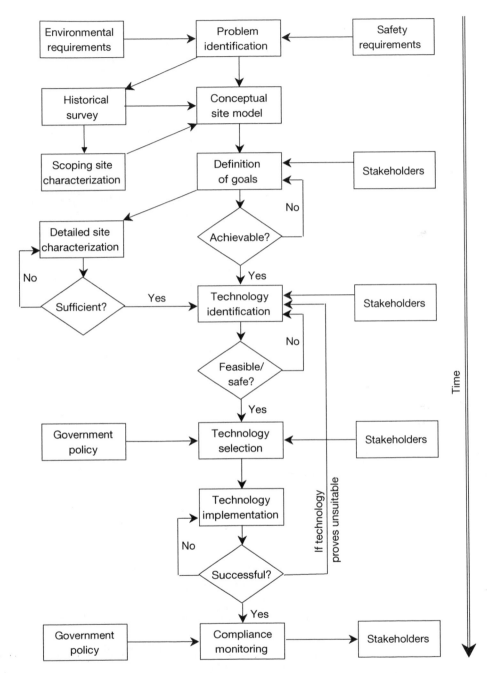

FIG. 2. Phases of decision making in remediation strategies and technologies.

These techniques, alone or in combination, will usually be chosen by an analogous approach to that for the management. An iterative procedure to develop an integrated management and technological approach will almost always be required (Fig. 2). Criteria for technology selection are discussed in Section 7.

6.3. INTERACTIONS WITH NATIONAL AND LOCAL REGULATORY BODIES

It has been pointed out in Section 3 that different types of contaminant typically fall under the remit of different regulatory authorities. As a consequence, the interactions with regulators and licensing authorities tend to be more complex in cases of mixed contamination. To simplify the process, typically one authority is mandated to take the lead. Normally, it would be the authority within the remit of whom falls the highest risk.

The regulatory authorities would have monitored the ongoing process, but at this stage the target levels for the remediation activities will be defined. Remediation targets or goals are media specific cleanup criteria for a given remedial action. They can be qualitative statements or numerical values, expressed as concentrations of a contaminant in an environmental medium, or they can be specified residual risks. They will be developed for all contaminants that are major contributors to the risk.

In practice, one risk may be dominant and the remediation targets are chosen to address this risk alone, notwithstanding any implications for the management of residues from remedial action.

6.4. PARTICIPATION OF OTHER STAKEHOLDERS

Early interaction with relevant stakeholders, including for example, regulators, local and regional government, the public and special interest groups, to identify long term management goals, acceptable management strategies, remediation targets and long term uses of the site, and is generally considered to facilitate the process. However, this report focuses on technological issues and more details on participation of other stakeholders are provided in recent and forthcoming technical reports [16, 75].

6.5. SITE ASSESSMENT

6.5.1. The process

Once a site has been identified as of potential concern, there is a generic overall process of assessment that is usually followed [2]. Assessment may be curtailed at any stage if it is judged that the risks are insufficient to warrant further action. Throughout the process the emphasis for mixed contaminant sites is on the consideration of all of the contaminants and hazardous substances present rather than only those with a radioactive nature. There are a number of key stages in this process that are outlined in the following.

6.5.2. Historical review

It is very important to understand the source of contamination, and the processes involved in its generation, in order to better understand the potential chemical form of the contaminant and the species present. The presence of other contaminants may alter the general form and behaviour of the contamination.

The historical review is a valuable tool with which to narrow down the range of contaminants that have possibly to be dealt with. Such a review is comparatively cheap, as it does not involve actual work on the site. It comprises a review of the history of the site, identification and examination of any records available, (industrial) processes used that may have resulted in contamination, potential contaminants present, any known past contamination incidents on- and off-site, and any monitoring or past characterization studies. It is at this first stage that consideration needs to be given to the potential mixed nature of contamination.

6.5.3. Scoping site characterization

A scoping characterization will then be undertaken on the basis of the results of the historical survey to determine whether a site is likely to pose significant risks and warrants further consideration. Assessment will use the above data with site observations to establish an overview of the extent of contamination and the degree of threat to human health and the environment. The need for additional physical characterization, for example, radiological surveys, and soil sampling and analysis, will be established at this stage to fully define the nature and extent of contamination. For large complex sites with mixed contamination, it may be expedient to outline a number of smaller subunits of similar characteristics within the site.

6.5.4. Conceptual site model

A conceptual model of contaminant distribution and potential migration patterns will be developed on the basis of the data gathered. This serves to both summarize the results and direct further investigations. As the site characterization process advances, the model is further refined. Site characterization and the development of the conceptual model are iterative steps.

6.5.5. Detailed site characterization

If warranted and needed, a detailed site characterization programme is developed on the basis of the conceptual model. This aims to delineate in sufficient detail the nature and extent of all contaminants, clearly identifying 'hot spots', and to delineate areas that do not require further attention. The objectives of a detailed site characterization are to:

— Guide the following remedial action;
— Enable quantitative assessments of the hazards posed by all of the contaminants on the site to workers, the public and the environment, both on- and off-site, at present and in the future;
— Establish the 'background' conditions in and around the site for baseline comparisons;
— Establish 'initial' conditions against which the performance and effectiveness of the remedial action is judged;
— Guide the selection of appropriate remediation techniques;
— Identify potential waste streams, in order to develop waste minimization strategies and plan disposal routes.

6.6. RISK AND PRELIMINARY ENVIRONMENTAL IMPACT ASSESSMENTS

The conceptual site model and the results from the site characterization are used to perform risk and environmental impact assessments. These consider the site in its present state, as well as the remediation process and the foreseen end state of the site.

The assessment considers the level of risk posed by the contaminants present and the pathways of significance to site users, the public and the environment. Both the current contamination situation, and its evolution in time with and without remedial action are investigated. Current and potential site uses need to be considered. Site use is the driver for developing long term management strategies for a site. It is also the basis for determining acceptable residual contamination levels, i.e. cleanup targets, for given, acceptable, levels of residual risk [11].

The presence of multiple contaminants introduces particular complexities into these assessments through, for example, the presence of wider ranges of possible concentrations, changes in chemical forms due to interactions between contaminants, combined toxicities and other hazards, and new or accelerated migration pathways. These can result in zones containing different levels of activities and representing different levels of risk. Discriminating between these is also a major challenge in characterization, if the areas and volumes of material are to be managed effectively [7, 82].

In certain cases, the non-radiological component of a contaminated site may be determined to be the greater, or a more immediate risk, to the public or environment, and thus may be the higher priority for remediation. The reasons may be inter alia that some radionuclides are less mobile, i.e. not migrating as quickly as the non-radiological components.

7. TECHNOLOGY EVALUATION AND SELECTION

7.1. TECHNICAL FACTORS TO BE CONSIDERED

Fundamentally, there is a much greater range of toxic chemicals and hazardous materials than there are radionuclides. These contaminants have a very wide range of chemical and physical properties. When selecting a remediation technique or combinations of techniques one has to beware of introducing synergistic effects by mixing hazards, and different methods of quantitative risk assessment may be required. There is a further fundamental difference between contaminants relating to their lifetime: radionuclides cannot be destroyed and only disappear by radioactive decay. For radionuclides with short half-lives, such as tritium, risks will fall over a relatively short period of time. However, radionuclides with long half-lives pose potential risks over very long timescales. Heavy metals represent the ultimate expression of this case, as they are persistent. This considerably limits the technical options for the treatment of radioactive and metal wastes. Such wastes can only be either contained or diluted and dispersed.

This is typically not the case for organic contaminants. All organic compounds can be destroyed by suitable processing. Ideally the processing destroys the contaminant to leave simple benign products, for example CO_2 or H_2O, or it can remove the hazardous properties, for example by oxidation of flammable organic compounds. Some compounds can be removed or destroyed with relative ease in the environment, for example by biochemical or chemical degradation, or by volatilization. Other compounds, for example PCBs, are very persistent and degrade extremely slowly in the normal environment [22]. They are also difficult to degrade in situ, particularly when present at low, but toxicologically significant, levels. Organic compounds are generally degraded in stages, often giving rise to other organic compounds as stable intermediate compounds. These degradation products have different chemical, physical and toxic properties. It may be noted that in some cases the intermediate degradation products may be more toxic than the parent organic compound, for example, formation of vinyl chloride from the degradation of some chlorinated solvents. In addition, they may have different solubilities and mobilities from the parent, leading in some cases to higher migration rates. These differences introduce greater difficulties than those experienced with conventional radioactive contamination, but also opportunities to apply a much greater range of treatment processes. They also introduce opportunities in some cases to reduce chemical and radionuclide contaminant migration rates by, for example, selective removal of carrier phases.

The following are general considerations related to sites where there are co-mingled radioactive and non-radioactive components:

(a)　In situ treatment processes must be fully assessed to ensure that they do not worsen the contaminant situation, for example, by enhancing the mobility of some radionuclides through introducing lixiviants.

(b)　Intentionally altering the geochemistry of a contaminated site, using, for example, in situ treatment techniques affecting chemical, thermal, pH and redox potential properties, can potentially alter the forms and mobilities of non-target contaminants in a detrimental way.

(c)　Additional challenges are introduced into the remediation process by DNAPLs and LNAPLs.

(d)　Complexation of radionuclides and heavy metals by certain organic contaminants may have occurred and needs to be considered when developing the conceptual model of the site and when selecting remediation approaches.

(e)　A site containing several different types of contaminant may require several different stages of treatment, for example, a separation process followed by thermal treatment, resulting in multiple waste streams.

(f)　Some techniques, for example, separation and concentration techniques, selected for a non-radioactive contaminant could potentially induce nuclear criticality of the radioactive component. A criticality analysis may be required prior to selecting and implementing a specific remediation process.

7.2. FUNDAMENTAL TECHNICAL CHOICES

The objective of any remedial action is to reduce risks to human health, the environment and property to acceptable levels by removing or reducing the source of contamination or by blocking exposure pathways. Once the decision has been made that some remedial action is necessary, there are various potential options for achieving that objective. These need to be selected and tailored to the environment affected, the type of contaminants present, the behaviour of the contaminants in the environment and the exposure pathways that exist. For sites with mixed contamination, it is often necessary to use several remediation technologies, sometimes in series, i.e. treatment trains, to effectively address risk from the radioactive, chemical and physical hazards that could be present. In addition, sites may have contamination in different media. It is not uncommon, for example, on sites with extensive soil contamination, to also have groundwater contamination. Different technologies will probably be needed for remediating the different problems.

There are three basic choices for any intended remedial actions. These are:

(1) Leave the site under consideration undisturbed while establishing a monitoring scheme for determining the evolution of the site. This option relies on natural processes to prevent significant exposure. The entire process needs to be carefully monitored so that an alternative can be initiated if required.

(2) Contain or restrict the mobility of the radioactive contaminants. Such technologies aim to immobilize the contaminants inside the area where they already exist, reducing the potential for further migration or entry into active pathways for exposure.

(3) Remove or destroy contaminants, using an appropriate treatment scheme. Such treatment technologies aim to extract, concentrate and then safely dispose of the contaminants at another location. In the case of organic compounds (bio)degradation may be a possible way to remove the source term.

The above generic options can be summarized using the brief expression 'monitored non-intervention, containment or removal'. Each one of the above fundamental technical choices will direct decision makers to substantially different paths with regard to their subsequent choices, actions and potential results, making available significantly different technological options for application (Fig. 3).

It may be worth noting that in certain cases the radionuclide(s) present may have a sufficiently short half-life, allowing it/them first to decay to a level below that of concern, i.e. applying monitored non-intervention, before treating the other contaminants, thus reducing the problem to a 'conventional' contamination problem.

This choice, as discussed in the relevant IAEA publications [2, 16], cannot be made solely on the basis of scientific or engineering considerations. In addition to technical constraints, there may a wide range of regulatory and socioeconomic constraints to selecting an appropriate remediation or disposal strategy [16]. Regulations in Member States may favour certain techniques and prohibit or discourage others. International agreements may also preclude or restrict some strategies. As has been discussed in great detail elsewhere [83], because public acceptability can be a major factor in selecting a particular remediation technique, the local population should participate in the remediation decision making process. Active inclusion of the public may increase their knowledge/awareness of the problem, their acceptance of the remediation technology selected for deployment and their acceptance of any

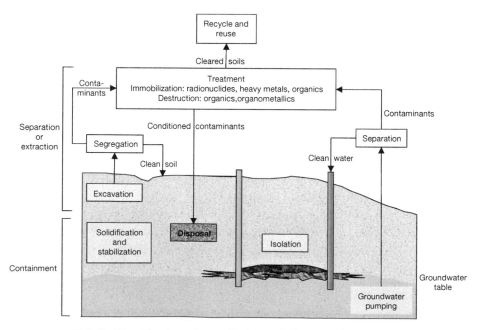

FIG. 3. Classification of remediation techniques by function [84].

restrictions on land use that may result. Participation may also enhance the public's willingness to support the long term maintenance of remediation measures/installations. Decision aiding tools make clearer the evaluation criteria used to support the selection of a technology to meet remediation objectives [16].

Once these points have been clarified, measures may be chosen taking the following considerations into account.

7.3. TECHNOLOGY SOURCES

A wide variety of remediation techniques are now commercially available or at the demonstration stage. Although most of the techniques are of a generic nature, others use proprietary formulations of reactants and other agents, or applications that are protected by patents and similar means. Because the field is continuously developing, formal methods to assess the applicability and effectiveness of technologies have been developed [85]. Approaches to selecting technologies vary from Member State to Member State. Some countries regularly undertake technology assessments to help ensure that proposed projects are effective and efficient. The findings are typically made accessible in technology directories or bibliographies, see, for example Ref. [86]. There are also international, semi-governmental, industrial or research community sponsored initiatives, see, for example, Ref. [87]. Technology and technology supplier directories are also available [88]. Other Member States and organizations rely on informal approaches, for instance on the basis of personal judgement by experts and managers, to select technologies.

7.4. EVALUATION CRITERIA

Once measurable remediation objectives have been established, several factors have an impact on the decision making process [16]. These basic evaluation criteria include engineering and non-engineering considerations:

— Effectiveness in remediating the contamination;
— Cost associated with the remediation programme;
— Occupational safety and health risks associated with the technology;
— Potential secondary environmental impacts (collateral damage);
— Prior experience with the application of the technology;
— Sustainability of any institutional control required;
— Socioeconomic considerations.

7.4.1. Effectiveness

The term 'effectiveness' is a measure of the ability of a technology to remove or reduce contaminants to prevent exposure or undue detriment to other properties of the site [89]. There is often a preference amongst regulatory bodies for selecting remedial actions that employ treatment technologies that, as their principal element, permanently and significantly reduce the toxicity, mobility or volume of the hazardous contaminants. Permanent and significant reductions can be achieved through destroying toxic contaminants, reducing total mass, irreversibly reducing the contaminant mobility or reducing the total volume of contaminated media. This criterion focuses the evaluation of an alternative on a variety of specific factors:

— Treatment processes used and materials they treat;
— Amount of hazardous materials destroyed or treated;
— Degree of expected reduction in toxicity, mobility or volume described as a percentage of reduction;
— Degree to which the treatment is irreversible;
— Type and quantity of treatment residuals that remain following treatment;
— Ability of the alternative to satisfy the statutory preference for treatment as a principal element.

Another key objective is often that the remediation should not only improve the situation by eliminating contaminant exposure pathways for health risk but also not be detrimental to the long term environmental qualities of the site. For example, the functionality of soils has to be retained to avoid unnecessary restrictions on future land use.

Another factor to consider in assessing long term effectiveness is the magnitude of the residual risk, i.e. the risk remaining from untreated wastes or treatment residuals remaining after remedial activities have been completed. The characteristics of the residual wastes need to be considered to the degree that they remain hazardous, taking into account their volume, toxicity, mobility and any propensity to bioaccumulate.

The adequacy and reliability of controls, for example, containment systems and institutional controls used to manage the residual risks, need to be considered. These include the long term reliability of the management controls necessary for continued protection from residual risk and assessment of the potential needs for maintaining and replacing the technical components of the remedial solution.

Site specific considerations have an impact on the effectiveness and efficiency of the chosen remediation method. Because the mineralogical and geochemical characteristics of the contaminant vary among contaminated sites, remediation methods are not universally effective and efficient. Methods to model and predict the effectiveness of technologies under consideration have been developed. The anticipated performance of a given technique can be simulated and compared with similar results from other techniques to facilitate the selection. The remediation action will be complemented by a post-remediation assessment and monitoring programme to assure its efficacy [90] and that may also be part of any institutional control required on residual contamination [12, 91].

Steps have already been undertaken to incorporate remediation activities into the ISO 9000 quality management systems [81]. Record keeping is an integral part of quality assurance and quality control. It is essential that records are kept of remedial actions undertaken, so that at any later point in time their performance can be evaluated against that of the original design. Having comprehensive documentation available also facilitates interventions in the case of unsatisfactory performance.

7.4.2. Ease of implementation

An assessment is required of the ease or difficulty of implementing the option. This will involve both technical and administrative/regulatory consider-ations. The former include difficulties in constructing and operating the process, the likelihood of technical problems during implementation that might lead to delays in schedule, the ease of undertaking additional remedial action, should it be necessary, and the ability to monitor the effectiveness of the remedy. The administrative considerations are in essence project risk factors. They include the ease with which the option can be coordinated with other on-site works, etc., and the potential for new regulatory constraints to develop, for example, uncovering buried historical remains or encountering endangered species. They also include the availability of any required off-site treatment, storage and disposal facilities with sufficient capacity, availability of necessary equipment and specialists as well as provisions to ensure any necessary additional resources, availability of services and materials, and availability of prospective technologies.

7.4.3. Cost

The term 'cost' in this section is intended to cover the direct expenditure of funds associated with the remediation technology. This includes the costs for design, construction management, equipment, labour and materials to deploy the technology, licensing the technology, treatability studies, operations and maintenance, monitoring, and disposal of residual wastes. Standard engineering cost principles can be applied to develop cost estimates for remediation technologies.

Cost data for a wide variety of remediation techniques are available from various sources. For example, the appendix of a recent IAEA report [16] provides an overview of remediation cost, drawing on national directories, such as the HCAS [92] in the USA, that provide useful material for relative cost assessments of the techniques listed.

Long term monitoring, surveillance and maintenance can be a major cost element. Depending on the time for which institutional control is required, provisions have to be made for funding these activities over periods of decades or even centuries.

In any comparison of technologies, discounted lifetime costs can also be determined for each option using nationally approved procedures, for example, discounted cash flow or net present value calculations, and discount rates. Consideration may also be given to different cash flow–time options, for example, uniform cash flows and low capital costs. The cost of remediation should be commensurate with the added level of protection afforded to the public by its implementation.

The costs associated with remediating a mixed contaminant site are likely to be higher than for those for 'simple' sites due to the added complexity and multiple waste streams.

7.4.4. Occupational safety and health

The term 'occupational safety and health' in this section is intended to cover the potential hazards and risks to workers involved in implementing the remediation technology [2]. Safety risks may result from accidents during deployment. Health risks may result from workers being exposed to radionuclides and other contaminants. Because the occupational risks of different technologies can vary substantially, these risks may be an important consideration in selecting a technology.

Worker and public health and safety is a critical component of any remediation project and is an essential consideration in developing characterization strategies and choosing a particular remediation option(s). The remediation of a mixed contaminant site is typically complex and requires a significant amount of evaluation. The costs of a remediation project can rise significantly as a result of establishing the necessary health and safety practices.

During a remediation programme at a mixed contaminant site, the health and safety programme will cover all phases where workers and the public are at risk, including site characterization. For example, during the characterization phase, workers may be exposed to toxic chemicals while taking samples and undertaking other field work. As another example, during extraction and treatment of organic contaminants, site workers could become exposed to vapours if working in confined spaces (e.g. in an excavation pit) or through leaks in a soil vapour extraction (SVE) system. Another possibility is that the remediation technique may be subject to an accident that results in a fire, with release of toxic emissions. The types of hazard that might be addressed in a mixed contaminant remediation project include, but are not limited to, radiological, chemical, biological, explosive, industrial, electrical and transportation hazards.

The following steps may be considered in ensuring a proper health and safety programme:

(1) Establish an effective multidisciplinary project team and conduct comprehensive work planning to avoid unsafe operations and work stoppages.
(2) Conduct a hazard characterization and exposure assessment to determine the breadth of the health and safety programme, and the associated cost and impact.
(3) Develop a site specific health and safety plan.
(4) Establish access and hazard controls during the characterization and remediation activities through the application of a hierarchy of access and hazard control methods; this may include, for example, using remote handling equipment, establishing special, enclosed, working areas, or using appropriate levels of personal protective clothing [77].
(5) Establish place and procedures for decontamination of personnel and equipment.

These elements are commonly accompanied by rigorous training and medical surveillance programmes for the site workers, as well as an emergency preparedness and response plan.

Remediation of a contaminated site involving the removal of large numbers of drums or other packaged wastes may give rise to specific safety concerns. Drums may be corroded and containment not assured. Special attention may need to be given to the risks associated with, for example, mechanical or manual handling, inhalation of contaminated vapour or dust, and fire and explosion hazards. In this respect, the risks associated with chemical, flammable and explosive materials may be greater than those associated with radiological hazards. The remediation of some chemically contaminated sites has already given rise to severe accidents and deaths.

Many remediation projects will involve a wide range of conventional civil engineering activities including:

— Decommissioning and decontamination of buildings;
— Stabilization of excavations;
— Transport and storage of excavated soils;
— Contouring and similar civil engineering activities;
— Excavations;
— Drainage of excavations;
— Sorting of contaminated soils.

These lead to typical building site exposures and hazards such as weather, draughts, dust, fumes, gases, noise and vibration, suspended loads and moving machinery. Some of these may be associated in addition with toxic or radioactive exposures. The toxicity or radioactivity of hazards may be known or unknown in quantity and intensity, and may vary over the project duration.

A variety of precautions can be taken, such as the establishment of safe procedures, technical measures and personal protective measures. Technical measures include, for instance, use of remote handling equipment and enclosed cabins on earth moving equipment, while personal protection measures largely consist of protective clothing and use of respirators [77]. Monitoring of the concentrations of hazardous materials in the various workplace media is an integral part of health and safety measures.

Safe procedures are designed to minimize the handling of hazardous material and to handle it in such a way that a minimum of dispersion occurs. Such procedures also ensure that the organizations and people involved in the remediation project are adequately qualified for the project in hand.

7.4.5. Secondary environmental impacts

The implementation of a remediation project may result in a variety of environmental impacts in addition to those resulting from the contamination itself. When a remediation strategy is selected, the impact of this strategy on the local environment may need to be evaluated (operational safety cases) to determine the net reduction in hazards, i.e. it will not be reasonable to cause more harm as a result of the remediation than by undertaking no remediation at the site. For instance, certain technologies, such as removal of topsoil or soil washing, may remove surface contamination at the cost of destroying the soil ecosystem.

Environmental risk involves adverse impacts on ecological receptors located on-site or off-site due to significant disturbance to the site ecosystem and its surroundings as a result of remediation. Impacts to be considered will be:

— Nuisances, for example noise, vibration, dust and traffic;
— Impacts on water resources, for example surface and groundwater contamination;
— Impacts on soils, for example, reduced fertility.

Depending on the size of the site, an area larger than the actual contamination may be required for installations, intermediate storage of wastes, etc. Removal, transport and disposal of residual wastes may result in environmental impacts and risks at locations other than those of the original contamination. There is, for example, little benefit in removing a contaminant that is well fixed on a low volume of soil, only to produce a high volume of aqueous wastes with the contaminant in a soluble or mobile form. In addition, the remediation techniques chosen may generate large quantities of secondary wastes and may pose risks of exposure to the public or operators that exceed the risks of quiescent contamination [93].

Environmental risk arising from the implementation of remedial actions may also extend to possible impacts on natural resources, such as surface water, groundwater, air, geological resources or biological resources. The potential for environmental risk may be an important factor in decision making because some remediation technologies are more likely than others to produce adverse impacts on ecological receptors, including habitat disruption, or to generate damage to natural resources.

7.4.6. Prior experience

The term 'prior experience' in this section is intended to cover the track record associated with implementing the remediation technology at other sites. It can be very useful to know whether the technology has been used successfully in the past. Information about previous deployments is available from a number of sources including vendors, regulatory authorities, professional organizations, internet databases, trade associations and publications (Section 7.3).

7.4.7. Socioeconomic considerations

The term 'socioeconomic considerations' in this section is intended to cover political, social and economic factors that may influence the selection of a remediation technology and its application to a site with dispersed radioactive contamination. The legal and institutional framework, prevailing socioeconomic boundary conditions and public perceptions can influence the choice and deployment of technologies for remediation of sites with dispersed radioactive contamination [17]. The level of public reassurance generally increases with the degree of intervention and, hence, with the cost of the operation [84].

7.5. OVERVIEW OF REMEDIATION TECHNIQUES

In Tables 7–11 an overview of available remediation techniques is given together with an indication of the groups of substances for which they are suitable. The lists are by no means exhaustive. Details of the remediation techniques and strategies that appear particularly suitable for mixed contamination are discussed in more detail in subsequent sections.

Tables 7–11 combine both techniques for recovering contaminants from soils and groundwater, as well as techniques for concentrating and conditioning contaminants. Unlike radionuclides and heavy metals, organic compounds can also be destroyed. Various in situ and ex situ techniques are listed in Tables 7–11.

It must be emphasized that almost certainly and for almost all practical cases any of the methods and technologies discussed will not 'remediate' a given contamination on its own. Owing to physicochemical properties, behaviour and initial conditions, any one technology will leave behind a certain residual level of contamination. Other remediation technologies, more appropriate and effective for this residual contamination level, will then have to be applied.

8. MONITORED NON-INTERVENTION

8.1. JUSTIFICATION

A variety of naturally occurring physical, chemical and biological processes in the subsurface can reduce contaminant concentrations at a given point in space and time without human intervention. The combination of these processes is known as natural attenuation. A special technical report is

TABLE 7. CONTAINMENT TECHNIQUES USED IN REMEDIATION

Technology	Medium	Contaminant	Brief characterization
Reactive barriers	Ground-water	Organic compounds, heavy metals and radionuclides	This is an in situ method of funnelling the natural or enhanced groundwater flow through a physical barrier containing reactive chemicals (oxidation or precipitation), metal catalysts (redox reactions), bacteria (biodegradation) or adsorbents.
In situ chemical oxidation	Soil and ground-water	Organic compounds (heavy metals and radionuclides)	The injection of ozone (O_3), hydrogen peroxide (H_2O_2) or chlorine compounds induces a redox reaction that chemically converts contaminants into less toxic compounds. This may reduce the mobility of contaminants throughout a plume.
Ex situ solidification	Soil or sludge	Radionuclides and heavy metals (organic compounds)	A low solubility solid is produced from contaminated soil by mixing it with a reactive binder (cement, gypsum, organic or inorganic polymer). The solid material may be disposed off in situ or at a designated repository.
In situ solidification	Soil and sludge	Radionuclides and heavy metals	The aim is to lower the mobility of contaminants by injecting binding materials (cement, organic or inorganic polymers) that react with the contaminant, the water and/or the soil to produce a low solubility solid.
Isolation	Soil	All types	Physical barriers, such as slurry walls or sheet piling, are installed to prevent movement of contaminants.
Vitrification	Soil and sludge	Radionuclides and heavy metals	The contaminated material is mixed with glass forming constituents and fluxes to produce solid glass blocks or slag-like products.
In situ vitrification (ISV)	Soil and sludge	Radionuclides and heavy metals	Soil is vitrified in situ to immobilize contaminants by applying electrical resistance or inductive melting.
Biosorption	Surface water and ground-water	Radionuclides and heavy metals	Certain microorganisms take up metal ions in their cell walls or on their surface; the processes involved can be used to concentrate these contaminants. Facilities can be designed as bioreactors or like sewage treatment plants (organic stationary phase).

TABLE 8. PHYSICAL REMOVAL TECHNIQUES USED IN REMEDIATION

Technology	Medium	Contaminant	Brief characterization
Excavation	Soil and sludge	All types	Contaminated materials are removed from the site and transferred to a designated disposal site. Conditioning may be required before disposal.
Pump and treat systems	Ground-water	All types	Groundwater is pumped to the surface and treated by a variety of methods. The efficiency depends on the type of contaminant and the concentration.
Funnel and gate systems	Ground-water	All types	The pump and treat methods and reactive barriers can be improved by constructing impervious walls, funnelling the water flow towards the well or the reactive barrier.
Physical segregation	Soil	Radionuclides and heavy metals	Often contaminants (including radionuclides) adsorb to fine grain size fractions in the soil. Size fractionation by sieving or flotation may thus result in a much smaller volume of contaminated material to be treated.
In situ soil washing	Soil	All types	This technique consists of flushing contaminated material in situ. It entails the injection and extraction of acidic or basic solutions, with added surfactants, chelates, etc., to dissolve, desorb and remove contaminants.
Ex situ soil washing	Soil	All types	This ex situ technique uses pH controlled solutions with the addition of acids or bases, surfactants or chelates to dissolve, desorb and remove contaminants. Organic solvents may be used for organic contaminants. A preceding size fractionation improves efficiency and reduces the volumes of material to be treated.
Ex situ filtration	Ground-water	Radionuclides and heavy metals	Contaminated ground or surface water is passed through a filter column to remove contaminated suspended solids. The resulting filter cake requires further treatment and disposal.

TABLE 8. PHYSICAL REMOVAL TECHNIQUES USED
IN REMEDIATION (cont.)

Technology	Medium	Contaminant	Brief characterization
Membrane separation	Ground-water	VOCs	A vapour–air separation method is used that involves the diffusion of VOCs through a non-porous gas separation membrane.
Air sparging	Ground-water and soil	VOCs and organic compounds	A method is used that promotes volatilization of organic compounds by air injection into the saturated zone; also promotes natural aerobic biodegradation.
Ex situ air stripping	Ground-water	VOCs and organic compounds	Removes volatiles in pumped surface or groundwater. Stripping towers (e.g. packed columns) have a concurrent flow of gas and liquid. The waste airstream may undergo further treatment by, for example, activated carbon or incineration.
Vapour phase carbon adsorption	Off gases	VOCs and organic compounds	Off-gases collected from ex situ or in situ stripping methods are routed through canisters containing granular activated carbon.
Soil vapour extraction (SVE)	Soil	VOCs	Removes VOCs from the unsaturated zone by creating a zone of low vapour pressure. SVE is most effective in highly permeable soils.
Vacuum extraction	Ground-water	VOCs	A vacuum created inside a well forces the groundwater to rise, allowing additional groundwater to flow in. Once in the well, the airflow causes some of the trapped volatile contaminants to vaporize, thus enabling the capture of VOCs through vapour extraction.
Free product recovery	Ground-water	Organic compounds	A non-miscible, liquid phase organic compound, either lighter or heavier than the groundwater, is removed by pumping from a defined horizon.

dedicated to this subject with respect to radioactive contamination [18]; hence this section focuses specifically on the applicability to mixed contamination.

In general, natural attenuation is considered a viable option when it can be determined that contaminants are degrading or becoming immobilized at a rate faster than the rate of migration and are not expected to reach human or

TABLE 9. CHEMICAL REMOVAL TECHNIQUES USED IN REMEDIATION

Technology	Medium	Contaminant	Brief characterization
Ex situ dehalogenation	Soil	Halogenated VOCs	Contaminants in excavated soils are dehalogenated using one of two processes. Base catalysed dehalogenation involves mixing the soils with sodium hydroxide (NaOH) and a catalyst in a rotary kiln. In glycolate dehalogenation, an alkaline polyethylene glycol (APEG) reagent dehalogenates the VOCs in a batch reactor. The resulting compound from either reaction is either non-hazardous or less toxic.
Ex situ oxidation	Ground-water	Organic compounds	Organic contaminants are oxidatively destroyed in extracted groundwater by UV irradiation, ozone (O_3) sparging and/or hydrogen peroxide (H_2O_2). Off-gases are generally treated by ozonation.
Ex situ chemical treatment	Ground-water	Radionuclides and heavy metals (organic compounds)	Ion exchange, precipitation, reverse osmosis, etc. are applied to concentrate contaminants for further conditioning.

ecological receptors. Doing 'nothing' may be considered the baseline option in any remediation case. In terms of expenditure on actual remediation activities, this is certainly the cheapest option. Nevertheless, it may entail a variety of other costs, including social and economic, at a later stage. Most notably cost for monitoring would arise. The cost efficiency of active remediation would be compared with this baseline option, taking all cost elements into account for all possible remediation options. The advantages of natural attenuation include reduced generation of remediation waste and possible reductions in the cross-media transfer of contaminants. The disadvantages include slower cleanup, the creation of transformation products that may be more toxic than the original contaminants, more costly site characterization, a reliance on uncertain institutional controls to ensure long term monitoring, and the chance that subsurface conditions will not support natural attenuation as long as necessary.

When natural attenuation is considered as a remediation option, monitoring is performed to assess contaminant migration, degradation and retardation. This is often referred to as monitored non-intervention. The

TABLE 10. BIOLOGICAL REMOVAL TECHNIQUES USED IN REMEDIATION

Technology	Medium	Contaminant	Brief characterization
In situ bioremediation	Soil	Organic compounds	Enzyme activity of natural soil microbes to break down contaminants is stimulated by the injection of nutrient, oxygen (for aerobic microbes) or surfactant containing solutions.
Biosorption	Surface water and ground-water	Radionuclides and heavy metals	Certain microorganisms take up metal ions in their cell walls or on their surface, a process which can be used to concentrate these contaminants. Facilities can be designed as bioreactors or like sewage treatment plants (organic stationary phase).
Constructed wetlands	Surface water and ground-water	Radionuclides and heavy metals	Contaminated waters are routed into artificial 'swamps', where the metals are taken up by plant tissue. The plants are harvested and incinerated. The resulting ashes are disposed off.
Biological wastewater treatment	Surface water and ground-water	Organic compounds (radionuclides and heavy metals)	Biological sewage treatment plants will also destroy certain organic contaminants. Bacterial populations specialized for certain contaminants may be used. The resulting sludge will also contain the majority of radionuclides and heavy metals and can be collected for further treatment.
Bio-degradation	Soil	Organic compounds	The generic process utilized in composting, landfarming and other bioremediation processes.
Composting	Soil	Organic compounds	Contaminated soil is excavated and placed in specialized facilities. Cellulose, biomass, nutrients and sometimes additional indigenous microbes are added to promote degradation. Specialized bacteria may be added to break down a particular compound.
Bioventing	Soil	Organic compounds	In situ process of injecting air into contaminated soil at an optimal rate, increasing soil O_2 concentration and thereby stimulating the growth of indigenous aerobic bacteria. Low injection rates keep volatilization to a minimum.

TABLE 10. BIOLOGICAL REMOVAL TECHNIQUES USED
IN REMEDIATION (cont.)

Technology	Medium	Contaminant	Brief characterization
Ex situ bioremediation	Soil	Organic compounds	The enzyme activity of natural soil microbes to break down contaminants is stimulated in bioreactors, treatment beds and lagoons by the addition of nutrients, oxygen (for aerobic microbes), surfactant, etc. to soils or surface water and groundwater. The process is similar to composting or sewage treatment.
Landfarming	Soil	Organic compounds	Once excavated, contaminated soils are spread over a clean area. The soil is aerated by regular turning or tilling to promote biodegradation.
Slurry phase bioremediation:	Soil and sludge	Organic compounds	An engineered process for treating contaminated soils or sludge that relies upon the mobilization of contaminants to the aqueous phase, where they are susceptible to microbial degradation.

purpose of monitoring is to ascertain compliance with regulatory requirements and to recognize emerging problems well in advance and thus to be able to implement contingency plans in good time. A strategy relying on monitored natural attenuation consists of the following three main elements: a site assessment and monitoring programme, a model to predict the site development and a contingency plan. These three elements are developed interactively, whereby modelling results are used to optimize the monitoring programme while the model in turn is refined using the monitoring and site assessment data. The contingency plan is periodically revised on the basis of conclusions from the other two elements. Mathematical methods to deal with spatial and temporal parameter uncertainty in this context have been developed (see, e.g., Ref. [94]).

The physical, chemical and biological processes as well as the rate and extent to which these natural attenuation processes occur depend on the contaminant and site hydrogeological and geochemical conditions. These processes are typically categorized as either destructive or non-destructive. Destructive processes reduce the potential risk from a contaminant by converting it to a less toxic form and include biodegradation and hydrolysis. Biodegradation is by far the most prevalent destructive mechanism. Non-destructive processes reduce potential risk from a contaminant by reducing its concentration and thus its bioavailability in groundwater or surface water.

TABLE 11. THERMAL REMOVAL TECHNIQUES USED IN REMEDIATION

Technology	Medium	Contaminant	Brief characterization
Thermally enhanced soil vapour extraction	Soil	VOCs and organic compounds	Contaminated soil is heated by the injection of hot air or steam, or by electrical resistance or microwave heating, thereby volatilizing contaminants. Off-gases are captured for further treatment.
Thermal desorption (ex situ)	Soil and sludge	VOCs and organic compounds	Excavated soils and sludges are heated to approximately 425°C (high temperature thermal desorption) or to approximately 200°C (low temperature thermal desorption) in an effort to volatilize organic contaminants. An off-gas treatment system is attached to capture and treat vapour phase contaminants.
Catalytic oxidation	Soil	Organic compounds	The use of a catalyst helps to lower the reaction temperature, and thus the energy input, for thermal treatment methods.
Incineration	Soil and sludge	Organic compounds	This process involves the combustion of excavated soils and sludges in, for example, rotary kilns or fluidized bed incinerators for the thermal destruction of contaminants. Often conducted off-site, but also on-site in mobile facilities.
Pyrolysis	Soil and sludge	Organic compounds	This process involves anaerobic thermal decomposition of organic contaminants in excavated soil or sludge.

Non-destructive processes include hydrodynamic dispersion and dilution, and adsorption, which reduce the mobility and solution concentration by binding to soil minerals and organic matter.

Each contaminant tends to be unique in the way different environmental processes affect its fate, so making generalizations that apply to all contaminants inappropriate. Especially significant is the difference between organic and inorganic contaminants. The fate of organic and inorganic contaminants is controlled by a combination of physical, chemical and biological processes. The physical processes control the rate and direction of travel as contaminants migrate through soil away from the source. The chemical and biological processes determine the extent to which the initial compounds will be transformed in the soil. Although organic contaminants may be completely degraded to carbon dioxide and water, some intermediate degradation products may pose a greater risk than the original contaminant. For example, vinyl chloride is more persistent, more mobile and more toxic than its parent chlorinated compounds. Some inorganic contaminants are amenable to destructive attenuation, for example, oxyanions, nitrate, sulphate, chromate and arsenate. The resulting products, however, may or may not be of lesser concern: for instance, nitrogen gas, ammonia and Cr^{3+}. In general, inorganic contaminants may be transformed by non-destructive processes to forms that have lower mobilities or bioavailabilities. It is important to note that inorganic contaminants persist in the environment because chemical elements are not amenable to attenuation by destructive processes, except for radioactive decay.

The presence of a contaminant mixture can enhance or inhibit natural attenuation of any one component of the mixture. In some cases the presence of co-contaminants may be aiding natural attenuation reactions to occur, but in other cases co-contaminants can interfere with these processes. For example, the presence of fuels can enhance the biodegradation of chlorinated solvents, whereas the degradation reactions that reduce pH can mobilize radionuclides and metals. Conversely, the presence of metals, including radionuclides, can inhibit biodegradation.

8.2. APPLICABILITY TO INORGANIC CONTAMINANTS

As has been pointed out above natural attenuation of radionuclides and (heavy) metals results not from destructive processes, but only from those that reduce their mobility or increase their dispersion. The passage of time can either enhance or reverse immobilization, depending on the type of reaction, the contaminant and the environmental conditions. The basic criteria and conditions for reliance on monitored natural attenuation for radionuclides are discussed in a companion report [17] in more detail. For heavy metals, the same geochemical and mineralogical processes as for radionuclides control their source terms and migration in principle. Solubility and mobility 'windows', however, might be markedly different for different metal species. This has to be taken into account explicitly when assessing the option of relying on natural attenuation.

8.3. PROCESSES AFFECTING ORGANIC CONTAMINANTS

8.3.1. General observations

Organic substances may exhibit a rather different behaviour from inorganic, ionic contaminants, depending on their 'polarity', i.e. their miscibility with water. The literature on the properties and behaviour of organic contaminants is extensive. In the following, some basics only are reviewed and the reader is referred to standard textbooks, for example Ref. [26].

The dominant process in natural attenuation of organic contaminants is usually biodegradation, since this is almost always the primary process responsible for reducing contaminant mass.

8.3.2. Biodegradation

Biodegradation is a process or collection of processes in which naturally occurring microorganisms such as yeast, fungi and bacteria break down organic substances into less toxic or non-toxic compounds. The ability of microorganisms to metabolize nutrients depends on the chemical composition of the environment. In most organisms, the metabolic process requires the exchange of oxygen and carbon. Biodegradation can occur in the presence or absence of oxygen. Nutrients and essential trace elements must be available in sufficient quantity in order for the microorganisms to break down all of the organic contaminant mass.

In general there are three biodegradation processes:

(1)   Those where the contaminant is used by the microbes as the primary food source;
(2)   Those where the contaminant is used to transfer energy;
(3)   Those where the biodegradation occurs in response to a chain reaction between the contaminant and an enzyme produced during an unrelated reaction (termed co-metabolism).

For fuel hydrocarbons, the first process is dominant. The full degradation of chlorinated solvents requires all three processes. Until recently, scientists believed that chlorinated organic compounds were generally highly resistant to biodegradation in the environment, but in the past two decades a variety of biological processes have been discovered that can transform these compounds in nature [95, 96]. It is worth noting that many microbial communities are very adaptable to the local circumstances and in the absence of other readily available energy sources may evolve to utilize highly resilient organic compounds. These processes are extremely complex and not yet fully understood, but are a topic of a significant body of research:

(a) *The contaminant is used as the primary food source.* In the presence of oxygen, bacteria are able to use the carbon in organic contaminants as their primary food source. This relatively rapid process has greater potential for fuels and chlorinated solvents with few chlorine atoms per molecule. Highly chlorinated organic compounds are less susceptible to this type of degradation. In the absence of oxygen, microorganisms can sometimes still use contaminants as their primary food supply. This form of degradation under anaerobic conditions depends not only on the compound but also on temperature, pH and salinity. In breaking down chlorinated solvents, bacteria use nitrate, iron, sulphate and carbon dioxide to help metabolize the carbon in the organic contaminants. If degradation is complete, the products are usually carbon dioxide, water and chlorine.

(b) *The contaminant is used to transfer energy.* All living organisms respire in that they use organic substances and other nutrients by breaking them down into simpler products. In the absence of oxygen, microorganisms may use chlorinated compounds as an aid to respiration rather than as a food source. This is accomplished through an electron transfer process. Where carbon in a contaminant is the food source, the contaminant is an electron donor. In the case where food is obtained from a different source, the contaminant sometimes aids this transfer by accepting electrons that are released during respiration. The most common anaerobic process for degrading chlorinated compounds is an electron transfer process termed reductive dechlorination. In this process, hydrogen atoms are sequentially substituted for chlorine atoms in the contaminant molecule. The major requirement for reductive dechlorination is the presence of other organic compounds that can serve as the food source.

(c) *Co-metabolism.* In co-metabolism microbes do not degrade the contaminant directly, but the contaminant degrades by enzymatic reactions that occur during metabolism of other substrates. Reductive dehalogenation occurs only under anaerobic conditions, although some chlorinated compounds can be biologically degraded by other mechanisms in aerobic environments. Aerobic co-metabolism requires the presence of electron donor compounds, such as methane, toluene, phenol or other organic compounds, that leads to production of the enzymes.

The biodegradation process most frequently observed at sites where natural degradation of chlorinated solvents occurs is reductive dehalogenation, where microbes use the chlorinated compounds for energy metabolism and remove a chlorine atom. For example, reductive dehalogenation can transform tetrachloroethene (PCE), which has four chlorine atoms, to TCE, which has three, and then transform TCE to cis-dichloroethene (cis-DCE), with two chlorine atoms. Cis-DCE can then be reduced to vinyl chloride, which can be further reduced to ethylene, an essentially harmless compound. A potential risk of this process is a buildup of intermediate transformation products, such as vinyl chloride, that are more toxic than the parent compound.

Natural attenuation of chlorinated compounds is a slow process and may not occur at all at a given site. Thus it is not likely to be an appropriate strategy at sites where rapid and sure cleanup of contamination is required. Monitoring for natural attenuation can also be costly. Nevertheless, the presence of intermediate and final degradation products indicates that at some sites natural degradation processes do take place [97]. A primary advantage, however, is that it can eliminate the need for an engineered solution that may disrupt the site or it can reduce the size of an area requiring treatment with an engineered system [98]. Engineering intervention, such as supplying nutrients to stimulate the natural degradation processes, can greatly enhance the attenuation (see, e.g., Ref. [99]). It is discussed in more detail in Section 9.1.

8.3.3. Sorption

Sorption, the process by which particles such as clay and organic matter 'hold onto' liquids or solids, retards migration of some organic compounds. This increases the time for biodegradation to occur before contaminants can migrate to a potential receptor. Sorption is controlled by the organic content of soil, soil mineralogy and grain size.

Certain functional groups, notably the carboxylic or phenolic groups, on organic molecules will dissociate to a certain degree when the substance is dissolved in water. Such substances are termed 'polar'. These groups, being anionic in nature, will give the molecules an overall negative charge and thus in general disfavour attenuation by hydrolysed mineral surfaces that are also negatively charged. There may be, however, more complex interaction mechanisms via hydrogen bonds or whereby metal ions act as bridges between the hydrolysed mineral surfaces and the charged molecule. In addition, complex soil organic constituents that are attached to the mineral surfaces can act as intermediates [100].

The interaction between non-polar organic molecules, i.e. those that do not dissociate in water, and solid mineral surfaces is much more complex. Such molecules may form surface coatings on clays, for example, and hence become immobile.

8.3.4. Physical processes

Physical processes, such as volatilization and dispersion also contribute to natural attenuation. The transport and retention mechanisms for dissolved organic contaminants are largely the same as for inorganic constituents.

In some instances of contamination, concentrations of non-miscible organic compounds may be so high that they form a three phase system together with the solid substrate and the groundwater (often referred to as NAPLs). In cases where the vapour pressure is high at ambient temperatures, even a four phase system may develop, with a separate gas phase. In the unsaturated zone a four phase system may be present in the sense that in-phase polar liquids fill some of the pore space.

Volatilization removes contaminants from groundwater or soil by transfer to a gaseous phase, eventually reaching the unsaturated zone. For highly volatile organic compounds such as benzene, volatilization may account for 5–10% of the total mass loss at a site, with most of the remaining mass loss due to biodegradation (see, e.g., Ref. [101]). For less volatile organic compounds, the expected mass loss due to volatilization would be lower, of course. Volatilization and transfer into the unsaturated zone may actually enhance biodegradation of certain organic compounds [102].

Where a separate phase of non-miscible organic compounds exists, two cases can be distinguished (cf. Fig. 1):

(1) The density of the organic liquid is lower than the density of water. In this case the contaminant will float on the groundwater table.
(d) The density of the organic liquid is higher than the density of water. In this case the organic liquids will collect at the bottom of an aquifer, often referred to as DNAPLs.

The potential for attenuation by physicochemical processes is lower for those lighter, and also more volatile, organic phases. They may readily migrate as liquid or gas phase. Conversely, the denser liquids collect in depressions at the bottom of the aquifers and remain rather stationary, also due to the typically rather higher viscosity. This, indeed, makes them rather inaccessible to pump and treat remediation techniques, as can be gathered from Fig. 14. While the bulk of the contaminant may remain stationary, a small fraction may dissolve in the water and thus lead to a persistent source term. Natural biodeg-radation processes may give rise to a continuing source term of degradation products that may be of concern. It is further possible that such DNAPLs act as an in situ solvent extraction process, concentrating heavy metals, including radionuclides. On the other hand, lighter organic phases are often more amenable to biodegradation.

Lighter-than-water organic liquids floating on the water table may become entrapped in the capillary fringe due to a fluctuating groundwater table. The migration and retention processes in the four phase system of the type soil solids–pore water–soil gas–liquid organic are rather complex and controlled inter alia by the surface tension of the organic liquid and its vapour pressure.

The dispersion of DNAPLs is initially driven by gravity and controlled by the capillary forces in the unsaturated zone. Once they reach the saturated zone, a three phase system develops. The further downward movement is controlled by the surface tension of the organic phase and the hydrodynamics in the aqueous phase. These factors may result in dispersion of the organic phase. If the amount of DNAPLs is not sufficient for a complete in-phase flow, droplets of the organic phase may become trapped and isolated in pores due to their surface tension. This in turn will reduce the permeability of the aquifer concerned. The trapped droplets can act as a long term source for small releases of organic contaminants and are not amenable to removal by techniques such as pump and treat.

9. BLOCKING OF PATHWAYS

9.1. ENHANCED NATURAL ATTENUATION

Interest in enhanced natural attenuation has increased recently as more reliable field data have become available on the specific mobility and persistence of the most frequently observed groundwater contaminants. Enhanced natural attenuation relies on naturally occurring environmental processes that have been optimized or stimulated by human intervention. These enhancements can consist of stimulating biodegradation of organic compounds, improving soil retention capacities, for example improving the sorption capacity, or changing the geochemical environment, for example changing the bulk redox state, such that migration of metals is hindered. As with many in situ techniques, it is difficult to distinguish between enhanced natural attenuation, reactive permeable barriers and in situ remediation, and the distinction would often depend on the actual operational configuration. The deployment methods, operational processes and reactants involved are often the same.

Biodegradation can be enhanced by the addition of a substrate, nutrients or essential elements to the subsurface to stimulate the growth of a target group of microorganisms. Usually the target microorganisms are indigenous; however, enriched cultures of bacteria that are highly efficient at degrading particular contaminants can also be introduced. Enhancing biodegradation is considered where it is desired to increase the rate of contaminant biotransformation, which may be limited by lack of required nutrients, electron donors or electron acceptors. The type of amendment required depends on the target metabolism for the contaminant of interest. Aerobic reactions may only require the addition of oxygen. Anaerobic reactions often require the addition of an electron donor (e.g. a lactate) as well as an electron acceptor (e.g. a nitrate or sulphate). Chlorinated solvents, in particular, often require the addition of a carbon substrate to stimulate reductive dechlorination.

A typical application is to supply electron donors or acceptors to enhance biodegradation of dissolved organic contaminants during their downstream migration. The resulting reactive zones are intended to be shorter than is the case for natural attenuation. Another application is injection of a reactant into the subsurface to enhance conversion of mobile metals into a reduced redox state that is less mobile, for example, U(VI) as anionic UO_2^{2+} versus U(IV) as cationic U^{4+}.

A wide variety of pure chemicals or organic waste materials have been investigated for use as in situ bioenhancements. Because of concerns over the introduction of additional chemicals to the subsurface, research on the use of readily degradable carbon sources, for example vegetable oil, was initiated. While simple compounds, such as lactate, are often found to be effective [103], industrial process residues, such as molasses, may be more economical. Complex organic contamination often requires a variety of electron donors to satisfy the needs of the specialized biodegrading microorganisms.

Electron acceptors, for instance either pure oxygen or some oxygen releasing compounds (peroxides and permanganates), are injected mainly to promote aerobic degradation of organic contaminants. The amount of oxygen to be delivered has to take into account the natural oxygen demand or the oxidation capacity of the groundwater and the geomatrix [104]. The efficient stimulation of the authigenic microbial communities for the degradation of specific contaminants requires a control over both the total amount of oxygen delivered and the amount delivered per unit time and volume of geomatrix. The reactant has to be prevented from becoming spent prematurely. Injection of air, pure oxygen or simple peroxides appears to be efficient in the short term, but some applications require a delayed delivery. Various proprietary slow release compounds, such as HRC® (hydrogen release compound) [105], ORC® (oxygen release compound) [106], MRC® (metals remediation compound) [107] or PermeOx® Plus [108], have been introduced into the market and shown to be effective also with radionuclides [109, 110]. The delivery characteristics for various generic and proprietary formulations have been reviewed recently [111].

Fixation can be further enhanced by sulphate reduction being induced, with the resulting sulphide forming low solubility precipitates with the radionuclides and heavy metals of interest (see, e.g., Refs [112, 113]). Solid sulphides in the geomatrix might be involved in dehalogenation processes [99].

Also marketed is an organosulphur compound (MRC®) [107] that is intended to complex metals, whereupon the complex sorbs to the solid substrate. The sorbed metal–organosulphur compound is subject to biodegradation and the metal eventually precipitates as a sulphide. It is worth noting that such precipitates can be redissolved, when the bulk groundwater returns to oxidized conditions after the reactant is spent.

Electron acceptors or donors introduced into the system will interact with the geomatrix, leading to oxidative or reductive dissolution of minerals. Certain minerals that are affected may contain toxic elements, such as arsenic, themselves, or may act as a sorption substrate, for example, for heavy metals that are released upon dissolution of the substrate. These effects have to be taken into account for the overall assessment of the effectiveness of such treatments.

When applying suspensions (solid containing liquids) or emulsions (fine dispersions of two non-miscible liquids), the potential clogging of the pore spaces in the soil and the resulting permeability losses must be carefully evaluated [114]. The reduction of permeability might be intended but frequently also leads to the groundwater bypassing the treated zone and thus making it ineffective or at least inefficient. The ability to disperse the reactant over a larger volume will determine its mode of application. The shorter the distance over which it can travel, the more injection boreholes are needed.

The use of specific bacteria to effect reduction of radionuclides and other metals together with reductive biodegradation in situ is still at a development stage [115] and apparently has not been tested outside the laboratory.

9.2. BARRIERS AND LINERS

9.2.1. The concept

Applicable to radiological, non-radiological and mixed contamination, one of the most straightforward means of dealing with contaminated sites appears to be to isolate them from human and other receptors by constructing physical barriers:

(a) Surface barriers, which are intended to minimize surface water infiltration into the contaminated area, to provide a barrier inhibiting direct contact and intrusion by plants and animals, and to inhibit inadvertent human intrusion. There are several general types of surface barrier, such as single layer covers, engineered multilayer covers and biotic barriers.

(b) In situ barriers, which are constructed vertically or horizontally below ground level to contain contaminated material. Vertical barriers are comprised of low permeability trenches, walls or membranes to impede lateral migration, usually keyed into a naturally occurring low permeability basal stratum. Horizontal barriers are installed beneath contaminated areas using in situ techniques such as grouting or soil mixing.

Surface containment systems are fully accessible during construction, allowing checking and testing, i.e. comprehensive quality control. They may be constructed on an uncontaminated surface to act as a liner on to which contaminated material is placed or they may be constructed above contaminated material to act as a cover. Liners form the basis of a dedicated landfill or 'containment cell' and invariably are used in combination with covers, for total encapsulation.

A surface barrier alone may not provide sufficient containment or isolation of contaminants so that a combination of technologies may be required to control contaminant migration and or exposure to contaminants. A cover system and active hydraulic control, i.e. a drainage system, will be needed to limit groundwater rise within the containment.

Physical containment can be used in an integrated fashion with other remedial methods. Excavation of hot spots may precede the construction of a covering system in order to reduce the size of the area to be contained. In situ stabilization may be employed as a pretreatment step to enhance immobilization of contaminants and to provide a stronger base to support a final cover, thus reducing the maintenance needs caused by subsidence. Alternatively, physical barriers can aid other forms of remediation by limiting the volume of contaminated material to be treated when using methods such as groundwater pump and treat.

Forming barriers in situ by injection (Fig. 9) from the surface can reduce construction and waste disposal costs and can be useful for replenishing barriers that have lost their effectiveness over time. Development of barrier emplacement methods that do not involve soil excavation is a significant advantage of this technology.

9.2.2. Surface barriers

Surface barriers, often referred to as (landfill) caps, are a common form of remediation for many types of contamination because they are a conceptually easy to understand and fairly inexpensive way to manage some of the risks associated with a contaminated site, such as direct exposure of humans and release of contaminants. They usually also enjoy a high public acceptance, as they seem to indicate visibly that something 'is being done'. Surface barriers or caps can be used to:

— Minimize direct exposure on the surface of the contamination from both radioactive and other hazardous substances;
— Prevent vertical infiltration of water into contaminated zones and wastes that would produce contaminated leachate;
— Contain waste while treatment is being applied;
— Control gas emissions from underlying contaminated materials that might be hazardous by themselves (e.g. radon and VOCs) or act as a carrier for contaminants, for example, ^{210}Pb and ^{210}Po;
— Create a land surface that can support vegetation and/or be used for other purposes.

The design of surface barriers is site specific and depends on the intended functions of the system. Surface barriers can range from a one layer system of vegetated soil to a complex multilayer system of soils and geosynthetic products (Fig. 4). In general, less complex systems are required in dry climates and more complex systems are required in humid climates. The materials used in the construction of surface barriers include low permeability and high permeability soils and low permeability geosynthetic products. The low permeability materials divert water and prevent its passage into the contaminated zone. The high permeability materials carry away water that percolates into the barrier. Other materials may be used to increase slope stability.

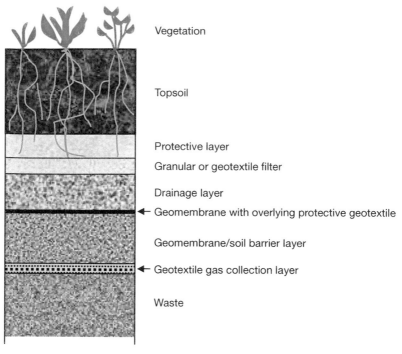

Vegetation

Topsoil

Protective layer

Granular or geotextile filter

Drainage layer

← Geomembrane with overlying protective geotextile

Geomembrane/soil barrier layer

← Geotextile gas collection layer

Waste

FIG. 4. Generic layout of surface capping.

Low permeability barrier layers are either natural clays and other low permeability soils or geosynthetic clay liners. Soils used as barrier materials are generally clays that are compacted to a hydraulic conductivity no greater than 1×10^{-8} m · s^{-1}. Compacted soil barriers are generally installed in lifts of at least 15 cm to achieve a thickness of 0.5 m or more. A flexible synthetic geomembrane (plastics) liner is placed on the top of this layer. The candidate list of polymers commonly used is lengthy, and includes polyvinyl chloride, polyethylenes of various densities, reinforced chlorosulphonated polyethylene, polypropylene, EIA and many new materials. Geomembranes are usually supplied in large rolls and are available in several thicknesses (0.5–3.6 mm), widths (3–30 m) and lengths (60–275 m). A composite barrier uses both soil and a geomembrane, taking advantage of the properties of each. The geomembrane is essentially impermeable, but, if a leak develops, the soil component prevents significant leakage into the underlying waste. Inspections of existing geomembranes have, however, shown that their functionality cannot be guaranteed even a few years after their installation. Differential settlement and imperfect seams during installation are the main causes [116]. In addition, there is no experience with the really long term stability of synthetic materials, as these have been in existence for generally less than 50 years.

For barriers placed over degradable contaminants, the collection and control of methane and carbon dioxide, which are potent greenhouse gases, must be part of the design and operation of the surface barrier. It is, however, generally accepted wisdom that degradable materials should not be emplaced into engineered landfills.

Surface barriers may be temporary or final. Temporary barriers can be installed before final closure to minimize generation of leachate until a better/ the final remedy is selected and implemented. They are usually used to minimize infiltration when the underlying contaminant mass is undergoing settling. A more stable base will thus be provided for the final cover, reducing the cost of post-closure maintenance. Surface barriers may also be applied to residue and waste masses that are so large that other treatments are impractical. At mining sites, for example, surface barriers can be used to minimize the infiltration of water to contaminated tailings piles and to provide a suitable base for the establishment of vegetation. In conjunction with water diversion and retention structures, surface barriers may be designed to route surface water away from the waste area while minimizing erosion [10].

Landfilling does not lessen toxicity, mobility or volume of mixed contamination but does mitigate migration. Surface barriers are most effective where most of the underlying contamination or waste materials are above the water table. A surface barrier, by itself, cannot prevent the horizontal flow of groundwater through the contaminated material, only the vertical entry of water into it. In many cases, surface barriers are used in conjunction with subsurface barriers, such as vertical walls, to minimize horizontal flow and migration. The effective life of physical barrier components can be extended by long term inspection and maintenance. In addition, precautions must be taken to ensure that the integrity of the cap is not compromised by land use activities [11].

9.2.3. Subsurface barriers

9.2.3.1. The concept

Underground containment barriers are an important method for limiting or preventing the movement of radiological and non-radiological contaminants into the surrounding geological media and groundwater. In the past, containment has been used primarily at sites where there was no other efficient and cost effective option. However, subsurface barriers can be used in any number of situations where it is necessary to prevent the migration of contamination. Barriers are currently used, for instance as an interim step, while final remediation alternatives are being developed (or considered) in conjunction with other treatment techniques, for example, reactive barriers (Section 9.3.1). In many instances (e.g. Example 5), subsurface barriers are capable of effectively confining the contaminant for extended time periods in a cost effective way.

Example 5. Example of in situ containment.

In 1984, in France the BRGM (Bureau de Recherches Géologiques et Minières) [117] successfully designed and realized the entombment of a soil deposit contaminated with pesticide residues (hexachlorocyclohexane). A volume of 3500 m^3 of polluted soil was buried in an engineered trench of which the bottom, sides and cap were made of compacted clay, with $(1–4) \times 10^9$ m · s^{-1} permeability. That clay was covered with shaly soil. The 'tomb' was equipped with a peripheral drainage system to collect rainwater, and with an inner piezometer to control potential water infiltration into the tomb.

There are many subsurface barrier technologies commercially available and others are at various stages of development. The purpose and function of the containment system must be determined prior to designing and constructing the barrier. Site characterization is an essential part of choosing an appropriate barrier. Some of the factors that may need to be considered when designing a subsurface barrier are [118]:

(a) It is important to establish the barrier placement criteria, including location, depth and thickness.
(b) A stress–deformation analysis needs to be performed on the surrounding area in order to assess the potential impacts of barrier construction.
(c) A compatibility test needs to be performed to select the most effective barrier materials and, when necessary, appropriate mixture combinations.
(d) It is necessary to determine the most effective and feasible construction methods.
(e) Construction quality assurance/quality control is a crucial component of subsurface barrier emplacement.

Different types of subsurface barrier have different construction quality assurance criteria; however, there are two primary concerns. First, the installed barrier must have a hydraulic conductivity equal to or less than that specified in the design. The second concern is barrier continuity, which is difficult to assess; the methods available have had varying degrees of success. There is currently no method of guaranteeing the continuity of a subsurface barrier [119]. Discontinuities may occur during grout application/installation and joint formation. Cracking due to curing, settling or wet/dry cycling may occur over time. Proper emplacement of a subsurface barrier is critical in ensuring the overall effectiveness of the containment system. Once a barrier has been installed, verification and monitoring are crucial. At this time, there is no uniform method for monitoring the emplacement, long term performance or integrity of the barrier.

The construction of subsurface barriers can be grouped into three basic technologies:

(1) Replacement of excavated materials with materials of lower permeability;
(2) Displacement with materials of lower permeability;
(3) Reduction of the permeability of the soil (Fig. 5).

Impermeable liners made with clays or cement and clay mixtures are widely used in the construction of new landfills. Clay is subject to chemical attack by leachates from the waste material that can degrade the barrier and lead to increased infiltration and contaminant dispersal. Proper moisture content must be maintained to prevent shrinkage cracks in the clay. The development of new barrier concepts, materials and construction techniques is in the process of overcoming these deficiencies however. The long term stability and effectiveness of new synthetic binders and polymers as sealants is being evaluated. Inorganic grouts are also being studied for use with or without clays.

9.2.3.2. Bored piles

Bored piles (Fig. 5(a)) are a series of overlapping large size boreholes. Rotary drilling equipment, soil mixers or line shaft excavators may be used. The boreholes are backfilled with a cementitious grout or concrete before the next hole in the row is drilled. Depending on the cement and aggregate used, nearly complete sealing can be achieved. Depths of several tens of metres can be reached. In principle the technique can be applied to many types of soil and rock, but the cost increases with the hardness of the material. Very inhomogeneous soils, containing boulders for instance, may prevent successful application. The technique may be combined with that of slurry walls.

9.2.3.3. Slurry walls or trenches

Slurry walls or trenches (Fig. 5(b)) are constructed by excavating a vertical trench around waste areas to a depth that is at or below the bottom elevations of contaminated soil or waste materials. Trench stability is maintained by placing a liquid slurry of bentonite and water in the trench as excavation progresses. When the trench reaches the proposed maximum depth, the slurry is displaced from the bottom upwards with a dense barrier material

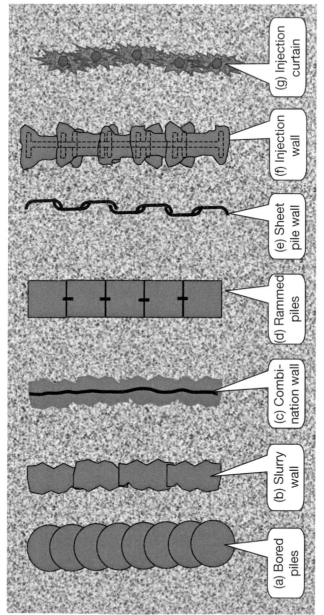

FIG. 5. Various containment construction techniques.

consisting of soil bentonite, cement grout, polymers, plastic concrete or other low permeability materials. Using a continuous trenching construction method (Fig. 8), cavities for slurry walls can be continuously excavated with a backhoe or excavator, filled with slurry, and backfilled with low permeability material until the waste disposal areas are completely encircled. Slurry walls can be excavated to depths of more than 30 m and can have permeabilities as low as 10^{-8} to 10^{-9} m $\cdot$ s^{-1}.

This technique is easiest to apply in sand and gravel formations and to a certain extent to cohesive materials, such as clays. It is more difficult to implement in hard rocks. Amendments can be added to the injected grouts that will act as additional sorbents for contaminants such as heavy metals and radionuclides. Slurry walls may also be combined with a plastic membrane to form combination walls (Fig. 5(c)).

9.2.3.4. *Keyed rammed piles*

Prefabricated concrete piles may be rammed into the ground using a pile driver. In order to ensure water tightness, they are interlocked with slots and keys (Fig. 5(d)). The applicability of this technique is largely restricted to unconsolidated or weakly consolidated sediments without large boulders.

9.2.3.5. *Sheet piles*

Sheet piling consists of vertical cut-off walls constructed by driving strips of steel, precast concrete, aluminium or wood into the soil. Sheet metal piling, which are corrugated sheets of iron that are shaped in such a way that they interlock (Fig. 5(e)) with sealable joints, is commonly used. Interlocking sheets are assembled before installation and driven or vibrated into the ground by about a metre at a time until the desired depth is achieved. Sheets are sealed by injecting grout into the joints between the metal sheet piles. Continuous sheet piling walls can potentially be driven to depths of some 90 m in unconsolidated deposits lacking boulders. Bulk hydraulic conductivities of 10^{-8}–10^{-10} cm $\cdot$ s^{-1} have been achieved in test cells constructed of joint sealed sheet piles.

9.2.3.6. *Injection walls*

An I shaped pile is driven into the ground and upon extraction the remaining hollow space is backfilled with a bentonite or cement–bentonite slurry (Fig. 5(f)). Each section overlaps with the preceding one to provide good keying in and water tightness.

9.2.3.7. Injection curtains

Injection curtains (Fig. 5(g)) are constructed by pushing hollow injection tubes into the ground (unconsolidated materials) or by drilling injection boreholes (rocks). A variety of inorganic and organic grouts may be injected to fill the pore space of the soils or rocks. Typical inorganic grouts are ordinary Portland cement (OPC), bentonite and water glass. The organic grouts used in civil engineering applications include polymers of methacrylate and epoxy resin. The possible interaction of organic grouts with organic contaminants has to be carefully studied before application, as the contaminants may lead to a dissolution or breakdown of the sealing components, or may prevent polymerization. The technique, in principle, is applicable to all types of soils and rocks. The sealing success depends very much on the homogeneity of the permeability distribution. Preferential pathways may lead to incomplete sealing. Some geological formations may have a too low permeability for injection, but still provide long term migration pathways. In such a case hydrofracturing allows successful creation of injection curtains. To this end, sand, zirconia or other high strength spherical materials are injected under very high pressure to 'fracture' the rocks. Spherical materials stabilize the open fracture while providing a high permeability infill that allows injection of the actual grout. In addition to providing a hydraulic sealant, injected grouts can also act as sorbents for contaminants. This effect may be less effective for organic contaminants than for metals, including radionuclides.

A variant of injection curtains is the injection of non-miscible fluids with the intention to reduce water permeability. In recent times the effect on water permeability of injecting biodegradable oils has been explored [114].

9.2.3.8. Ground freezing

Temporary containment can be achieved by a variety of measures, including grouting and ground freezing [120–122] (Fig. 6). Either an impermeable screen around a contamination can be established or the contaminated material itself can be frozen in order to facilitate its handling or excavation (Section 10.1.4.1). Artificial ground freezing (AGF) has been used for over 100 years to form impermeable barriers and temporary support for excavations, shafts and tunnels [123]. Techniques such as grouting and AGF are standard in civil engineering and mining for stabilizing, for instance, highly saturated soils or creating impermeable walls for tunnelling purposes. They are also used when constructing foundations below the groundwater table.

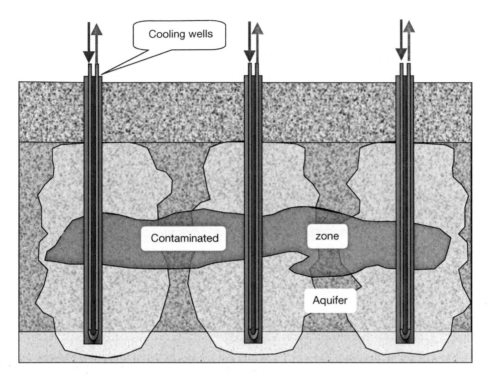

FIG. 6. The principle of ground freezing as a barrier and to immobilize contaminants.

Laboratory studies have shown that frozen soil barriers with very low hydraulic conductivities ($<4 \times 10^{-12}$ m $\cdot$ s^{-1}) can be formed under saturated soil conditions. The formation of a frozen soil barrier in arid conditions will require a suitable method for homogeneously adding moisture to the soils to achieve saturated conditions. Formation of frozen soil barriers in areas where plumes of low freezing point contaminants (TCE, etc.) exist may require low temperature and more expensive cryogenics (e.g. liquid nitrogen and CO_2) [124].

Freezing is effected by a system of pipes that are inserted into or around the contaminated zone (Fig. 6). A cooling liquid (brine) is circulated (a one phase system) in this pipe system. Another option is an open two phase process whereby liquid nitrogen is pumped into the ground. The N_2 vaporizes and thereby extracts the heat from the soil. Thermosyphons forming a closed two phase system are an alternative. The working fluid is contained in a closed sealed vessel (a thermopile or thermoprobe) that is partially buried. Thermosyphons can function passively in cold climates during the winter months, at which time the above ground portion is subjected to cold ambient air that cools and condenses the working fluid. The condensed fluid gravitates to the below ground portion. Below ground, subjected to warmer temperatures, the working fluid warms, vaporizes and rises upwards to repeat the cycle. A closed two phase system can also be used in an active mode and is applicable when the ambient air temperature is above freezing [125]. Such systems utilize 'hybrid thermosyphons'. A typical system consists of multiple thermoprobes, an active (powered) compressor and condenser, an interconnecting supply and return piping network, and a control system. Thermoprobes consist of an evaporator and a passive condenser section. The hybrid system can function simultaneously in both passive and active modes when the ambient temperatures are sufficiently low, thereby reducing energy costs. Hybrid thermosyphons may operate in northern climates (locations that experience air temperatures below the target soil temperature) without external power. The temperature of the barrier can be adjusted to ensure the necessary liquid–solid phase change even though contaminants may lower the phase change temperature.

9.3. IN SITU TREATMENT

9.3.1. Reactive permeable barriers

9.3.1.1. The concept

Permeable reactive barriers or walls are distinguished from outright containment by the fact that the contaminant carrier as such, i.e. the groundwater, is not prevented from moving [126–129]. The objective is rather to remove the contaminants from the mobile phase. Permeable reactive barriers are installed by excavating a portion of the aquifer, disposing of the excavated material and replacing it with a permeable material designed to react with the contaminant and remove it from the flowing water. The advantages over pump and treat systems are that no active pumping or process operation and maintenance is required, reducing energy, operation and maintenance costs, no treatment sludges are produced, reducing waste disposal costs and there is no surface facility required, which allows land to be returned to productive uses. The systems typically rely on the natural gradient of the groundwater table as the driving force. The barrier materials must be designed to remain reactive for periods of many years to decades. Furthermore, the barrier permeability must be sustained throughout the duration of groundwater treatment. The performance of permeable reactive barrier systems, therefore, must be monitored so that corrective action can be taken when required.

Permeable reactive barriers have been designed and implemented for the remediation of dissolved metals [126, 130, 131], acid mine drainage [132–134], radionuclides [135–138] and dissolved nutrients [139–141]. Contaminant removal can be achieved in a variety of ways [142–144]. Treatment processes include adsorption [145, 146], simple precipitation [147], adsorptive precipitation [140], reductive precipitation [126, 136] and biologically mediated aerobic or anaerobic transformations [132, 133, 139, 148].

Changing the redox state can be a very effective method of immobilization for certain radionuclides (e.g. uranium and technetium). These radionuclides have two or more oxidation states, and radionuclides with more reduced oxidation states are less mobile. For example, reduction of the hexavalent uranyl ion UO_2^{2+} to the tetravalent U(IV) state, results in the precipitation of sparingly soluble precipitates including $UO_{2(s)}$ or mixed U(VI)–U(IV) precipitates. Zero valence iron is an abundant and inexpensive reducing agent that has been observed to reduce and precipitate uranium and technetium in laboratory studies [135, 136, 149–151]. Oxidation products generated, for example ferric hydroxides, can also provide a high capacity sorption substrate for non-redox sensitive species [152], but their long term stability vis-à-vis changes in redox conditions has to be carefully evaluated [153].

9.3.1.2. Applicability

Permeable reactive barrier systems containing zero valence iron have been installed for the treatment of uranium, technetium and other metals [136, 137, 154–156]. These barriers demonstrate excellent removal of uranium and technetium. Examination of the reaction products has been conducted at a series of permeable reactive barrier sites [136, 157, 158]. Although the results of these characterization studies are inconsistent, all of the reports indicate that a portion of the uranium entering the barrier system is reduced to U(IV), whereas some portion may remain in the U(VI) oxidation state. Other metals that are commonly associated with uranium mine waste, including As, Mo, Se, V and Zn are also removed from the groundwater, possibly as reduced phases (e.g. V_2O_3) or as sulphide minerals (As_2S_3 and ZnS) [137, 159].

Organic reductants, such as sawdust or shredded bark, have also been explored to promote reduction and precipitation of uranium as well as heavy metals from mixed wastes [160]. Passive treatment systems containing organic carbon have been used to remove both uranium and NO_3 from groundwater at sites where these two constituents coexist as a result of releases from nuclear weapons production facilities [161].

Sorption can remove contaminants from groundwater and maintain low concentrations of radionuclides. Sorptive materials that have been evaluated or deployed in permeable reactive barrier systems for treating radionuclides include zeolites (e.g. clinoptilolite [162]), phosphate based adsorbents (e.g.

bone char apatite [154] and apatite II [163]) and hydrous ferric oxides (e.g., amorphous ferric oxyhydroxide) [145, 154].

Hydrocarbon treatment with a reactive barrier is extremely viable. This is due to the flexibility of microbial degradation systems that can be stimulated in the barrier. Arrangements for the injection of air, nutrients, co-metabolites and other chemical supplements are technically straightforward. Redox conditions can be controlled, as well as stimulation of the specific microbial enzymatic systems required to degrade xenobiotic hydrocarbons. The most critical issue is control over the generation of biomass. Overgrowth will destroy the hydraulic permeability of the barrier.

Reactive barriers containing zero valence iron are being used to degrade chlorinated hydrocarbons by the process of reductive dechlorination. The metal serves as a source of electrons for the reduction step that removes chlorine atoms from the hydrocarbons and releases chloride and ferric iron into solution. The end products are primarily ethane and ethene, however, partially dechlorinated products may form if the reaction time is insufficient. Enhancements to granular iron that result in faster degradation are being investigated; iron plated with palladium appears to offer some advantages [164]. However, deconvolution of the various surface and bulk processes is not easy but may be necessary in order to improve the efficiency of the applications [165, 166]. A wide variety of inorganic and biologically mediated processes appear to be at work [167].

The availability of literature specifically on the application to mixed contaminant problems is rather limited and often restricted to laboratory experiments rather than to field testing or even full scale application. Several reactants may have to be used for different contaminants. Examples include experiments to treat together zinc, arsenate, PCE, TCE and BTX [168].

9.3.1.3. Deployment

The majority of the reactive barriers installed to date have been continuous barriers installed across the entire width of the plume. Contaminant fluxes can also be focused on the reactive barrier by an array of non-reactive barriers, such as slit or slurry walls [169], to form a funnel and gate system [170, 171] (Fig. 7). Funnel and gate systems reduce the physical length of the treatment portion of the barrier and prevent contaminants from flowing around the treatment zone. The volume of reactive material required to treat contaminated groundwater is determined by the contaminant concentrations, groundwater geochemistry and flow rate. For many contaminant plumes, the volume of reactive material will be similar whether a continuous barrier or funnel and gate configuration is employed. Because the installation of continuous barriers is typically less expensive than for funnel and gate systems, this installation technique has been preferred. Furthermore, because funnel and gate installations focus flow to across a small cross-sectional area, there is greater potential for clogging by the formation of secondary precipitates.

Depending on the reactive material to be used, deployment techniques may include injection wells (for grouts, gels and soluble reactants) or trenches (Fig. 8) cut by a suitable excavator (for grouts and particulate material such as granular iron and sawdust). Development work on efficient methods to emplace reactive barriers with minimal disturbance, even in awkward places, is still underway. This includes adapting more novel civil engineering techniques, such as directional or horizontal drilling [172] and the use of guar gum slurries for barrier installation [134]. Hydraulic fracturing [173] and jet grouting techniques [174] can be used for emplacement of barriers at depths beyond the limitations of conventional excavation techniques (Fig. 9).

The possibility of putting reactive barrier walls in place by colloid deposition has been investigated. The advantages are that much less material is required and deep contamination or inaccessible areas are less of a problem than they are with the trench and backfill approaches [175].

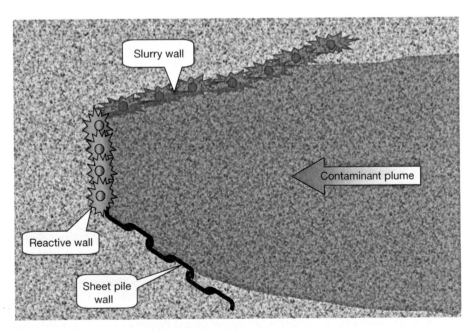

FIG. 7. Sketch of a permeable reactive wall in combination with a 'Funnel and Gate™' system.

FIG. 8. (a) Continuous trenching machine used to install a 46 m long, 7.3 m deep and 0.6 m wide granular iron permeable reactive barrier; (b) Simultaneous excavation and replacement of aquifer material with granular iron as the horizontal trencher advances [151].

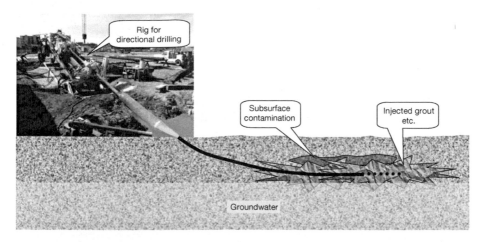

FIG. 9. The principle of directional drilling and jet grouting.

9.3.1.4. Long term performance

The limitations on permeable reactive barrier performance and lifespan include constraints on the reactive material longevity and the barrier permeability. Of these concerns, the potential for barrier clogging and the permeable reactive barrier evolving into an impermeable reactive barrier is the most significant. Because the total mass of contaminant that accumulates in the barrier is modest, the principal precipitates resulting in clogging are the products of reactions either between the barrier materials and the major ions present in the water or between the barrier materials and the water itself. The use of zero valence iron (Fe^0), the most commonly used reactive material, results in a reduction of water and an increase in the pH to between 10 and 11. This increase in pH favours the precipitation of carbonate minerals, principally calcite ($CaCO_3$) and siderite ($FeCO_3$). Over periods of several years to decades, the potential accumulation of these precipitates may be sufficient to reduce the pore space of the reactive material and limit the barrier permeability. Reactive barrier technology has evolved recently, and the oldest barriers are now approaching ten years of age. Clogging to a degree that is sufficient to impair barrier performance has yet to be observed. Long term monitoring programmes are required to assess this concern.

The long term fate of the reactive barrier, after remediation is complete or after the barrier becomes ineffective, depends on the nature of the contaminant and the characteristics of the barrier. Concerns include the potential for remobilization of contaminants retained in the barrier and for clogging in the barrier to alter the natural groundwater flow conditions. For many barrier systems, the contaminant is converted to a form that is stable in the geochemical environment that prevails in the aquifer. Furthermore, because the mass of contaminant is small relative to the mass of the barrier materials, the residual barrier materials may be classified as non-hazardous materials. It may be acceptable in these systems for the barrier to remain in place. In other cases, the mass of contaminant may exceed the guidelines for soil, the contaminant may have the potential for remobilization or the contaminant may be sufficiently hazardous to warrant excavation of the reactive material and placement in a secure waste disposal facility. In these cases, excavation of the barrier or a portion of the barrier may be required.

Although a considerable amount of research on the performance of reactive walls is still going on worldwide, some technologies have reached commercial maturity [176, 177].

9.3.1.5. Limitations

There are various technical and operational constraints on the usefulness of permeable reactive barriers:

(a) Applications currently are limited to shallow depths (less than 20 m) because of construction challenges associated with the installation of barriers.
(b) To be effective the barrier must be constructed to intercept a large portion of the contaminated area and configured to direct the captured groundwater to the treatment unit (gate).
(c) Inflow of groundwater from deeper uncontaminated flow systems must be prevented or controlled to minimize unnecessary water flow through the barrier and possible consumption of reactive materials.
(d) The hydraulic properties and reactive characteristics of the barrier must be consistent with the requirements of a gravity driven flow regime.
(e) Operating costs associated with periodic replacement of the reactive material may be incurred.
(f) In settings with a very low hydraulic gradient, installation of pumps to create and direct an artificial groundwater flow through the barrier and to overcome the hydraulic resistance of the barrier may be needed.

9.3.2. Biological barrier walls

9.3.2.1. The concept

Biological barrier walls, also termed biowalls, are in situ barriers that rely on biological processes in order to restrict the migration of contaminants. The principle of the biowall is illustrated in Fig. 10. They are installed across the flow paths of plumes of contaminated groundwater so that contaminated groundwater moves through the barrier. These barriers consist of an excavated trench filled with a sorbent media that retards the movement of organic compounds and supports microbes that biodegrade the sorbed organic compounds. The volume of the barrier provides localized control of the in situ environment by the addition of nutrients, co-substrates and/or electron donors or acceptors to optimize biodegradation. The target contaminant groups for biological barriers are aerobically and anaerobically biodegradable compounds such as halogenated and non-halogenated volatile organic compounds, semivolatile organic compounds and PCBs. Application of the technology is most appropriate to geological formations with significant permeability (e.g. sands, sandstone and permeable limestones) and no preferential flow paths such as open cracks and fissures.

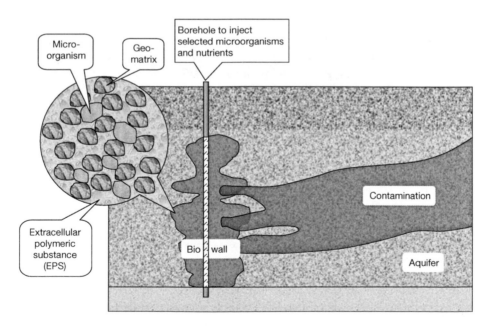

FIG. 10. The principle of the biowall.

The effectiveness of biowalls results from:

(a)   The physical reduction of permeability and hence groundwater flow by the microbial population. This effect can be enhanced by the use of 'ultra-microcells' (less than 100 nm). In the course of growth by metabolism these increase in size and may completely fill the pore space.

(b)   The generation of metabolites capable of restricting the migration of radionuclides through the barrier wall. Such metabolites are mainly extracellular polymeric substances (EPSs), commonly termed slimes, which the microbial cells use for attaching themselves to the substrate. These EPSs also fill pore spaces and thus reduce permeability.

(c)   The sequestering of radionuclides from groundwater by complexation, though it should be noted that subsequent mobilization of these colloidal species could constitute an additional transport mechanism.

(d)   Degradation of organic contaminants by microorganisms. The type of mechanism and necessary operational conditions are discussed in more detail in Section 8.3.2.

As in many comparable instances, fractured rocks pose particular problems, partly because their hydraulic behaviour is difficult to predict, and partly because comparatively high flow velocities along the fractures may make attachment of microorganisms difficult. An example of a successful development of a biobarrier in fractured shale is given in Ref. [178]. Another example of a biowall is given in Example 6.

Biowalls for the purpose of specifically retaining radionuclides are discussed in more detail in a companion report [17].

Example 6. Example of a biobarrier.

A pilot unit for groundwater remediation by means of a biobarrier has been realized in the north of France, on the pathway of groundwaters contaminated by nitrates (more than 1000 mg/L). By means of 27 injection pipes, a nutrient ethanol solution has been injected directly into the groundwater stream everyday [179]. The system, maintained in anaerobic conditions, gave rise to a dramatic increase of the denitrating local microflora, using ethanol as an energy source and nitrates as electron acceptors, turning nitrates into gaseous nitrogen. After more than one year, the pilot unit allowed reduction factors of about 95%, and kept the nitrite concentration in water at a very low level.

9.3.2.2. Limitations

The following factors may limit the applicability and effectiveness of the process:

— Possible toxicity of very high contaminant concentrations to micro-organisms;
— Possible toxicity of heavy metals not treated by this method to micro-organisms;
— Proximity of the plume to the site boundaries or receptors;
— Depth and width of the contaminated plume;
— Cost of the treatment medium;
— Generation of biomass, which may limit the permeability of the treatment barrier.

9.3.3. In situ immobilization/solidification

Immobilization, as opposed to physical containment, is intended to treat contaminated material in place to reduce migration potential without excavation. Two basic options can be distinguished: in situ and ex situ immobilization/stabilization treatments [180, 181]. In situ immobilization treats contaminants in place without the contaminated material being removed, while ex situ immobilization/stabilization requires removal of the contaminants for processing in a treatment facility, either on-site or off-site. After treatment, the material is either returned to the original site or disposed of in an engineered repository. A number of treatment technologies can be used for both in situ and ex situ treatments, the method of application varying in each case. Ex situ methods are discussed in Section 11. The objective of immobilization/stabilization is to chemically stabilize and or encapsulate contaminants to reduce or eliminate the potential for migration of the contaminants.

Three major methods for the implementation of in situ immobilization/stabilization can be distinguished, based on chemical, biochemical and heat treatment, respectively. Chemical immobilization/stabilization is based on the injection of a variety of grouts or on changing, for example, the pH and/or redox conditions in the groundwater. These grouts can be based for instance on OPC, water glass (sodium silicate), gypsum or organic polymers, for example, methacrylic or epoxy resins. Prices probably increase in this order, but this may vary and depend on the availability of the agent as a waste product from industrial processes. Price, in fact, will be a crucial determinant for the viability of a method.

The importance of redox reactions, either in terminal or intermediate reactions, is being studied increasingly, for both reactive walls and other in situ applications [182, 183]. Electron shuttles, such as humic acids or quinones, increase the bioavailability of naturally occurring electron acceptors, mainly iron and manganese oxides, that may convert radionuclides and heavy metals into less mobile forms [184]. This will also find application in other in situ methods, such as the permeable reactive barriers discussed above.

The deployability of immobilizing agents via injection depends largely on the hydraulic properties of the contaminated material. Ordinary Portland cement and epoxy resins typically have a high viscosity, while water glass and gypsum solutions or methacrylic acid suspensions can be made up with viscosities close to that of water.

Organic polymers and water glass are also used to immobilize surface contamination. The main effect is to enhance the cohesive properties of topsoils, thus preventing wind and water erosion [185, 186]. Depending on the formulation, the infiltration of rainwater may also be impeded and thus the downward migration of radionuclides retarded. If used not only as a temporary solution, for example to reduce wind blown dispersion of contaminated soils, the long term stability of the polymer stabilized material has to be carefully assessed. Breakdown products containing functional groups, such as carboxylic or phenolic groups, may actually act as a vehicle to facilitate transport of radionuclides.

The advantage of in situ solidification/stabilization techniques employing inorganic agents is that these techniques typically need little follow-up and monitoring once their functionality has been verified. In the case of organic solidification agents, the possibility of biodegradation has to be taken into consideration and some monitoring may be needed.

In situ solidification/stabilization techniques may present some drawbacks or specific difficulties. Since most of the chemical reactions employed are exothermic, the dissipating reaction heat can give rise to a volatilization of organic contaminants before these are effectively bound.

9.3.3.1. Limitations

Factors that may limit the applicability and effectiveness of in situ immobilization and solidification include:

— The depth of contaminants may limit some types of application techniques.
— Certain contaminants are incompatible with solidification agents.

— Reagent delivery and effective mixing are more difficult than for ex situ applications.
— Future use of the site may be limited after treatment.
— Treatment of contamination below the water table may require prior dewatering.

9.3.4. In situ vitrification

9.3.4.1. The concept

Heat treatment is aimed at in situ vitrification (ISV) whereby loose sand is fused into a lump containing the contaminants (Figs 11 and 12); see, for example, Refs [4, 187, 188]. Resistance or inductive heating methods are available. They are best suited to areas with contamination in relatively homogeneous media. Mixed contaminated sites that are very heterogeneous, such as buried waste sites, require careful pretreatment characterization in order to assess the safety of the process implementation and production of a uniformly high quality product. Characterization is needed to identify waste forms, such as intact containers of liquids, pressurized gas cylinders and residues of explosives, which can cause significant pressure excursions during treatment. Characterization is also needed to ensure that the base chemical constituents are suitable and adequate to form an acceptable vitrified product. If not, addition of glass forming constituents, for example sand, may be necessary. Care is also needed if substantial amounts of metal debris are present.

The vitrification process will either destroy organic compounds or volatilize them in its early stages. It has to be considered, however, that an incomplete combustion process may lead to more toxic degradation products, such as dioxins. Another problem with heat treatment may be the volatilization of ^{210}Po, ^{137}Ce, Pb and Hg, where present. This can be overcome, albeit at additional cost, with the installation of abstraction hoods, high efficiency particulate air (HEPA) filtration and exhaust gas scrubbing. Secondary wastes from air emission control may require special treatment and disposal at licensed facilities. The vitrified block may be either left in situ or removed (Fig. 13) to an engineered disposal facility.

The evolution of ISV technology resulted in three different configurations of the process:

(1) Traditional ISV;
(2) Planar ISV;
(3) Plasma arc (or bottom-up) ISV.

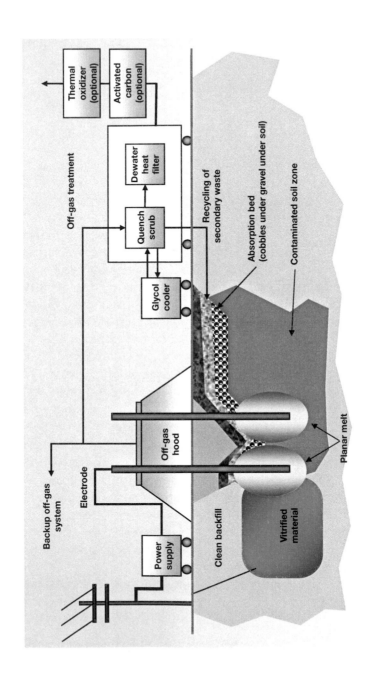

FIG. 11. In situ vitrification (after GeoMelt™ [189]).

FIG. 12. Examples of ISV (after GeoMelt™ [189]).

9.3.4.2. Traditional in situ vitrification

The traditional ISV process employs an array of electrodes placed vertically into waste or contaminated soil, and an electric current is passed through the soil between the electrodes. The heat generated from the resistance of the soil to the passage of the current is referred to as Joule heating. As the heated soil melts progressively downwards, the electrodes are allowed to sink through the melted soil, enabling melting depths of 7 m or more.

An off-gas hood covers the entire melt and some distance around the outside edge to control release of gases and airborne particles generated within or near the melt. The off-gases are drawn into the hood by the negative pressure created by a fan, then treated in a process train before being discharged to the atmosphere. When the melting has progressed to the desired depth, the power to the electrodes is shut off and the melt is allowed to cool. The electrodes are left in place in the melt and are sawn off at the ground surface. New electrodes are installed at each new melt location. The final melt is smaller in volume than the original waste and associated soil due to:

— Removal of volatile contaminants;
— Reduced void space;
— Higher density of glass relative to waste materials.

Each melting produces a single block shaped monolith of glass. Most vitrification projects require multiple, overlapping, melts to cover the area and volume of the contaminated site.

9.3.4.3. *Planar in situ vitrification*

Like traditional ISV, planar ISV employs the same Joule heating principle but differs in the application of electric current and in the starter path configuration. In planar ISV, the current travels between pairs of electrodes, causing two parallel planar melts to form. As the melts grow downwards and spread laterally, they eventually meet in the centre of the electrode array and fuse together into one melt. The final planar melt has the same size and shape as a traditional ISV melt.

9.3.4.4. *Plasma arc ISV*

Plasma arc ISV is a newer and much less tested technique based on established plasma arc technology. In this process, electrical energy is applied as direct current between two electrodes within a torch, creating a plasma of highly ionized gases at very high temperatures. The resistance to the flow of current between the two electrodes generates the plasma.

The operation involves lowering the torch into a predrilled borehole of any depth and heating the wastes and soil as the torch is gradually raised. The organic fraction of the wastes is pyrolysed and the inorganic fraction is vitrified, thus converting a mass of soil and or waste into a highly stable, leach resistant slag column.

Although this 'bottom-up' ISV process is experimental, it has advantages over the traditional and planar ISV applications. A primary advantage is the ability of gases and vapours to escape the subsurface above the melt zone rather than being trapped beneath it. As a result, the likelihood of melt expulsions is reduced.

The ISV process can immobilize extremely hazardous materials and radionuclides that may be difficult to treat.

9.3.5. In situ chemical oxidation

In situ chemical oxidation is based on the delivery of chemical oxidants into the vadose zone and/or groundwater to oxidize contaminants into carbon dioxide and water. This technique is best applied at highly contaminated sites or directed at source areas to reduce contaminant concentrations. In general this technique is not cost effective for plumes with low contaminant concentrations. The effectiveness of in situ chemical oxidation is sensitive to variations in the hydraulic conductivity of the soil as well as to the distribution of contaminant mass. Therefore, performance is improved by detailed site characterization.

To date the most common oxidant delivery methods involve injection of oxidants only. Should a significant hydraulic gradient exist, targeted delivery of oxidant to the contaminant zones may require injection and extraction wells. The major benefits of a passive oxidant delivery mode are that treatment of groundwater and disposal of secondary hazardous wastes are avoided.

The common oxidants are hydrogen based Fenton's reagent and potassium permanganate. In the application of Fenton's reagent, hydrogen peroxide is applied with an iron catalyst creating a hydroxyl free radical. This hydroxyl free radical oxidizes complex organic compounds. Residual hydrogen peroxide decomposes into water and oxygen in the subsurface and any remaining iron precipitates out. Fenton's reagent is produced on-site by adding an iron catalyst to a hydrogen peroxide solution. A 50% solution is common for this application. A pH adjustment may be required as Fenton's reagent is more effective at acidic pH. The main difference to the oxidation techniques discussed in Section 9.1 is that here the contaminants are oxidized directly, rather than being broken down in an aerobic microbial process.

The volume and chemical composition of reactants are based on contaminant levels and volume in addition to subsurface characteristics, and may be derived from pre-application testing results. The methods for delivery of the oxidants vary; they can be injected through a well or directly into the subsurface through an injector head; they can be mixed with a catalyst and injected, or combined with groundwater extracted from the site and then re-injected. In the case of hydrogen peroxide, stabilizers are needed because of the inherent instability of this compound.

In situ oxidation is being used for groundwater, sediment and soil remediation. It can be applied to a variety of soil types (silt and clay). It is used to treat volatile organic chemicals including DCE, trichloroethene, TCE, benzene, toluene, ethylbenzene and xylene, as well as semivolatile organic chemicals including pesticides, polycyclic aromatic hydrocarbons and PCBs [190, 191].

The limitations of the in situ chemical oxidation technique include:

(a)   Target contaminants may be difficult to oxidize.
(b)   Areal extent of contamination may be too large, in situ oxidation is best applied to 'hot spots' and source zones rather than very large groundwater plumes.
(c)   Geotechnical and hydraulic characteristics of the site may restrict drilling and limit ability to inject oxidant.
(d)   Presence of underground human made structures (i.e. buried pipelines and other utilities) can create short circuits for injected fluids.
(e)   High natural organic content will create a high oxidant demand, thus requiring larger amounts of oxidant that will increase the cost of treatment.
(f)   Inadvertent mobilization of co-contaminant metals, including radionuclides, from increased oxidation states.

10. REMOVAL OF THE SOURCE TERM

10.1. EXCAVATION

10.1.1.   Preconditions and constraints

It should be noted that in general any method relying on the removal of contaminated soil is likely to require the substitution of the removed material with clean soil. Therefore, in addition to considerations with respect to technical feasibility, an economic source of clean soil will be required to make this option viable. Conversely, a precondition for any removal option is the availability of a suitable disposal site for the excavated materials, whether they are left untreated or whether they are conditioned before emplacement.

Retrieval consists of excavating and removing buried wastes or subsurface contaminated soil or sediments. For buried wastes, retrieval could entail removal of overburden soil, interstitial soil and possibly impacted underlying soil as well. Retrieving low level radioactive and hazardous soil and buried wastes from a site is a proven and reliable approach. Examples of retrieval actions conducted at USDOE facilities, including Hanford, Rocky

Flats, Los Alamos, Fernald and the Idaho National Laboratory, are provided, for instance, in Ref. [192]. However, retrieval and waste management techniques for transuranic wastes have not been proven to the same extent and may require site specific and innovative design elements to ensure protection of human health and the environment. In addition, problems with the acceptance of wastes in disposal facilities might arise.

The removal of wastes from a site allows them to be treated to reduce the toxicity and mobility of the various contaminants with a view to making the wastes suitable for disposal in a licensed engineered facility. Retrieval removes or greatly reduces the risks associated with the site if the retrieved wastes are disposed of off-site or isolated from the environment. This typically then results in significantly reduced long term site monitoring and maintenance requirements. Furthermore, with complete removal of the contaminants, the site can be released for unrestricted use. However, it has to be borne in mind that the disposal site may now need such monitoring and maintenance. Nevertheless, some advantage would be gained by concentrating contaminants at a smaller number of sites requiring supervision.

The retrieval and disposal of waste materials is time consuming and expensive. One of the greatest concerns in retrieving buried radioactive and hazardous wastes and contaminated soil is increased potential for worker exposure (Section 4), contamination spread and off-site release.

Two categories of technology are usually implemented during retrieval of contaminated materials and wastes from sites with mixed contamination — contamination control and excavation.

10.1.2. Contamination control

Controls during waste retrieval are needed to minimize the spread of contamination and control the source. Depending on site-specific conditions and materials present (e.g. soils, bulk debris, process sludges and containerized liquids), various controls may be used. In general, controls are grouped into two categories — those used before retrieval and those used during retrieval. Both types can be effective at controlling contamination, thus decreasing the potential for exposure, the costs of operation and maintenance of equipment and the cost of decontamination. Process options for contamination control include the following:

(a) *Confinement*: Enclosures constructed from plastic, metal, fibreglass or other materials are used to prevent the spread of airborne contaminants by enclosure of a piece of equipment, work area or an entire site. Enclosures may be relatively lightweight and portable or they may be more substantial, sturdier and less portable. Enclosures are typically double walled to minimize the potential for contaminant releases.

(b) *Ventilation and vacuum systems*: Ventilation systems use laminar airflow at the dig-face of an excavation and within enclosures to direct dust to HEPA filter units. Vacuum systems are used to remove loose particles from equipment and structures and draw in dust and debris generated during excavation activities.

(c) *Foams, sprays, misters, fixatives and washes*: Their application is intended to control odors, VOCs, dust and other emissions, creating a barrier between the work surface and the atmosphere, or to aid settling airborne particulates. They are also used in the decontamination of personnel and equipment. The materials selected are non-toxic, non-hazardous, non-flammable and biodegradable.

(d) *Electrostatics*: Electrically charged plastics and electrostatic curtains can be used to minimize the spread of contamination from enclosed areas. Curtains can be used upstream of emission filtering systems to neutralize charged dust particles.

(e) *In situ stabilization*: In situ stabilization can be performed before initiating excavation operations to control contamination in the soil and waste matrix. Grout, resin or polymers may be injected into wastes or soil to solidify material or sprayed onto the surface to suppress dust generation (Section 9.3.3). Stabilization can also be achieved by ISV (Section 9.3.4) or ground freezing technologies (Section 9.2.3.8).

10.1.3. Excavation techniques

A wide variety of excavation techniques and associated equipment are available on the market, including conventional heavy earth moving equipment, standard construction equipment with appropriate modifications (e.g. sealed and pressurized cabins with filtered intakes and extracts or supplied air) and remotely controlled equipment. Most equipment used for excavation of soil and buried wastes is standard heavy construction equipment proven for use at hazardous waste sites around the world. If the hazards at a site are particularly severe, remotely operated equipment and hermetically (airtight) sealed equipment with filtered or supplied air can also be used.

A number of hand-held tools of specialized designs have been developed to facilitate retrieval of various waste forms. Designs include grappling devices for waste containers and debris, as well as water jets, magnets and vacuum systems. A summary of potentially available hand-held tools is presented in Table 12.

TABLE 12. DESCRIPTION OF RETRIEVAL EQUIPMENT

Technology	Description
Remote excavators	
Remotely controlled demolition robots	Remotely controlled excavators with a fully articulated telescopic arm. Available with several different end-tools that can be used for hammering, cutting and scooping wastes. The largest varieties can reach approximately 4 m below the ground surface.
Remotely controlled confined space demolition equipment	Remotely controlled excavators with a telescopic boom capable of moving in three dimensions. Available with several end-tools. The largest Keibler Thompson machine can reach approximately 5 m below the ground surface.
Remotely operated excavator	The excavator is mounted on a wheeled undercarriage that was developed to retrieve unexploded ordnance. A television set provides images for remote control. The only such excavator in existence is currently used at an air force base.
T-Rex® front shovel excavators that require modification for use	Teleoperated, heavy lift, long reach excavators designed to retrieve boxes, drums and containers with a front shovel excavator. Controls can be operated from distances of up to 380 m (1250 ft) from the excavator.
Front end loaders with a bucket of 2 m³ volume	Front end loaders developed for use by remote control. They provide a three dimensional colour video/audio feedback and can be controlled from distances of up to 500 m. These systems can be modified for use on excavators.
Teleoperated excavators using T-Rex® remote control kits	Remotely controlled excavators (bucket and thumb) adapted for hazardous environments, such as unexploded ordnance (UXO), through sensors, controllers and hydraulic components.
Remotely controlled excavator vehicle system experimental platforms based on excavators	Remotely controlled, tethered platforms for excavators. Attachments can grasp objects, sift soil and make an excavator act as a bulldozer. A clam shell and air jet vacuum system can also be attached.
Automated ordnance excavators	Remotely controlled excavators with extended reach capability, developed for UXO removal. Can grasp objects such as drums and boxes.

TABLE 12. DESCRIPTION OF RETRIEVAL EQUIPMENT (cont.)

Technology	Description
Remote excavators (cont.)	
Small emplacement excavators	Military tractors with a front end loader and backhoe remote operation for retrieving buried wastes and soil. Systems can be controlled from distances of up to 800 m.
Remotely controlled excavators, Hitachi excavators, innovative end-effectors and self-guided transport vehicles	Standard excavators with end-effectors (such as buckets, rippers and breakers) used for buried waste retrieval. Systems can be controlled from inside a cab, via a remote tether or from distances of up to 750 m.
Modified Bobcats®	Remotely controlled skid steer loaders with a Bobcat® vehicle base with barrel grapple, sweeper and bucket attachments. Modified for use in hazardous environments, remote kit for other excavators.
Standard construction equipment with modifications	
Sealed and pressurized cabins, with filtered air intakes and extractors	Standard construction equipment with modifications made to the cabins. The sealed and pressurized cabins use filtered air (through HEPA filtration).
Sealed and pressurized cabins, with supplied air	Standard construction equipment with modifications made to the cabins. The sealed and pressurized cabins use supplied air.
Remote end-tools	
Safe excavators	High pressure probes dislodge compacted soil, other hardened materials using an air jet/vacuum end-effector system. Vacuums up soil.
Two armed, tethered, hydraulically powered interstitial conveyance systems	Crane deployed with two excavators and vacuums designed for low level radiation fields. Maximum pick-up load of 320 kg.
Highly manipulative tentacles	Teleoperated manipulators and bellows actuators.
Hydraulic impact end-effectors	Water cannons for tank applications; attached to a robotic manipulator arm and used to break up monolithic hard cake forming around risers in tanks.
Schilling Tital II®	Manipulators deployed by cranes for selective retrieval. Basic components include a hydraulic system, positioning system, electronics module and mechanical interface.

TABLE 12. DESCRIPTION OF RETRIEVAL EQUIPMENT (cont.)

Technology	Description
Remote end-tools (cont.)	
Mineclaw®	Manipulators with a strong electromagnet to pick up barrels. Custom grapple with a payload of several hundred kilograms and an electromagnet to retrieve metals.
Confined sluicing end-effectors	Water jets designed for waste tank cleanup. Use high pressure water jets to cut material into small pieces and evacuate with a vacuum jet pump. Captures slurry water.
Soil skimmers	Skimmers remove soil overburden, for example in 8, 10 or 15 cm increments. Adjustable depth controls determine the depth of cut without disturbing soil underneath.
Innovative end-effectors	These consist of three assemblies: a thumb, an attachable/detachable integrated transfer module and a shovel assembly capable of soil retrieval and dust-free waste dumping.
Quick-change couplers	These are available in manual and hydraulic versions. They are used on various buckets, rakes, clamps, rippers and other end-effectors.
Vacuum systems	Nuclear grade vacuum systems for contamination control and retrieval of soil with HEPA filtration and waste containers safe from criticality.

Note: Brand names are used for purposes of illustration only and do not constitute an endorsement of the supplier.

Most of the required equipment and techniques for excavation or retrieval have been proven in highly contaminated environments. For example, remote excavators have been proven successful in waste retrieval simulations and have been used throughout the facilities of the USDOE for decontamination and demolition work. In addition, shielded excavators and hermetically sealed vehicles have been used successfully. In general, hermetically sealed retrieval equipment is less expensive, needs less maintenance, is capable of more precise digging and can be operated faster than remote equipment. In some environments, shielding (e.g. Lexan™ windows) of equipment is required to protect workers from potential explosions and radiation. Filtered or supplied air can be added to equipment to protect operators, as has been proven at many sites. Additional information can be found in Refs [193–195].

It should be noted that where a medium, typically water, is being used, secondary mixed wastes or wastewater may arise that require treatment and disposal.

10.1.4. Waste stabilization as a pretreatment for excavation and retrieval

10.1.4.1. Soil freezing

Soil freezing can provide an in situ barrier for containment of contaminated groundwater and a bottom barrier at landfills or other contaminated sites, and provides temporary shoring for construction of permeable barriers or excavation of contamination. It creates a dry safe environment for construction and excavation. It also bonds soil and wastes together to prevent dangerous mixing during removal, reduces the volatility and inflammability of organic contaminants, and even helps with safe retrieval of unexploded ordnance.

10.1.4.2. In situ vitrification

As was discussed in Section 9.3.4, ISV may be used to generate blocks of waste or a slag-like product that can be safely and easily handled. The vitrified block would be excavated and the material removed for disposal at an engineered disposal facility (Fig. 13).

10.1.4.3. In situ chemical solidification

Some of the inorganic and organic grouting techniques described above and designed for the contaminated material remaining in situ can also be used

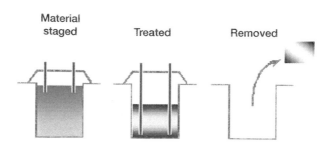

FIG. 13. In situ vitrification for removal and disposal (after GeoMelt™) [189].

to solidify the matrix for easier and safer handling. Following the curing of the grout, the contaminated material can be excavated as a block. Thus the dispersal, spilling or volatilization of contaminants during the excavation operation can be minimized. The technical arrangements for application of the solidification agent would be the same as those discussed in Section 9.2.3. The grout matrix will also reduce the solubility of contaminants, and the materials thus solidified may be suitable for direct disposal in an appropriately engineered facility. The solidification agent would be chosen such that it does not compromise the long term stability of the waste matrix in the engineered disposal facility.

10.2. PUMP AND TREAT FOR SURFACE WATER AND GROUNDWATER

10.2.1. The concept

The pump and treat technology for groundwater involves drilling wells into contaminated groundwater, pumping it to the surface and treating it to remove the contaminants (Fig. 14) [196]. After removal of contaminants, the treated water is either re-injected into the groundwater via a well in a suitable location or discharged to a surface watercourse or into the sewerage system, depending on availability and permits. The treatment method depends on the physicochemical properties of the contaminants to be removed. Pump and treat systems remove groundwater contaminated with a variety of dissolved materials, including VOCs, semivolatile organic compounds (SVOCs), fuels, heavy metals and radionuclides.

Pump and treat systems are designed to:

(a) Hydraulically contain and control the movement of contaminated groundwater and prevent continued expansion of the contamination zone;

(b) Reduce dissolved contaminant concentrations to comply with cleanup standards and thereby restore the aquifer;

(c) Combine the two objectives (a) and (b) [197].

The major advantage of pump and treat is that with it conventional technologies for water and wastewater treatment can be applied for decontamination of the pumped groundwater. These include biological treatment, activated carbon adsorption, air stripping of volatiles and metal precipitation.

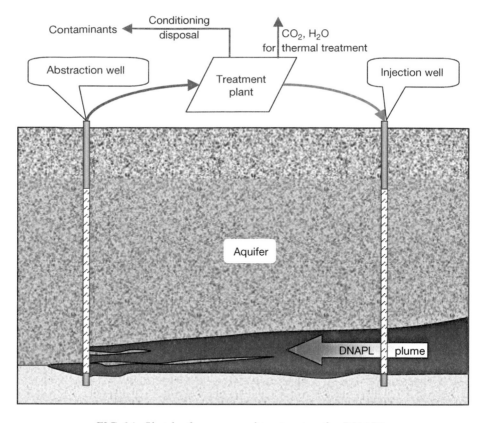

FIG. 14. Sketch of a pump and treat system for DNAPLs.

Pump and treat is most effective when it is combined with measures of isolation and/or removal of the contamination source in order to prevent further introduction of contaminant into the groundwater.

The pump and treat remediation requires passage of a sufficient volume of groundwater through the contaminated section of the aquifer in order to remove not only the dissolved contaminants but also the ones that desorb from the geological media, diffuse from zones of low hydraulic conductivity and dissolve from solid phases or non-aqueous phase liquids. The total volume of groundwater that must be treated at the surface is determined by the product of the pore volume and the number of pore volumes that must be pumped in order to reduce the contaminant concentration in the aquifer to the desired level. Typically, pump and treat systems are designed to remove 0.5–2 pore volumes of the contaminated section of the aquifer per year [197]. Pumping at higher rates may be limited by low permeability of some sections of the aquifer or interphase mass transfer. The remediation time may be approximated by comparison of the contaminant rate of removal, the initial mass and the mass remaining in the aquifer at any point in time. The use of a reaction transport model of the coupled type might be of advantage to estimate the times needed.

Monitoring contaminant concentrations with time at pump and treat sites reveals tailing and rebound phenomena. Tailing refers to the progressively slower rate of dissolved contaminant concentration decline observed with continued operation of pump and treat systems. Another problem arises when residuals are left on soil as groundwater is depressed during pumping. After the groundwater returns to normal levels, contaminants sorbed onto the soil become dissolved; this phenomenon is termed 'rebound'. Tailing and rebound may result from several physical and chemical processes that affect pump and treat remediation, including [197]:

— Contaminant desorption;
— Non-aqueous phase liquid dissolution;
— Precipitate dissolution;
— Groundwater velocity variation;
— Matrix diffusion.

10.2.2. Applicability

Pump and treat systems (Fig. 14) were the baseline for remediating groundwater during the 1990s [9, 198–201]. A basic condition for pump and treat is that an aquifer has to have a sufficiently high permeability to allow a significant water flow to be induced. Contaminant transport may be hindered in heterogeneous aquifers by low permeability areas. The target contaminants should have a limited affinity for the solid phase only, i.e. they should readily desorb; otherwise long tails will ensue.

The apparent advantage of pump and treat systems is that they are seemingly simple in operation and design. From a purely hydraulic perspective, pump and treat systems can indeed be effectively designed. In addition, as the operation and maintenance of pump and treat systems is very simple, the skilled workforce necessary for operation is quite small.

However, the effectiveness of pump and treat systems can be compromised by a number of factors that are related to the contaminants of interest and the characteristics of the site. As a result, it is usually impossible to reduce dissolved contaminants to below drinking water limits in reasonable time frames, for example less than 10 years at many sites [202]. A United States National Academy of Sciences report [203] provides a comprehensive assessment of the effectiveness of pump and treat systems for remediation of subsurface contamination. The report found that pump and treat is inefficient as a source removal technology, although it can reduce source term volumes. In line with other methods that are based on changing the distribution between two different phases of a contaminant, this method becomes increasingly inefficient as the concentration gradient between, for example, species sorbed on the solid matrix and aqueous species diminishes. Large quantities of groundwater may have to be pumped and treated to remove only small amounts of contaminant. Removal underground is inefficient due to tailing or mass transfer limitations. A further complication arises from the fact that not all pore water is mobile. Contaminants (e.g. NAPLs) may be trapped in dead-end pores and released into the mobile pore water only by diffusion, which is one of the mechanisms responsible for the 'tailing'. DNAPLs may become trapped in various aquifer features and thus become inaccessible to pumping (cf. Fig. 1). Although various configurations of, for example, abstraction wells have been investigated to increase the degree of hydraulic connectedness and hence the efficiency [204, 205], these configurations have been unable to overcome the fundamental constraints on diffusion. The efficiency of the pump and treat method can be enhanced in some cases by using flushing chemicals, by combining it with techniques that aim to increase the solubility of contaminants, such as electrolysis [206] or (reverse) osmosis [207] (see Section 10.3 for details), or by pulsed pumping. The pump and treat method may also be used in combination with other remedial alternatives such as vacuum extraction and/or bioremediation.

For the reasons given pump and treat is currently considered more a containment method — with an appropriate configuration of the abstraction and injection wells — than a removal method.

Unusual conditions of the water, such as low pH values, as is often the case for mine effluents or disposal facility leachates, may pose special problems during the processing [208]. A neutralization step might be required [209].

Additional problems arise in multiphase systems. As can be gathered from Fig. 1, the placement of abstraction wells can be crucial. Depressions in low permeability strata underlying an aquifer may collect dense non-miscible fluids that can only be retrieved if an abstraction well is actually placed in such a depression. The differences in surface tension in multiphase fluid systems and the affinity to clay surfaces of many non-polar liquids may also make recovery by pumping almost impossible due to capillary forces at phase boundaries. Addition of surfactants to enhance recovery may be required (Section 10.3.2).

Pumped waters can be treated in a variety of ways to remove and concentrate contaminants [9, 198–201]. Ion exchange or sorption [210] and precipitation are the main processes employed [211]. More esoteric methods, for instance, involve electrolysis [206] or (reverse) osmosis. The contaminant concentrates arising require treatment by an appropriate conditioning method before they can be sent for long term storage and/or ultimate disposal.

A particular instance of the pump and treat technique is discussed in Example 7.

10.2.3. Pumping techniques

In most cases submerged centrifugal pumps would be used. Where the water table is less then 8 m below ground, surface (centrifugal) pumps can also be employed. The layout of pumping wells would be designed to suit the specific application and the hydraulic boundary conditions. Special precautions may need to be taken in cases where volatile and explosive contaminants may be drawn into the pumping wells. This concerns in particular degassing and the accumulation of explosive gases in the headspace of pumping equipment. Provisions for bleeding off headspace gases and their treatment may have to be made. Pumps and associated power supply systems may need to be made to a specification that gives them protection against explosions.

Airlifts are an alternative to centrifugal pumps. Using these, compressed air is pumped down a well and the rising air bubble induces an upward water flow. Since no moving parts in the hole are involved in this technique, it is particularly suitable for water with high solid contents. The disadvantage can be that large quantities of oxygen are introduced and that the large surface area created by injecting the air promotes degassing. However, both effects can be beneficial: the gasses can be collected for treatment, and with appropriate process control, deliberate oxidation processes can be induced (Section 10.3.7.2).

10.2.4. Treatment systems

Various techniques are available to treat ex situ abstracted waters for dissolved contaminants and gases. Section 11 describes ex situ treatment techniques in more detail. Many techniques are borrowed from drinking water treatment and other industrial processes and include:

(a) *Adsorption*: In the presence of a solid phase, contaminants may partition from the liquid onto this solid phase, thereby reducing their concentration in the bulk liquid. The surface processes active there are usually summarily termed adsorption. The most commonly used adsorbent for organic constituents is granulated activated charcoal. Other natural and

Example 7. Pump and treat applied to drinking water (courtesy of L. Pillette-Cousin).

The pump and treat remediation technique has been applied to the water table near the city of Strasbourg (France), which is used as a source of drinking water [212]. In this case, an industrial pollution of water by tetrachloroethene was detected at more than one kilometre from the pumping station providing drinking water to a part of the city. As the treatment started, the monitoring of the contaminant concentration in the pumped water demonstrated its effectiveness, as shown below:

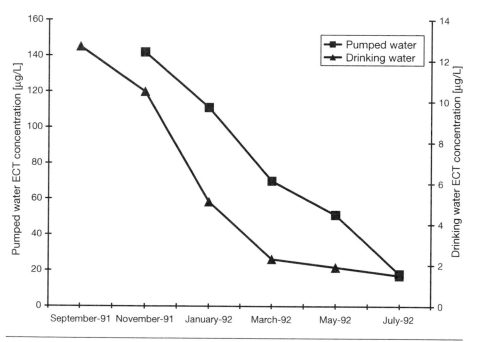

synthetic adsorbents include forage sponge, lignin, clays and synthetic resins, which are more suitable for ionic contaminants.

(b) *Biological treatment*: Organic contaminants are broken down and removed in various types of biological reactor system. In suspended systems, such as activated sludge, contaminated groundwater is circulated in an aeration basin. In attached systems, such as rotating biological contractors and trickling filters, microorganisms are established on an inert support matrix.

(c) *Air stripping*: VOCs are partitioned from groundwater by increasing the surface area of the contaminated water and a pressure gradient. Aeration methods include packed towers, diffused aeration, tray aeration and spray aeration.

(d) *Ion exchange*: This is a process whereby certain cations, such as protons, or anions on a stationary solid phase are exchanged for contaminants in ionic form that have a higher affinity for the substrate. Typical ion exchangers are certain synthetic resins, natural organic polymers and some types of clay. Once the exchange capacity has been exhausted, the ion exchanger is removed and regenerated by backwashing it with concentrated solutions of inert salts.

(e) *(Co)-precipitation, coagulation and flocculation*: These related processes transform dissolved contaminants into an insoluble solid, facilitating its subsequent removal from the liquid phase by sedimentation or filtration. Precipitation or co-precipitation is brought about by the addition of ions that form low solubility solids with the target contaminants, or by inducing hydrolysis by increasing pH. Subsequent flocculation is aided by various agents.

(f) *Separation*: These processes are aimed at detaching contaminants from their medium (i.e. groundwater and/or binding material that contain them). Ex situ separation of waste streams can be performed by many processes:

(1) Distillation;
(2) Filtration, ultrafiltration and microfiltration;
(3) Membrane pervaporation;
(4) Reverse osmosis.

10.3. ENHANCED RECOVERY

10.3.1. The concept

Recent research has led to a better understanding of the processes involved in the transport and transformation of contaminants in the subsurface. In recognition of the fact that pump and treat systems often require protracted periods of time to make significant reductions in the quantity of contaminants in the subsurface and may not be able to mobilize the whole reservoir of contaminants, methods for improving the efficiency of pump and treat technology have been developed [207]. These methods aim at either detaching the contaminants from soil surfaces, releasing them from the bulk soil and breaking down organic contaminants into more mobile forms, or improving the hydraulic conductivity or accessibility of the pore space.

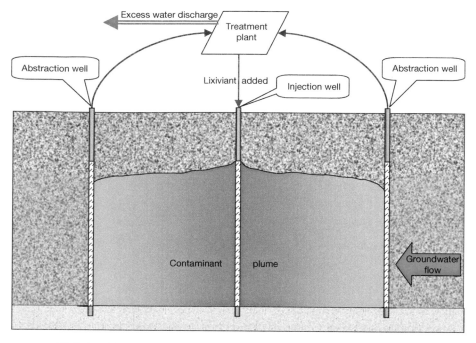

FIG. 15. Sketch of in situ leaching or enhanced recovery arrangement.

10.3.2. *Chemical agents*

Methods to speed up recovery of contaminants or to lower residual concentrations in pump and treat scenarios are often termed soil flushing [213]. After removing the contaminant and before being re-injected, the pumped water is dotted with lixiviants, for example, acid, surfactants [214], complexing agents, such as EDTA and other macromolecules, or inert electrolytes to replace sorbed radionuclides (Section 10.3.4). Figure 15 shows the principal layout for the treatment of an aquifer, while Fig. 16 shows the arrangement for treating the unsaturated zone above an aquifer. A similar arrangement to that of Fig. 16 might be used to stimulate biodegradation in the vadose zone by adding nutrients.

The typical target contaminants for soil flushing are inorganic compounds including radionuclides [215]. While the technology can be used to treat VOCs, SVOCs, fuels and pesticides, it is often less cost effective than alternative technologies for these other contaminant groups [216].

Factors that may limit the applicability and effectiveness of the process include:

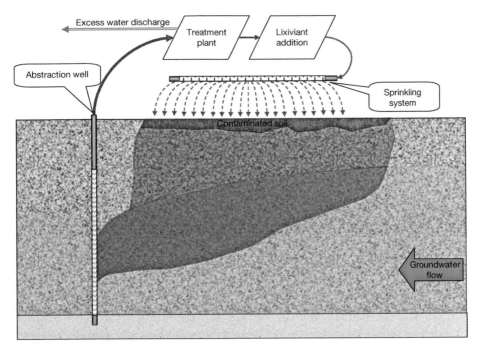

FIG. 16. Sketch of contaminated soil in the vadose zone being sprinkled to remove contamination.

(a) Difficulty of treating low permeability or heterogeneous soils;
(b) Possible adherence of surfactants to soil and reduction of effective soil porosity;
(c) Reduction of contaminant mobility caused by reactions of flushing agents with the geomatrix;
(d) The potential for washing the contaminant beyond the capture zone due to insufficient hydraulic control;
(e) Regulatory concern over the introduction of alien substances;
(f) Technical feasibility and cost of recovering contaminants and separating flushing agent.

It is imperative to understand thoroughly the hydraulic and geochemical system to which the enhancement methods are to be applied. Not all contaminations are amenable to chemical enhancement methods; in particular, if retention is dominated by physical processes then chemical enhancement will have no effect on the recovery rate. If the retention of the contaminant appears to be dominated by chemical or surface processes, specific knowledge of these processes needs to be acquired before an enhancement technique is designed and implemented.

The key issues for consideration when designing a chemical enhancement method are:

(1) Feasibility of delivery of the reactive agent to target areas in the aquifer;
(2) Efficiency of removal by the enhancement process;
(3) Fate of reactant in the subsurface,
(4) Impact of the reactive agent on any ex situ treatment process;
(5) Volume of removed contaminant to be disposed of.

Different agents can be chosen depending upon the processes that control the retention, such as:

— Competition for adsorption sites;
— Complexation of the contaminant;
— Co-solvent effects;
— Mobilization and solubilization by surfactants;
— Oxidation and reduction;
— Dissolution.

These mechanisms are not necessarily exclusive. For example, a reactive agent may change the redox state of the contaminant and then form a complex with the altered form. Complex formation can be an effective means to solubilize contaminants because aqueous complexes are often not adsorbed as readily as the respective ion; hence, they are more mobile and easier to remove by pumping. For example, it was found that citric and diethylene-triamine-penta-acetic (DTPA) acid complexed Cr(III) sufficiently to maintain useful solution concentrations [217]. Similar organic complexants, such as EDTA, are routinely used as decontamination agents.

Considerable operational experience is available in the metals industry, including the uranium mining industry, in the application of in situ leaching techniques to recover metal value. However, if the reactive agents are chosen on the basis of incorrectly identified limiting processes and site properties, there is a risk that their application will provide no net benefit and may even become counterproductive.

10.3.3. Electrokinetic extraction

Electrokinetic extraction technology is a treatment process that is intended to concentrate, separate and extract contaminants, primarily heavy metals, radionuclides and charged organic material, from saturated or unsaturated soils, sludges and sediments, and groundwater. The principle of electrokinetic extraction relies upon application of a low intensity direct current through the soil between ceramic electrodes that are divided into a cathode array and an anode array (Fig. 17). This mobilizes charged chemical species, causing ions and water to move and concentrate towards the electrodes. Cations, such as simple metal ions or the ammonium ion, and positively charged organic compounds move towards the cathode. Anions such as chlorine, cyanide, fluorine, nitrate and negatively charged organic compounds move towards the anode. The current creates an acidic front at the anode and a basic zone at the cathode. This generation of an acidic condition in situ helps to mobilize sorbed metal contaminants for transport to the collection system at the cathode.

The primary mechanisms that transport contaminants through soil towards one or the other electrode are electro-osmosis, electromigration and/or electrophoresis. Electro-osmosis is the movement of soil moisture or groundwater from the anode to the cathode of an electrolytic cell. Electromigration is the transport of ions and ion complexes to the electrode of the opposite charge. Electrophoresis is the transport of charged particles or colloids under the influence of an electric field; contaminants bound to mobile particulate matter can be transported in this manner.

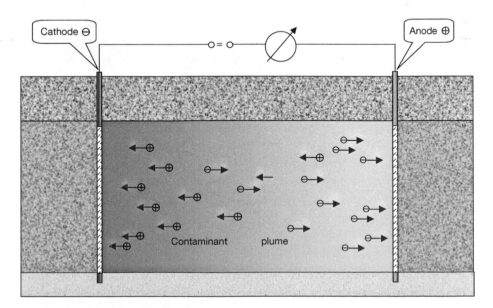

FIG. 17. Generic layout for remediation by electrolysis and electro-osmosis.

Among the transport mechanisms, electromigration is the main mechanism for the electrokinetic remediation process. The direction and rate of movement of an ionic species depends on its charge, in both magnitude and polarity, as well as on the magnitude of the electro-osmosis induced flow velocity. Non-ionic species, both inorganic and organic, will also be transported along with the water flow induced by electro-osmosis. Extraction rates and efficiencies depend upon many subsurface characteristics, such as soil type and grain size, contaminant concentration, ionic mobility, total ionic concentration, types of contaminant species and their solubility.

The concentrated contaminants can be extracted from the vicinity of the electrodes by precipitation or co-precipitation, pumping near the electrode or complexing with ion exchange resins, or become electroplated on the electrodes and then removed with them. In both cases ex situ treatment and disposal will follow.

The ensuing electrolytic reactions can also be utilized to change the redox state of various inorganic and organic contaminants. In the latter case this can lead to in situ destruction of the contaminant. However, unwanted by-products, such as halogenated organic compounds, may result.

Owing to the ionic nature of most radionuclides and heavy metals in aqueous solutions, electrochemical methods appeared at first to be rather promising [206, 218–221]. However, the application of electrochemical techniques to remove organic contaminants has met in practice with limited success. Addition of chelating agents, such as citric acid or EDTA, will increase the effectiveness of this process [222–224]. The effectiveness of electrochemical methods can also be enhanced by the introduction of co-solvents and surfactants (see also Sections 10.3.5 and 10.3.6) [225–228]. The addition of surfactants, however, may change clay permeabilities for the worse through swelling [229].

Different types of electrode materials have been tested to improve performance, including porous ceramics and the rather novel carbon aerogels that increase the effective surface area [210]. Electro-osmosis may be combined with other techniques to remove contaminants from low permeability geomatrices, such as clays. LASAGNA™ is a technology demonstration project designed to evaluate a combination of technologies [230]:

(a) A permeable zone in the contaminated soil region is created for instance by hydrofracturing, and appropriate sorbents or reactants are introduced.
(b) Electro-osmosis is applied to move contaminants from low permeability areas.
(c) The contaminant collects in the high permeability zone and is removed or degraded (organic compounds).

A similar configuration can be used to create electrically induced redox barriers, but this work is still very much in the development stage [231].

Limitations of this technology include:

(a)   There is a lack of understanding of its effects on naturally occurring ions and the impact these effects have on mobilization and removal of target contaminants.

(b)   Reduced effectiveness for wastes and soil with moisture contents less than 10%. The maximum effectiveness occurs for moisture contents between 14 and 18%.

(c)   The presence of buried metallic or insulating materials can cause variability in the electrical conductivity of the soil; therefore, the (natural geological) spatial variability should be delineated carefully. Additionally, deposits that exhibit very high electrical conductivity, such as ore deposits, cause the technique to be inefficient.

(d)   The need to use inert electrodes of, for example, carbon, graphite or platinum to avoid introducing degradation products into the treated zone. Metallic electrodes may dissolve as a result of electrolysis and introduce corrosion products into the treated zone.

(e)   Electrokinetics is most effective in clays because of the negative surface charge of clay particles. However, the surface charge of clay is altered by both changes in the pH of the pore fluid and the adsorption of contaminants. Extreme pH values at the electrodes and reduction–oxidation changes induced by the electrode reactions may reduce effectiveness, although acidic conditions may help remove metals.

(f)   Electrolysis can result in undesirable and potentially hazardous products, such as hydrogen, hydrogen sulphide or chlorine gas, trihalomethanes and acetone.

10.3.4. Displacement by inert electrolytes

If the retention of the contaminant is primarily controlled by adsorption processes, a reactive agent can be chosen to compete for the adsorption sites. The aquifer may be swamped with an inert electrolyte to replace contaminants from sorption sites on the geomatrix. The effectiveness of these methods depends very much on the nature of the contaminants and the geomatrix. Competition is usually most effective for ionic solutes and least effective in displacing neutral organic molecules partitioned into soil organic matter. In general, competition will be significant only when the adsorption sites are near saturation or when the affinity of the displacing ion for the sorption sites is significantly higher than that of the contaminant. The most effective cation to replace sorbed radionuclides would be protons, as indeed are used in in situ mining, but these would also affect acid dissolution of some matrix minerals, namely carbonates and oxyhydroxides. Such dissolution of the matrix may be rather undesirable, because it affects the structural and hydrodynamic properties of the rock and consumes large quantities of acid. An inert, toxicologically acceptable and cheap cation is the sodium ion administered in the form of NaCl (rock salt).

10.3.5. Co-solvent solubilization

The rate of removal of hydrophobic organic contaminants is often limited by their relatively low solubility in water. However, the solubilities of many of these contaminants are much greater in other solvents. Co-solvents are chemical compounds that are miscible in water and also have a certain affinity for NAPLs. These co-solvents promote NAPL removal through a number of complementary mechanisms, including: reduction of interfacial tension between the aqueous and NAPL phases; enhanced solubility of the chemical contaminants (NAPL components) in the aqueous phase; swelling of the NAPL phase relative to the aqueous phase; and, under certain conditions, complete miscibility of the aqueous and NAPL phases. The relative importance of these different mechanisms depends on the ternary (water, co-solvent and NAPL) phase behaviour of the specific system [232]. Co-solvents that preferentially partition into the NAPL phase are capable of mobilizing the NAPL as a separate phase due to swelling of the NAPL and reduction of interfacial tension. In cases where the co-solvent strongly partitions into the NAPL phase, the NAPL is effectively removed with about one pore volume of injected fluid. Co-solvents that preferentially stay with the aqueous phase can dramatically increase the solubility of NAPL in the aqueous phase, and removal occurs by enhanced dissolution rather than in a separate phase.

Given a sufficiently high initial co-solvent concentration in the aqueous phase (the flooding fluid), large amounts of co-solvent will partition into the NAPL. As a result of this partitioning, the NAPL phase expands, and formerly discontinuous NAPL ganglia can become continuous, and hence mobile. This expanding NAPL phase behaviour, along with large interfacial tension reductions, allows the NAPL phase to concentrate at the leading edge of the co-solvent slug, thereby increasing the mobility of the NAPL. Under certain conditions, a highly efficient piston-like displacement of the NAPL is possible. Because the co-solvent also has the effect of increasing the NAPL solubility in the aqueous phase, small fractions of the NAPL that are not mobilized by the above mechanism will be dissolved by the co-solvent slug.

Examples of co-solvents that preferentially partition into the NAPL include higher molecular weight miscible alcohols, such as isopropyl and tert-butyl alcohol. Alcohols with a limited aqueous solubility, such as butanol, pentanol, hexanol and heptanol, can be blended with water miscible alcohols to improve their overall phase behaviour.

In field applications the co-solvent mixture is injected uphill of the contaminated area. The solvent with the dissolved contaminants is extracted downhill of the contaminated area and treated above ground. Physical barriers may be installed to prevent uncontrolled migration of solvent and contaminants.

Co-solvents that are used as substrates by microbes may have the added advantage of promoting co-metabolism of primary contaminants. Small amounts of biodegradable co-solvent that are difficult to remove from the subsurface will be of less concern because of their eventual transformation. Thus, co-solvents, such as alcohols, are potentially effective reactive agents for chemical enhancement for pump and treat of hydrophobic organic compounds.

Order of magnitude decreases in adsorbed contaminants are generally achieved with co-solvent concentrations greater than 20%. Fluids containing this amount of co-solvent will have densities and viscosities that differ substantially from the groundwater. Thus, the transport behaviour of these fluids is more complex and more difficult to predict than that for fluids with homogeneous properties.

Co-solvent interaction with clays in the aquifer matrix may either increase or decrease the permeability of the soil. The formation of such high permeability pathways may be particularly troublesome at sites where DNAPLs are present. Co-solvents such as methanol can serve as a substrate for subsurface microbes, resulting in biofouling of the aquifer. Biotransformation may substantially alter the geochemistry of the aquifer and promote the reductive dissolution of iron and manganese oxides. These metals can create problems with well clogging and interfere with surface treatment.

10.3.6. Surfactants and micro-emulsions

10.3.6.1. Basic mechanisms

Surfactants are molecules that have both hydrophilic and lipophilic moieties. The amphophilic nature of surfactant molecules causes them to accumulate at interfaces, such as air–water, oil–water and water–solid, and significantly reduce the interfacial tension [233]. Because of this property, surfactants are useful in enhanced oil recovery [234] and may also be applied to remediation of NAPL contaminated sites [235]. Surfactants are classified by the nature of their head group. The different types are: cationic, anionic, non-ionic and zwitterionic (both cationic and anionic groups). Different types of surfactant can be more or less effective depending on the particular contaminant involved.

The surfactant must be chosen to be compatible with the solvent under the conditions of use. Inadequate surfactant formulations may result in high viscosity macroemulsions that are difficult to remove. The surfactant can alter the wetting properties of the soil matrix and cause the NAPL to become the wetting phase. The NAPL would then occupy the smaller pores of the soil matrix, thereby exacerbating cleanup efforts.

Introducing alien substances, such as surfactants, into an aquifer is always a concern and may meet with resistance from regulatory authorities. It has to be shown that they are non-toxic and, if possible, biodegradable; otherwise, the surfactant itself will have to be removed from the treated zone.

There are two main mechanisms by which surfactant can affect recovery of subsurface NAPLs: micellar solubilization and mobilization of the NAPL due to reduced interfacial tension.

10.3.6.2. Micellar solubilization

A unique characteristic of surfactant molecules is their ability to self-assemble into dynamic aggregates known as micelles (Fig. 18) [236, 237]. The surfactant concentration at which micelle formation commences is known as the critical micelle concentration (CMC). Micelle formation generally distinguishes surfactants from amphophilic molecules (e.g. alcohols) that exhibit a much lower degree of surface activity and do not form micelles.

Figure 18 shows an example of a micelle. The presence of micelles increases the apparent solubility of the contaminant in water. This in turn improves the mass removal per pore volume. To determine the appropriate amounts of surfactant to add to the systems, batch or column experiments are usually performed. Such experiments have determined that surfactant additions are often rate limited [238, 239]. As the surfactant concentration increases, additional micelles are formed and the contaminant solubility continues to increase.

Winsor Type I micelles have a hydrophilic exterior (the hydrophilic heads are oriented towards the exterior of the aggregate) and a hydrophobic interior (the hydrophobic tails are oriented towards the interior of the aggregate). Thus, micelles are analogous to dispersed oil drops; the hydrophobic interior of the micelle acts as an oil sink into which hydrophobic contaminants can partition. Winsor Type II surfactants are soluble in oil, i.e. they have a low hydrophile–lipophile balance, will partition into the oil phase and may form reverse micelles.

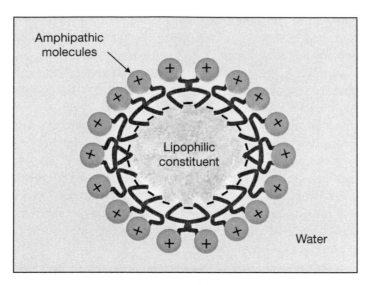

FIG. 18. The principle of micelle formation.

Reverse micelles have hydrophilic interiors and lipophilic exteriors; the resulting phenomenon is analogous to dispersed water drops in the oil phase. Surfactant systems intermediate between Winsor Type I micelle systems and Winsor Type II micelle systems can result in a third phase with properties (e.g. density) between oil and water. This third phase is referred to as a middle phase microemulsion (Winsor Type III system). The middle phase system is known to coincide with ultralow interfacial tensions; thus, middle phase systems will result in bulk extraction of organic compounds from residual saturation.

Microemulsions are a special class of Winsor Type I system in which the droplet diameter of the dispersed phase is very small and uniform. Droplet diameters of oil-in-water microemulsions generally range between 0.01 and 0.10 mm. These microemulsions are single phase, optically transparent, low viscosity, thermodynamically stable systems that form spontaneously on contact with an oil or NAPL phase. A properly designed microemulsion system can be diluted with water and transported through porous media by miscible displacement. This is in contrast to surfactant based technologies that utilize Winsor Type III middle phase microemulsions that depend on an immiscible displacement process to transport the NAPL phase.

Microemulsions are usually stabilized by a surfactant and a co-surfactant. A mixture of water, surfactant and co-surfactant form the microemulsion 'precursor' and should also be a stable single phase, low viscosity system. Low molecular weight alcohols (propanol, butanol, pentanol, hexanol, etc.), organic acids and amines are all suitable as co-surfactants. There are many surfactants that will form oil-in-water microemulsions in the presence of alcohol co-surfactants. Some of these surfactants have been given direct food additive status, for example by the United States Food and Drug Administration, are non-toxic and are readily biodegradable so that there is little concern over their release into the environment.

However, it is important in applications that surfactant losses due to sorption, precipitation, coacervate formation or phase changes are minimal, and that environmental acceptance and biodegradability are assured. Co-solvents can be used to stabilize the system and avoid macromolecule formation. Recovery and reuse of surfactants will improve the cost effectiveness of a remedial system. Designing a system to recover and reuse the system requires trade-offs based on ease of recovery versus efficiency of the remedial system.

10.3.6.3. Mobilization

The second mechanism utilized in surfactant treatment is NAPL mobilization due to a decrease in interfacial tension. The interfacial tension between the groundwater and NAPL produces large capillary forces that retain the NAPL. This is the reason that conventional pump and treat operations cannot remove the majority of NAPL at a given site [240]. As the interfacial tension diminishes, the phase becomes virtually miscible. This results in direct mobilization of the NAPL. Caution must be exercised, however, because the surfactant could cause the contamination to spread too easily and too quickly [241]. This is particularly true with DNAPLs, which can quickly spread to underlying uncontaminated zones.

In the pump and treat scenario, dilute surfactant solutions are injected into the contaminated aquifer and withdrawn together with the solubilized DNAPLs. Vertical circulation wells (VCWs) are an alternative application under consideration. Chen et al. [242] discuss the effectiveness of using VCWs with surfactant injection and recovery systems. The surfactant is injected from one screened section of the well and the contaminant plus the surfactant is extracted from another screened section. The possible advantages of using VCWs over the multiwell system are:

(a)   Reduced cost;
(b)   Effective hydraulic control over limited volumes of the formation;
(c)   Ability to capture NAPLs that might sink when mobilized;
(d)   Application to both LNAPLs and DNAPLs;
(e)   Minimal loss of surfactants;

(f)   Reduced volume of fluid requiring treatment;

(g)   Induced mounding, which can remediate portions of the contaminated vadose zone around the well.

10.3.7. Physical methods

10.3.7.1. Hydraulic and pneumatic fracturing

These mechanical methods to enhance recovery typically strive to improve the hydrodynamics of the system as a whole or of individual contaminants. Insufficient permeability or hydraulic connectivity can be overcome by hydrofracturing techniques. These technologies are borrowed from the oil industry, where they were developed in the 1970s for deep wells, and it has recently been shown that the yield of wells for recovering contaminating liquids and vapours from low permeable media at shallow depths can be stimulated [243].

The fracturing process begins with the injection of water into a sealed borehole until the pressure of water exceeds the natural in situ pressures present in the soil or rock (e.g. overburden pressure and cohesive stresses) and at flow rates exceeding the natural permeability of the subsurface. A slurry of coarse grained sand and guar gel or similar mixture is then injected. As bedding planes and fractures open up in hard rocks, the sand helps to keep open fractures propagating away from the injection point. Fracture propagation distances of 10–20 m are common in hard rock, while unconsolidated materials, such as silts and clays, typically exhibit fracture propagation distances of 5–15 m. The oil industry also uses high strength solids, such as zirconia spheres, at greater depths, where higher lithostatic pressures have to be counteracted. The hydrofracturing increases the effective surface area and the radius of influence of the abstraction wells and promotes a more uniform delivery of treatment fluids and accelerated extraction of mobilized contaminants.

The increased permeability and hydraulic connectivity may be of benefit not only in pump and treat systems but also for in situ bioremediation, oxidation/reduction dechlorination and SVE applications. Delivery of liquid substrates and nutrients would be facilitated.

Alternatively, gases (air) may be used as a fracturing medium. Pneumatic fracturing allows treatment of the vadose zone for enhanced recovery of volatile contaminants. A comparative field demonstration of hydraulic fracturing to enhance mass recovery or emplace reactive barriers was conducted from the autumn of 1996 to the spring of 1998 at the Portsmouth Gaseous Diffusion Plant, Ohio. Hydraulic fracturing demonstrations showed that mass recovery increased from 2.8 to 50 times and radius of influence from

25 to 30 times for pneumatic fracturing at Tinker Air Force Base, Oklahoma. This demonstration treated chlorinated solvents (specifically TCE) in both the vadose and saturated zones within low permeability silt and clay deposits and was shown to double the hydraulic conductivity and increase the radius of influence by 33% [244].

Cohesive or hard low permeability geological media with distinct bedding planes or a pre-existing network of fractures, such as clays, shales or sandstones, are the most appropriate for hydraulic fracturing.

The baseline against which hydraulic fracturing plus an in situ remediation technology in low permeability media can be compared is excavation and ex situ treatment. The advantages of hydraulic fracturing include:

(a) Improved accessibility to contaminants and delivery of reagents (steam, oxidant, etc.) due to increasing permeability and hydraulic connectivity (e.g. improved mass transfer rates);
(b) Limited site disruption minimizing adverse effects on surface features as fewer wells can be installed.

Hydraulic fracturing is applicable to a wide range of contaminant groups with no particular target group. Factors that may limit the applicability and effectiveness of the process include:

— The technique should not be used in bedrock susceptible to seismic activity.
— Investigation of underground utilities, structures or trapped free-phase contaminant is required.
— A potential to open new pathways exists, leading to the unwanted spread of contaminants.
— Pockets of low permeability may remain after using this technology.
— It is almost impossible to control the final location and size of the fractures created.
— Fractures are anticipated to collapse due to overburden pressure if not reached by the stabilizing media.

10.3.7.2. Air sparging and venting

In the unsaturated zone, VOCs can exist in gaseous, aqueous, sorbed and liquid–organic phases. A venting system consists basically of wells, or 'extraction' vents, completed above the water table in zones of contamination, very similar to a pump and treat system below the water table. A pump is used to apply a vacuum that induces a subsurface gas flow pattern converging on the extraction vents. Prior to venting operations, the soil gas concentrations are in equilibrium with the existing contamination. The induced gas flow displaces the equilibrated soil gas with fresh air, resulting in mass transfer from the aqueous, sorbed and liquid–organic phases to the sweeping gas phase. Continuous subsurface flushing of fresh air leads towards an almost complete removal of the VOCs. Fresh air can be either injected through vents or allowed to seep in through the ground surface. The extracted contaminant vapours are collected from the extraction vents and treated as required.

Air sparging systems are designed to inject air below the water table through sparge wells. This process is analogous to above ground air stripping treatment of water. The process is based on increasing the gas exchange surface area and a steep distribution gradient into the clean air bubbles. As the injected gas rises through the saturated zone and contacts contaminated water or liquid–organic phase, VOCs transfer to the gas phase. The contaminated vapours emerge into the unsaturated zone, where the gas is collected.

While both technologies are limited to removing only volatile contaminants, they provide a means of encouraging biological degradation of organic pollutants by supplying an active source of oxygen to the subsurface. The permeability of the gas bubbles is a limitation. An unwanted side effect could also be the oxidation of iron bearing groundwater, leading to voluminous oxidation products clogging the pore space. However, the iron oxyhydrates that form may also provide a substrate for sorption and thus increase retention, if such is desired, for radionuclides and heavy metals.

10.3.7.3. In well aeration

The in-well aeration technology is also known as a 'vacuum vaporizer well'. This technology was developed in Germany and has been used at several sites [245]. The conceptual basis of this technology is to use air to strip volatile contaminants from water inside a well casing. The essential design of the system involves two screened intervals and a pump to generate vertical recirculation of water within the saturated zone. Depending on type and distribution of contaminants, water flow is either upwards or downwards. Air from the surface is introduced into the well to serve as the stripping agent. A slight vacuum is imposed on the well to collect the contaminated vapour, which can be treated at the surface. The goal is to remove volatile contaminants from the water before they are pumped back into the aquifer. Operation of the system continues until all volatile contaminant mass has been removed from the swept volume of the aquifer (aqueous, sorbed and immiscible liquid phases).

One potential advantage of the in-well sparging system in comparison with 'normal' air sparging involves vapour transport in vertically stratified porous media. In normal air sparging, the contaminant is recovered by use of SVE. However, the presence of a water saturated, low permeability stratum between the point of air injection and the vadose zone may impede the vertical movement of the airstream, thereby reducing recovery. This may affect the efficiency and safety of air sparging. The use of in-well aeration eliminates this potential recovery problem. Low permeability strata are advantageous in in-well aeration systems because they increase the swept volume affected by each well.

10.3.8. Thermal methods

Increasing the ambient temperature in situ serves two purposes: to reduce the viscosity of hydrocarbons and to increase the volatility of organic compounds, thus enhancing their recovery rate [246].

Steam injection is a technology originally developed by the oil industry to enhance recovery of crude oil from host rock [247]. The viscosity and the surface tension (capillary forces) of most hydrocarbons decreases with increasing temperature, thus improving the recovery of liquid phase organic compounds. The residual concentration for any combination of non-miscible organic contaminant and host rock type depends on these physicochemical parameters. The steam also helps to volatilize organic contaminants that are then transported in and recovered from the gas phase. During the injection process three stages can be observed:

(1) The injected steam raises the temperature around the injection well, thus improving the flow properties of viscous organic compounds.
(2) As more steam is injected and transfers its heat content to the ground-water, hot water is pushed away from the injection well into the formation, thus displacing the various liquid phases.
(3) Eventually, along the whole pathway between injection and abstraction wells, the boiling point for water is exceeded and only gas phase transport of volatile organic compounds occurs.

The increased temperature in stages 1 and 2 will also shift any sorption equilibria, both for organic and inorganic contaminants, towards the aqueous phase. The technique is applicable to both unconsolidated sediments as well as fractured rocks but requires a certain permeability.

10.3.9. Biological methods

Biological in situ leaching appears promising as a technically and economically feasible method to enhance contaminant recovery. The range of techniques appears to be especially suitable for large scale locations, such as former industrial sites. As compared with flushing with inorganic acid (Section 10.3.2), biological leaching has the advantage of a higher removal efficiency and/or less damage to the soil matrix. Biological leaching either aims at lowering the pore water pH without adding acid and/or changing the redox conditions due to the biological activity, thus increasing the solubility of inorganic contaminants. A more detailed discussion of biological methods in general is found in Section 10.4.5.

10.4. TREATMENT FOR CONTAMINANT DESTRUCTION AND REMOVAL

10.4.1. The mixed contamination context

As has been pointed out in Section 6.2, a single technique may not be sufficient for the remediation of a situation with mixed contamination. In the following a range of techniques that specifically address organic contaminants are described that would be complementary to other techniques addressing, for instance, heavy metals and radionuclides.

10.4.2. Dynamic underground stripping and hydrous pyrolysis oxidation

Dynamic underground stripping and hydrous pyrolysis oxidation (DUS/ HPO) is a combination of technologies that can rapidly remove organic contaminants from the subsurface where other technologies may take decades or more to achieve the desired cleanup criteria. For instance, in two field-scale applications, DUS/HPO has achieved remediation performance in less than one tenth the time of conventional pump and treat methods, both above and below the water table, and at less overall cost [248]. Major elements of the technique include steam injection, air injection, vacuum extraction, electrical resistivity heating, groundwater extraction, surface treatment of vapour and groundwater, and underground imaging and monitoring.

Dynamic underground stripping is an innovative thermal remediation technology that accelerates removal of organic compounds, both dissolved phase liquids and DNAPLs, from soil and groundwater. In DUS, steam is injected at the periphery of the contaminated area to volatilize and solubilize compounds bound to the soil. Centrally located vacuum extraction wells then remove this volatilized material from the subsurface. A steam front develops in the subsurface as permeable soils are heated to the boiling point of water, and volatile organic compounds are vaporized from the hot soil. The steam sweeps the permeable zones between the injection and extraction wells. Steam injection then ceases, while the vacuum extraction continues once the front reaches the extraction wells. The vapour and any groundwater pulled through the extraction wells are treated above ground. When the steam zone collapses, groundwater re-enters the treatment zone and the steam–vacuum extraction cycle is repeated.

For application in dense clays, electrical resistive heating can also be used to enhance contaminant removal. Water and contaminants in the conductive zone are vaporized and forced into the permeable zone, being swept by the steam and then subjected to vacuum extraction.

In HPO, steam and air are injected into paired wells, creating a heated oxygenated zone in the subsurface. When injection is halted, the steam condenses and contaminated groundwater returns to the heated zone where it mixes with oxygen-rich condensed steam, which destroys dissolved contaminants in situ.

An integral component of DUS/HPO is a sophisticated imaging system known as electrical resistance tomography (ERT), which allows real time three dimensional monitoring of the subsurface. Electrical resistance tomography is based on a cross-hole tomography system that maps changes in resistivity over time. Changes in resistivity both laterally and vertically can be related to the migration of steam through various zones between the injection and extraction wells. Electrical resistance tomography is utilized to make process adjustments to optimize the performance of DUS/HPO.

Limitations include:

— The process requires a large amount of energy.
— Above ground treatment systems must be sized to handle peak extraction rates and the distribution of VOCs in the extracted vapour and liquid streams.
— Steam adds significant amounts of water to the subsurface, and precautions must be taken to prevent mobilization of contaminants beyond the capture zone.
— It is not applicable at depths of less than 1.5 m; to date it has been used at depths of up to 40 m.
— Microorganisms destroyed by steam can foul the system, and small particles pumped to the surface can clog the system.
— Treated soils and groundwater can remain at elevated temperatures for years after cleanup, which could affect site reuse plans.

10.4.3. Soil vapour extraction

It may be necessary to capture and remove toxic or explosive gases before or while addressing other contaminants bound to the soil or in the groundwater. Soil vapour extraction uses a vacuum to remove volatile and some semivolatile contaminants from the soil. The vapour–soil gas mixtures will be treated and discharged according to the applicable air discharge regulations. Extraction wells are typically used at depths of 1.5 m or greater, and have been successfully applied as deep as 90 m. Groundwater pumps may be used in conjunction with SVE to keep groundwater from rising into the vadose zone as a result of the vacuum, or to increase the depth of the unsaturated zone. This area, termed the capillary fringe is sometimes highly contaminated, as it holds NAPLs lighter than water and vapours that have escaped from dissolved organic compounds in the groundwater below or from DNAPLs. In soils where the contamination is deep or when there is low permeability, injecting air into the soil assists in extraction. During full-scale operation, SVE can be run intermittently (pulsed operation) once the extracted mass removal rate has reached a steady state level. Because the process involves the continuous flow of air through the soil, it often promotes biodegradation of low volatility organic compounds that may be present.

Soil vapour extraction can also be used ex situ on piles of excavated soil. A vacuum is applied to a network of piping in the pile to encourage volatilization of organic compounds from the excavated media. A system for handling and treating off-gases is required.

A field pilot study is necessary to establish the feasibility of the method as well as to obtain information necessary to design and configure the system.

The SVE technique is typically applicable to VOC and/or fuel contamination. It works only on compounds that readily vaporize (i.e. that have a high Henry's law constant). Some limitations of the SVE technique include:

(a) A high soil moisture content requires higher vacua.
(b) Soils with high organic content or soils that are extremely dry have a high affinity and retention capacity for VOCs. These conditions limit its effectiveness.
(c) Soils with low permeability also limit its effectiveness.
(d) Applying a vacuum to the subsurface soils can raise groundwater levels. As the soils become saturated, some contaminants may dissolve into the groundwater. As a result, groundwater can show increased contamination levels, especially at the start of this process.
(e) It will not remove heavy oils, metals, PCBs or dioxins.

(f)   Exhaust air from in situ SVE systems may require treatment. Off-gas treatment is usually carried out by adsorption onto granular activated carbon.

(g)   It is not applicable to the saturated zone (except in the form of air sparging in wells).

10.4.4. Thermal methods

10.4.4.1. Electrical resistance heating

Electrical resistance heating uses an electric current to heat less permeable soils such as clays and fine grained sediments so that water and contaminants trapped in these low conductivity materials are vaporized and ready for vacuum extraction. An array of electrodes is placed directly into the soil matrix (Fig. 19) and an (alternating) electric current passed through the soil, the resistance loss of which then heats the soil and the contaminants, increasing the vapour pressure of the latter. The heat also dries out the soil causing it to fracture. These fractures make the soil more permeable, increasing the removal rate of contaminants by SVE. In addition, the heating creates an in situ source of steam to strip contaminants from the soil, inter alia reducing the viscosity of trapped liquids and eventually allowing them to be removed by SVE. Six phase soil heating is a typical layout that uses a low frequency electric current delivered to six electrodes in a circular array to heat soils.

The following factors may limit the applicability and effectiveness of the process:

(a)   It may be self-limiting, since as the clays heat up, they dry out and the current will stop flowing [246, 249].

(b)   Debris or other large objects buried in the media can cause focusing of the electrical field or short-circuiting.

(c)   The performance is very much dependent on the type of organic substance involved and its vapour pressure, as well as the temperature and heat flows that can be achieved in the process selected.

(d)   There is an optimum soil moisture content as the resistance increases with decreasing moisture content and the permeability in turn decreases with increasing moisture content.

(e)   A low permeability will hinder the flow of steam and organic vapours towards the SVE, thus leading to a low efficiency of the process due to the high energy input to increase vacuum and temperature.

(f)   Soil with a highly variable permeability may result in accessibility to the contaminated regions being uneven.

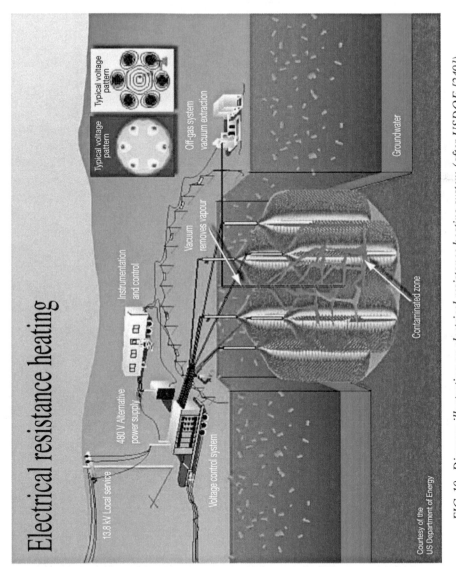

FIG. 19. Diagram illustrating an electrical resistance heating system (after USDOE [249]).

137

(g)   High soil organic matter content may reduce the efficiency of the technique due to the high affinity of organic contaminants for these constituents.

(h)   Air emissions will need to be controlled to be below the limits of regulatory concern or permissions may need to be sought. Off-gas treatment and permits will increase project costs.

(i)   Residual liquids and spent activated carbon may require further treatment or disposal.

10.4.4.2. Microwave heating

The operating idea of a microwave oven can be applied to soils in situ, albeit on a grander scale. Microwave heating is based on the phenomenon that dipole molecules, such as those of water, can be stimulated in their vibrational movements by high frequency electromagnetic radiation. This vibrational energy is then dissipated in the form of heat. While many organic molecules are flexible enough to adjust themselves to the electromagnetic field, they still absorb photons, which may lead to the breaking of weak bonds [250]. Such bonds can be either within the molecule or between the molecules and a surface. Thus, microwave applications will enhance recovery of organic contaminants by either volatilizing them, by reducing the viscosity due to increased ambient temperature or by detaching them from the geomatrix [251].

10.4.4.3. Thermal conductance

In situ thermal treatment to enhance contaminant removal can also be accomplished by a technique where heat and vacuum are applied simultaneously to soil, sediments or buried wastes. Heat flows into the soil by conduction from heaters operated at approximately 800–1000°C. Vertical thermal wells are used for deep contamination and horizontal thermal wells are used for shallow contamination. Multiple wells are installed to span the areas requiring treatment. Electric heaters are installed in the wells and wired together with power tapped from utility poles or other power sources. Vapours are extracted from some of the wells to ensure the boundaries of the heated zone are under vacuum.

Most of the contaminant destruction occurs underground near the heat source. As soil is heated, contaminants in the subsurface are volatilized or destroyed by several mechanisms, including:

— Evaporation;
— Boiling;

— Oxidation;
— Pyrolysis;
— Steam distillation.

Volatilized contaminants not destroyed in the subsurface are recovered and treated above ground. A wide range of soil types can be treated by this process. The high temperatures applied over a period of days result in an extremely high destruction and removal efficiency even of contaminants with high boiling points such as PCBs, pesticides and other heavy hydrocarbons.

Special consideration is needed when applying this process to sites with radionuclides and or toxic metals, such as mercury, as the heating process may change the oxidation state of these contaminants, which can make them more or less mobile in the environment.

10.4.5. In situ biological remediation

10.4.5.1. Concept

In general, bioremediation technologies employ engineered systems to heighten the effects of naturally occurring degradation mechanisms [252, 253]. Bioremediation techniques are destruction or transformation techniques directed towards stimulating microorganisms to grow by using the contaminants as a food and energy source through creating a favourable environment for the microorganisms. In general, this means providing some combination of oxygen, nutrients and in some cases moisture, and controlling the temperature and pH. Sometimes, microorganisms adapted for degradation of the specific contaminants are applied to enhance the process (Table 13). There is a conceptual similarity to techniques used in the context of enhanced natural attenuation (Section 9.1).

Biodegradation methods, both in situ and ex situ, are likely to gain ground, as disposal related legislation increasingly tends to discourage or prohibit landfilling of biodegradable materials. It was noted, however, that the application of bioremediation techniques, although often cost efficient, may be hampered by licensing procedures [254].

The main advantage of in situ treatment is that it allows soil to be treated without being excavated and transported, resulting in potentially significant cost savings. However, in situ treatment generally requires longer, and there is less certainty about the uniformity of treatment because of the variability in soil and aquifer characteristics and because the efficacy of the process is more difficult to verify.

TABLE 13. COMPONENTS OF IN SITU BIOREMEDIATION TECHNOLOGY [253]

Component	Example	Biodegradation mechanisms supported	Targeted CAHs[a]
Bio-augmentation	Seed the subsurface with non-native, CAH degrading bacteria	Aerobic oxidation (cometabolic and direct)	TCE, DCE, TCA, DCA, CA, CT, CF
		Anaerobic reductive dechlorination (cometabolic and direct)	TCA, DCA, CA, CT, CF, CM
Addition of nutrients	Add nitrogen, phosphorus or other growth factors that may be deficient in the subsurface	Aerobic oxidation (cometabolic and direct)	TCE, DCE, TCA, DCA, CA, CT, CF
		Anaerobic reductive dechlorination (cometabolic and direct)	TCA, DCA, CA, CT, CF, CM
Addition of electron donors	Add a substrate, such as toluene, propane or methane	Aerobic oxidation (cometabolic)	TCE, DCE, TCA, CF, MC
		Anaerobic reductive dechlorination (cometabolic and direct)	PCE, TCE, DCE, VC, TCA, DCA, CA, CT, CF, MC
Addition of electron acceptors	Add oxygen by bioventing, biosparging or adding an oxygen source such as hydrogen peroxide	Aerobic oxidation (direct)	TCE, DCE, VC, TCA, DCA, CA, CE, MC, CM
	Add an anaerobic reductant such as nitrate (cometabolic)	Anaerobic reductive dechlorination	PCE, TCE, DCE, VC, DCA, CT

[a] See glossary for abbreviations.

The metabolic activity of indigenous microorganisms can be stimulated to degrade organic contaminants by way of using them as a food source. This stimulation can consist of supplying nutrients or essential elements when their absence would constrain metabolic activity. Furthermore, metabolic products may be removed that otherwise would slow down metabolic activity. It is also possible to introduce microorganisms that are specifically adapted to the use of the target contaminant as a food source.

Separate techniques have been developed for surface soils, the vadose zone and the saturated zone. In the first case, nutrients, essential elements or specialized microorganisms are added to the soil by, for example, ploughing them in [255]. Nutrients can be brought into the vadose zone by injecting them in gaseous form [256]. The same applies to the saturated zone, where the respective growth stimulating agents are injected through wells. Gases may also be injected into contaminated groundwaters, thus combining growth stimulation with air sparging to remove volatile contaminants to the vadose zone for capturing or degrading them there.

10.4.5.2. Process variables

The rate at which microorganisms degrade contaminants is influenced by the specific contaminants present; oxygen supply; moisture; nutrient supply; pH; temperature; availability of the contaminant to the microorganism (clays can adsorb contaminants, making them unavailable to microorganisms); concentrations of the contaminants (high concentrations may be toxic to microorganisms); presence of substances toxic to microorganisms, for example mercury; or inhibitors to the metabolism of the contaminant. These parameters are discussed briefly in the following [257] and also pertain to ex situ methods:

(a) *Oxygen* levels are easier to control in ex situ applications than in situ applications and are typically maintained by mechanical tilling, venting or sparging.

(b) *Anaerobic* conditions may be used to degrade highly chlorinated contaminants. This can be followed by aerobic treatment to complete biodegradation of the partially dechlorinated compounds as well as of the other contaminants.

(c) *Water* serves as the transport medium through which nutrients and organic constituents pass into the microbial cell and metabolic waste products pass out of the cell. Moisture levels in the range of 20–80% generally allow suitable biodegradation in soils.

(d) The *nutrients* required for cell growth are nitrogen, phosphorus, potassium, sulphur, magnesium, calcium, manganese, iron, zinc and copper. If nutrients are not available in sufficient amounts, microbial activity will stop. Nitrogen and phosphorus are the nutrients most likely to be deficient in the contaminated environment and are thus usually added to the bioremediation system in a useable form (e.g. as ammonium for nitrogen and as phosphate for phosphorus).

(e) *pH* affects the solubility, and consequently the availability, of many constituents of soil, which can affect the biological activity. Many metals that are potentially toxic to microorganisms are insoluble at elevated pH levels; therefore, elevation of the pH of the treatment system can reduce the risk of poisoning the microorganisms.

(f) *Temperature* affects the microbial activity in the treatment unit. The biodegradation rate will slow down with decreasing temperature; thus, in northern climates bioremediation may be ineffective during part of the year unless it is carried out in a climate controlled facility or well below the frost penetration depth. The microorganisms remain viable at temperatures below freezing and will resume activity when the temperature rises. Too high a temperature can be detrimental to some microorganisms, essentially sterilizing the soil. Compost piles require periodic tilling to release self-generated heat.

(g) *Bioaugmentation* involves the use of cultures that have been specially bred for degradation of a variety of contaminants and sometimes for survival under unusually severe environmental conditions. The most successful method of application of bioremediation has been through stimulation of indigenous microbial species. Microbial stimulation is the process of ensuring that environmental conditions, nutrient availability and requirements for an electron acceptor are adequate in the contaminated portions of the aquifer.

(h) *Co-metabolism*, in which microorganisms growing on one compound produce an enzyme that chemically transforms another compound on which they cannot grow, has been observed to be useful. In particular, microorganisms that degrade methane (methanotrophic bacteria) have been found to produce enzymes that can initiate the oxidation of a variety of carbon compounds.

10.4.5.3. Process designs

A wide variety of process designs and technical layouts have been developed. These may be based on groundwater recirculation (Fig. 20), direct injection (Fig. 21) or bioventing (Table 14). Biowalls have already been discussed in Section 9.3.2.

10.4.5.4. Applicability

Natural microbiological systems are very complex, difficult to understand in their interactions, and, unlike many engineered systems, difficult to control.

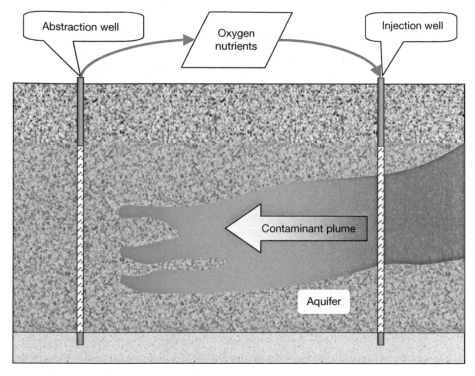

FIG. 20. Stimulation of in situ bioremediation by groundwater recirculation.

In this sense, bioremediation is not foolproof and it cannot be guaranteed to be successful even in instances where due care was taken in its design and application. It is essential first to understand the chemical systems to which bioremediation will be applied (Table 15).

On the basis of their origin and their susceptibility to microbial interaction, hydrocarbons may be divided into two broad classes:

(1) Petroleum hydrocarbons that are largely associated with the production, storage or use of fuels, lubricants and chemical feedstocks. Petroleum hydrocarbons have been demonstrated to be biodegradable by numerous species of bacteria. Over a period of 3.5 billion years bacteria have been able to evolve genetic resources that allow some of them to potentially use petroleum hydrocarbons as a source of food.

(2) Complex industrial hydrocarbons include chlorinated aliphatic and aromatic hydrocarbons, pesticides and herbicides, and polymers. It has only been in the last 100 years that the human race has manufactured these new industrial chemicals. Bacteria have not had time to evolve the

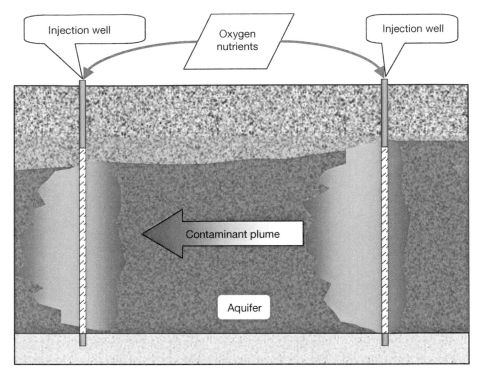

FIG. 21. Bioremediation by direct injection of nutrients.

genetic information required to utilize them as a source of food. Owing to their resistance to microbial attack these complex industrial chemicals are termed xenobiotic.

Cleanup goals may not be attained if the soil matrix prohibits contaminant–microorganism contact [253]. The circulation of water based solutions through the soil may increase contaminant mobility and necessitate treatment of underlying groundwater. Preferential flow paths may severely reduce contact between injected fluids and contaminants throughout the contaminated zones. Highly layered clay or heterogeneous subsurface environments will limit the effectiveness of this technology because of oxygen (or other electron acceptor) transfer limitations. High concentrations of radionuclides, heavy metals, highly chlorinated organic compounds, long chain hydrocarbons or inorganic salts are likely to be toxic to microorganisms. Concentrations of hydrogen peroxide higher than 100–200 ppm in groundwater inhibit the activity of microorganisms. Individually, many organic compounds are biodegradable, but, when mixed with other substances (pesticides and toxic heavy metals),

TABLE 14. BIOREMEDIATION SYSTEM CONFIGURATIONS [253].

Configuration	Purpose	Applicability/ advantages	Potential limitations
Direct injection	To enhance the biodegradation of contaminants in place in soil and groundwater	Less above ground equipment needed than for ex situ systems	Difficult to control dispersion of reactants in aquifers Regulatory concerns about discharges of chemicals to groundwater
Groundwater recirculation	To contain the contaminated groundwater plume and enhance biodegradation of contaminants in the recirculation area	Can provide containment of the plume Allows controlled amendment of groundwater	Re-injection of groundwater may be complicated because of regulatory concern Clogging of recirculation wells may reduce effectiveness of system
Bioventing	To enhance the degradation of contaminants in the vadose zone	Less above ground equipment needed than for ex situ systems Treats contaminated soil	Must be coupled with groundwater treatment (such as biosparging) of remediated contaminated groundwater

TABLE 15. BIODEGRADABILITY OF SELECTED ORGANIC COMPOUNDS [258]

Compound	Biodegradability
Acetone	Degradable
Benzene	Degradable
Toluene	Degradable
Fuel oil	Degradable
Phenol	Degradable
Trichloroethene	Difficult to degrade
Chloroform	Difficult to degrade
Pentachlorophenol	Difficult to degrade
Vinyl chloride	Difficult to degrade

inhibition processes may occur, sometimes to the extent of poisoning the microorganisms involved in the degradation process.

A surface treatment system, such as air stripping or carbon adsorption, may be required to treat extracted groundwater prior to re-injection or disposal.

A wide variety of stimulated biodegradation methods have been developed for ex situ and in situ application. While ex situ methods such as landfarming, biopiles, composting and bioreactors have reached a certain level of maturity, in situ methods are still in the development stage. One problem with the latter is the relatively greater difficulty of controlling process variables. The most common cause for failure of in situ bioremediation in saturated zones is the lack of adequate mass transport of the electron acceptor (usually oxygen). In this regard, the physical setting of the site is critical. Microbiologically specific reasons for the poor performance of in situ bioremediation systems include:

(a) There is uncertainty with regard to the effect of hydrocarbon availability on the effectiveness of biodegradation. Can bacteria degrade hydrocarbons adsorbed on surfaces or degrade hydrocarbons with low levels of solubility? Or must the hydrocarbon be solubilized before it can be biodegraded?

(b) Although petroleum hydrocarbons are amenable to aerobic biodegradation, for it to occur the indigenous bacteria must have the appropriate genetic information. This genetic information is precise. The presence of a specific hydrocarbon will stimulate the synthesis of an oxygenase enzyme that is expressly configured to react with that stimulating hydrocarbon. For remediation, the question is whether the indigenous microbes possess the genetic information required for appropriate enzyme production and whether the contaminant stimulates the production of those enzymes.

(c) General microbial stimulation has the potential to produce a large amount of biomass that may not take part in the biodegradation process and actually be harmful through biofouling and plugging of injection wells, galleries or surrounding formations. There is potential to lose critical subsurface mass transport capabilities.

(d) There are practical limits to the degree of cleanup obtainable using bioremediation. Hydrocarbons at the low ppm level may not be capable of supporting significant levels of microbial activity even under stimulation. Sites with relatively high levels of hydrocarbon impact may actually be better candidates for bioremediation than those on which the impact is small at levels slightly above regulatory action levels.

146

It should be noted that many of these factors are better controllable under ex situ conditions.

10.4.5.5. Anaerobic stimulation

In the absence of oxygen (anaerobic conditions), organic contaminants will be ultimately metabolized to methane, limited amounts of carbon dioxide and trace amounts of hydrogen gas. Under sulphate reduction conditions, sulphate is converted to sulphide or elemental sulphur, and under nitrate reduction conditions, dinitrogen gas is ultimately produced. A substrate, such as compost extract, is added to enhance the degradation. The contaminants are dehalogenated in several steps. Whether the dehalogenation process is fully completed depends on the contaminant, the substrate and the soil system. In the concepts mentioned below, the source area is often treated more intensively than the plume area. Other differences are the type and method of substrate addition.

Contaminants may be degraded to intermediate or final products that are less, equally or more hazardous than the original contaminant. For example, TCE anaerobically biodegrades to the persistent and more toxic vinyl chloride. To avoid such problems, most bioremediation projects are conducted in situ. Vinyl chloride can easily be broken down further if aerobic conditions are created.

Anaerobic stimulation can also be used to change the redox environment and thus fix radionuclides for which the reduced redox state is less mobile. In order to make the process more efficient and longer lasting, various proprietary formulations of reactants with delayed release of electron donors (hydrogen release compounds, HRC®) are now available [259]. The delayed release, however, may be achieved at a somewhat lower efficiency compared with application of pure H_2 [109].

10.4.5.6. Aerobic stimulation

In the presence of sufficient oxygen (aerobic conditions), and other nutrient elements, microorganisms will ultimately convert many organic contaminants to carbon dioxide, water and microbial cell mass. In addition to oxygen a co-metabolizer usually has to be added. Aerobic degradation is often a second remediation step that is preceded by a first, anaerobic, step. Enhanced bioremediation of soil typically involves the percolation or injection of groundwater or uncontaminated water mixed with nutrients and saturated with dissolved oxygen. Sometimes acclimatized microorganisms (bioaugmentation) and/or another oxygen source such as hydrogen peroxide are also added (see above). An infiltration gallery or spray irrigation is typically used for shallow contaminated soils, and injection wells are used for deeper contaminated soils.

Although in situ bioremediation has been successfully demonstrated in cold climates, low temperatures slow the remediation process down. For contaminated sites with low soil temperatures, heat blankets may be used to cover the soil surface in order to increase the soil temperature and the degradation rate.

Enhanced bioremediation may be classified as a long term technology which may take several years for cleanup of a plume [86].

10.4.6. Phytoremediation

In situ bioremediation may also employ higher plants and is then commonly known under the title phytoremediation. Here the contaminants are either taken up into the shoots or the roots, or the complex biogeochemical processes in the root zone either destroy or immobilize the contaminants.

The application of various types of phytoremediation to remove or contain contamination by radionuclides has been discussed in more detail in a companion publication [17]. There it was noted that the majority of published documentation concerns treatment of heavy metals and organic contaminants. Various variants of phytoremediation technologies can be used to degrade or destroy organic contaminants, but a clear distinction with respect to achieved effects and acting mechanisms is not always possible. The amenability to plant uptake appears to be related to the degree of hydrophobicity of the organic compound. Studies on the efficiency of biodegradation in the presence of radionuclides and heavy metals are important, since metabolic pathways can be inhibited in their presence [260]. Some fungi have been shown to be tolerant to high metal concentrations [261]. Laboratory research also indicates that fungi that are resistant to metals in symbiotic association with plant roots might positively influence phytore mediation [262]. Table 16 provides an overview of typical phytoremediation techniques and their applicability to various target contaminants as well as their respective states of development [263].

Most relevant research has focused on individual contaminants or on certain classes of contaminant and not on mixtures of different types of contaminant. Although there is some evidence that plants can tolerate mixed organic and metal contamination, it has generally not been investigated whether one type of vegetation can successfully remediate different classes of contaminant simultaneously. Thus, inhibition, for example, by heavy metals of plants grown for the purpose of the remediation of organic contaminants, appears conceivable but is not known systematically.

TABLE 16. OVERVIEW OF PHYTOREMEDIATION TECHNIQUES [263]

Mechanism	Process goal	Media	Contaminants	Plants	Status
Phyto-extraction	Contaminant extraction and capture	Soil, sediment and sludge	Metals: Ag, Gd, Co, Cr, Cu, Hg, Mn, Mo, Ni, Pb, Zn; Radionuclides: Sr-90, Cs-137, Pu-239, U-238, U-234	Indian mustard, pennycress, alyssum, sunflowers and hybrid poplars	Laboratory, pilot and field applications
Rhizofiltration	Contaminant extraction and capture	Groundwater and surface water	Metals and radionuclides	Sunflowers, Indian mustard and water hyacinth	Laboratory and pilot scales
Phyto-stabilization	Contaminant containment	Soil and sediment	As, Cd, Cr, Cu, Hs, Pb and Zn	Indian mustard, hybrid poplars and grasses	Field applications
Rhizo-degradation	Contaminant destruction	Soil, sediment, sludge and groundwater	Organic compound degradation (TPH, PAHs[a], pesticides, chlorinated solvents and PCBs)	Red mulberry, grasses, hybrid poplar, cat's tail and rice	Field applications
Phyto-degradation	Contaminant destruction	Soil, sediment, sludge, groundwater and surface water	Organic compounds, sludge, chlorinated solvents, groundwater phenols, herbicides and munitions	Algae, stonewort, hybrid poplars, black willow and bald cypress	Field demonstrations

TABLE 16. OVERVIEW OF PHYTOREMEDIATION TECHNIQUES
[263] (cont.)

Mechanism	Process goal	Media	Contaminants	Plants	Status
Phyto-volatilization	Contaminant extraction from media and release to air	Ground-water, soil, sediment and sludge	Chlorinated solvents, phytovolatili-zation releases (some inor-ganic com-pounds (Se, As and Hg) to air)	Poplars, alfalfa black locust and Indian mustard	Laboratory and field applications
Hydraulic con-trol (plume control)	Contaminant degradation or containment	Ground-water and surface water	Water soluble organic compounds and inorganic compounds	Hybrid poplars, cottonwood and willow	Field demon-strations
Vegetative cover (evapo-transpiration cover)	Contaminant containment and erosion control	Soil, sedi-ment and sludge	Organic and inorganic compounds	Poplars and grasses	Field applications
Riparian corridors (non-point source control)	Contaminant destruction	Surface water and ground-water	Water soluble organic and inorganic compounds	Poplars	Field application

[a] PAHs: polycyclic aromatic hydrocarbons.

11. EX SITU TREATMENT

11.1. PHYSICAL SEPARATION

11.1.1. Particle separation techniques

Ex situ soil separation processes, mostly based on mineral processing techniques such as floatation or cycloning, are widely used in northern Europe and the USA for the treatment of contaminated soil. The concept of reducing soil contamination through the use of particle size separation is based on the finding that most organic and inorganic contaminants tend to bind, either chemically or physically, to the finer grain size fractions, i.e. clay and silt, and to organic soil particles. The silt and clay, in turn, are attached to sand and gravel particles by physical processes, primarily compaction and adhesion. Washing processes that separate the fine (small) clay and silt particles from the coarser sand and gravel soil particles effectively separate and concentrate the contaminants into a smaller volume of soil that can be treated further or disposed of. Gravity separation is effective for removing high or low specific gravity particles, such as compounds containing heavy metals (e.g. lead or radium oxide). Attrition scrubbing removes adherent contaminant films from coarser particles. However, attrition washing can increase the fines in the soils processed. The clean, larger, fraction can be returned to the site for continued use.

Liquid–particle separation involves removal and collection of dispersed or colloidal solid particles in a fluid suspension. Liquid–particle separation categories include:

— Screening;
— Membrane filtration;
— Cycloning;
— Flotation;
— Thickening/sedimentation;
— Filtration;
— Centrifiguation.

Among these, filtration is the most widely used liquid–particle separation process.

There are two general processes for separating solid particulate matter from a liquid. In the first type, separation is accomplished by allowing an external force, such as gravity or an electrostatic potential, to move the suspended particles in the liquid. For example, in sedimentation and thickening, solid particles settle due to the density difference between the solids and liquid under the influence of gravitational or centrifugal acceleration. In electrostatic precipitation, particles are attracted towards an oppositely charged surface by applying an electrostatic potential difference.

In the second type of process, exemplified by filtration, the liquid–particle separation is accomplished by passing the liquid–particle suspension through a porous medium. The porous medium acts as a semipermeable barrier that allows the fluid to flow through its capillary channels while retaining the solid particles on its surfaces. This type of separation can be further divided into two classes: deep bed filtration and cake filtration.

Deep bed filtration, also known as blocking filtration, surface filtration and clarification, is preferred when the solid content of the suspension is less than 1%. In such an operation, a deep bed of filter material (sand, diatomaceous earth or synthetic fibres) is used to capture fine solid particles from a dilute suspension. Since the particles to be removed are several orders of magnitude smaller than the size of the filter media, they will penetrate a considerable depth into the bed before being captured. The particles can be captured by several mechanisms:

(a) The direct sieving action at the constrictions in the pore structure;
(b) Gravity settling;
(c) Brownian diffusion;
(d) Interception at the solid–fluid interfaces;
(e) Impingement;
(f) Attachment due to electrokinetic forces.

Cake filtration is the most commonly used process for separating fine particles from a liquid–particle suspension. In cake filtration, particles are trapped at the surface of a filter medium (a porous barrier) and allowed to accumulate to form a cake of increasing thickness. This cake of particles then forms the 'true' filtering medium. Often liquid will also be trapped in the cake, and, where total recovery of the solids is necessary, the cake is dewatered by applying mechanical, hydrodynamic, electrical or acoustic forces.

When the mean particle size is less than a few micrometres, the conventional cake filtration process loses efficiency, primarily due to the formation of a high resistance filter cake. To overcome this problem, cross-flow filtration is used to limit cake growth. In cross-flow filtration, the liquid–particle suspension flows laterally across the filter rather than vertically through the medium as in conventional filtration. The shear forces across the surface of the cake remove fine layers of the cake, thus limiting the accumulation of solid particles on the medium surface. In this manner, the rate of filtration can be maintained at a higher level to ensure a cost effective operation.

Ultrafiltration is a membrane process capable of separating or collecting submicron sized particles and macromolecules from a solution. It is widely used to concentrate solutions of colloids, salts or macromolecules. The ultrafiltration membrane is like a sieve with very small pore sizes, ranging from molecular dimensions to a few microns. Ultrafiltration membranes are made in sheet, capillary and tubular forms and are designed for high permeation flux and resistance to plugging.

The cost for a given fluid–particle separation process varies widely. The cost for purchasing industrial filtration equipment can vary from $500 m^{-2} to as much as $50 000 m^{-2} of filter area. This large variation in cost is due to a wide variety of individual features and materials of construction required by specific applications.

The cost for an ultrafiltration plant ranges from $600 to $1200 m^{-2} of membrane area, which is comparable to conventional filtration equipment. However, the operational costs are nearly an order of magnitude higher than those of conventional filtration.

11.1.2. Segmented gate systems

The segmented gate system (SGS) is a characterization and sorting technology that measures the radioactivity of soil, sand, dry sludge or any material that can be transported by conveyor belts, and mechanically separates radioactive contaminated material into clean and contaminated waste streams. This is accomplished by passing the material on a conveyor belt under an array of sensitive, rapidly reacting, radiation detectors that measure radionuclide concentrations. Material above the desired cleanup limits is automatically diverted into a separate waste stream. In this system, contaminants are isolated and removed by locating small particles of dispersed radioactive material, thus significantly reducing the overall amount of material requiring disposition as radioactive waste.

A variety of sensors can be utilized for detection of specific contaminants (i.e. sodium iodide, calcium fluoride or high purity germanium). Typical radio-nuclides that can be measured by SGS include ^{137}Cs, ^{60}Co, ^{226}Ra, ^{232}Th, ^{238}U and ^{241}Am. While the detection level for the system depends on the ambient radiation background, conveyor belt speed, thickness of the material layer on the conveyor, and contaminant γ ray energy and abundance, lower limits of detection, 0.074 Bq/g for ^{241}Am and 0.185 Bq/g for ^{226}Ra, have been success-fully demonstrated.

11.2. CHEMICAL AND PHYSICOCHEMICAL SEPARATION

11.2.1. Soil washing

As with respective in situ techniques, a variety of lixiviants can be used to separate contaminants from the soil matrix by dissolving or suspending them in the washing solution (which can be sustained by chemical manipulation of pH for a period of time). This typically is preceded by concentrating them into a smaller volume of soil through particle size separation.

Soil washing techniques are promising for an application to soils contaminated with a wide variety of heavy metal, radionuclide and organic contaminants. Complex mixtures of contaminants in the soil, such as a mixture of metals, non-volatile organic compounds and SVOCs, and heterogeneous contaminant compositions throughout the soil make it, however, difficult to formulate a single suitable washing solution that will consistently and reliably remove all of the different types of contaminant. For such cases, sequential washing, using different washing formulations and/or different soil to washing fluid ratios, may be required. Soil washing is a media transfer technology, i.e. the resulting contaminated water or other solvents need to be treated with a suitable technique and disposed of. The technique offers the ability for recovery of metals and can clean coarse grained soils from a wide range of organic and inorganic contaminants:

— Aliphatic hydrocarbons, i.e. mineral oils;
— Polycyclic aromatic hydrocarbons (PAHs);
— Heavy metals such as Cu, Zn, Pb, Cd, Cr, Hg, Co, Ni and Sn;
— Pesticides such as insecticides, herbicides and fungicides;
— Other organic halogenated compounds (e.g. PCBs) or phenolic compounds;
— Inorganic contaminants, such as arsenic or cyanide compounds (free or complexed).

The treatability of other contaminants has to be established on a case by case basis.

A major disadvantage of soil washing is that in many cases it will destroy the (biological) functionality of the soil, in particular when applied to topsoil. The functionality of topsoils depends on the mixture between different grain sizes, the clay and humus contents, and the indigenous microbial flora and fauna. Often a sterile product results, as the latter two constituents are removed or destroyed. Experiments are under way in various Member States to reconstitute functionality by adding compost to the soil before returning it to nature.

11.2.2. Adsorption

Adsorption mechanisms are generally categorized as physical adsorption, chemisorption or electrostatic adsorption. Weak molecular forces, such as Van der Waal's forces, provide the driving force for physical adsorption, while a chemical reaction forms a chemical bond between the compound and the surface of the solid in chemisorption. Electrostatic adsorption involves the adsorption of ions through Coulombic forces and is often referred to as ion exchange, which is addressed separately in the next section.

The physicochemical process of adsorption can be used to remove contaminants from liquids, slurries or gases. The process is based on the affinity of some constituents for certain types of surface. An adsorbent, for example certain types of clay, zeolites and granulated activated carbon, is brought into contact with a contaminated medium. After saturation has been reached, the adsorbent with the contaminant attached is removed for further processing. The contaminant is either desorbed, i.e. the adsorbent is 'regenerated', or the adsorbent is conditioned and treated, for example cemented into drums, for storage and disposal (Section 11.2.5).

The most common adsorbent is granular activated carbon; other natural and synthetic adsorbents include: activated alumina, forage sponge, lignin, sorptive clays and synthetic resins [264]:

(a) *Granular activated carbon*: Carbon, often derived from ground nut shells, is 'activated' by thermal processing to create porous particles with a large internal surface area (300–2700 m^2/g of carbon) that attracts and adsorbs organic molecules as well as certain metal and inorganic molecules. The capacity of carbon to adsorb contaminants depends on the properties of the contaminants. In particular, large polar molecules tend to adsorb more strongly than small non-polar molecules.

(b) *Activated alumina*: Activated alumina is an aluminium oxide (Al_2O_3) in the form of finely dispersed spheres derived by heat treatment of aluminum ore. It is highly porous, hygroscopic and has a high sorption capacity. It will remove a variety of inorganic contaminants, including fluorine, arsenic and selenium, as well as organic compounds. The medium can be regenerated by heat treatment or with acid depending on the type of contaminant.

(c) *Forage sponge*: Forage sponge is an open celled cellulose sponge incorporating a chelating polymer containing an amine that selectively absorbs heavy metals from solution. The functional groups in the polymer provide a selective affinity for cationic and anionic heavy metals, preferentially forming complexes with transition group heavy metals.

(d) *Lignin/sorptive clay*: Lignin/sorptive clays are used to treat aqueous waste streams with organic, inorganic and heavy metal contamination. The contaminants bind to surface complexation sites of the lignin or the clays. In the case of clays they may also be bound in the interlayers.

(e) *Synthetic resins*: Synthetic resins can be designed to achieve high degrees of selectivity and high exchange capacity for contaminants by providing selective binding sites. Resins are typically regenerated non-thermally using acids, bases or organic solvents. This property makes them suitable for thermally unstable compounds, such as explosives.

The target contaminants for adsorption processes are most organic contaminants and selected inorganic contaminants from liquid and vapour streams. Factors that may limit the applicability and effectiveness of these processes include:

(a) Poor sorption of water soluble organic compounds and monovalent ions;
(b) High costs if used as the primary treatment on waste streams with high contaminant concentrations;
(c) Typically not applicable to sites with high levels of oily substances;
(d) Not practical where the concentrations of contaminants are so high that sorption capacities are quickly reached and frequent replacement of the adsorption unit is necessary.

11.2.3. Ion exchange

The process of ion exchange is rather similar to that of adsorption, but the contaminant ions are bound to specific sites on surfaces that previously have been occupied by other (monovalent) ions, typically protons or sodium ions. The substrate is usually an organic resin or a certain type of clay. The equilibrium distribution between the substrate and the solution depends on the activity concentrations of the various constituents in the solution. Depending on the type of binding sites available, ion exchange may be highly specific for certain contaminant ions. Ion exchange treatment can be operated in a flow-through mode or as batch processing. Once the ion exchanger is saturated with the contaminant, it is removed from the system and 'backwashed'. Backwashing means that the ion exchanger is brought into contact with a solution containing a high concentration of protons, for instance concentrated HCl, that replaces the contaminants.

Ion exchange can remove dissolved metals and radionuclides from aqueous solutions. Other compounds that have been treated include nitrate, ammonia and silicate. There are a number of factors that affect the applicability and effectiveness of the process:

(a) Oil and grease in water may clog the ion exchange media.
(b) A suspended solids content higher than 10 ppm may cause resin binding.

(c) Low pH values of the influent may lead to effective competition of the protons with the contaminant ions for binding sites and, hence, a reduction in the efficiency of the process.

(d) Strong oxidants in the water may damage the ion exchange resin.

The literature on ion exchange as a method for radioactive waste treatment has been summarized recently [265].

11.2.4. Membrane pervaporation and reverse osmosis

Membrane pervaporation is a process that uses permeable membranes that preferentially adsorb VOCs from contaminated water. Contaminated water first passes through a heat exchanger, raising the water temperature. The heated water then enters the pervaporation module, which contains membranes composed of a non-porous organophilic polymer, similar to silicone rubber, formed into capillary fibres. Volatile organic compounds diffuse by vacuum from the membrane–water interface through the membrane wall. Treated water leaves the pervaporation module, while the organic vapours travel from the module to a condenser where they return to the liquid phase. The condensed organic materials represent only a fraction of the initial wastewater volume and may be subsequently disposed of with a cost savings.

Osmosis is the phenomenon of water flow through a semipermeable membrane that blocks the transport of salts or other solutes through it. When two water (or other solvent) volumes are separated by a semipermeable membrane, water will flow from the side of low solute concentration to the side of high solute concentration. The flow may be stopped, or even reversed, by applying external pressure on the side of higher concentration. This phenomenon is termedreverse osmosis or hyperfiltration. It is applied to water purification and desalination, waste material treatment and many other chemical and biochemical laboratory and industrial processes.

The membrane pervaporation process can be combined with reverse osmosis. The water containing the concentrated contaminants is recirculated to the pervaporation module for further treatment, in which the organic vapours (termed permeates) are extracted by vacuum, condensed and vented downstream of the condenser, thus minimizing air releases.

The resulting concentrates require further treatment or destruction of the organic phase.

11.2.5. Precipitation

Dissolved contaminants can be removed from solutions by precipitation and co-precipitation agents [266]. The concentrations of many contaminants, while of concern from a radiological or toxicological point of view, are too low for precipitating as a separate phase with a reasonable amount of precipitating agent. However, certain contaminant metal ions can substitute more common metal ions in bulk precipitates in a process termed co-precipitation. This technique has been used for many decades to remove toxic metals from drinking water together with iron by precipitation as iron oxyhydroxide.

In such processes it is often not possible to distinguish between precipitation and sorption as removal mechanisms. Iron oxyhydroxide may incorporate other metal ions as well as providing ample sorption sites and the possibility of non-specific interaction with the large charged surface area. In contrast to the adsorber beds discussed above, the precipitates are not normally regenerated, but further conditioned and processed for disposal.

Precipitation transforms dissolved contaminants into a scarcely soluble or insoluble solid, thereby facilitating the removal of the contaminants from the liquid phase by sedimentation or filtration. The process usually uses pH adjustment with the addition of a chemical precipitant followed by flocculation. Typically, metals can be precipitated from the solution as hydroxides, sulphides, sulphates or carbonates. The solubilities of the specific metal contaminants and the required cleanup standards will dictate the process used. In some cases, process design will allow for the generation of sludges that can be sent to recyclers for metal recovery.

Metals precipitation has long been a primary method of treating metal laden industrial waste and drinking waters. Because of the success of this process in these applications, the technique is often considered and selected for use in remediating groundwater containing heavy metals, including their radioactive isotopes. In groundwater treatment, the metal precipitation process may be used as a pretreatment for other treatment techniques (such as chemical oxidation or air stripping) where the presence of metals would otherwise interfere with the other treatment processes.

In the precipitation process, chemical precipitants, coagulants and flocculants are used to increase particle size through aggregation. In the primary precipitation process, very fine particles are generated that are held in suspension by electrostatic surface charges. These charges cause clouds of counter-ions to form around the particles, giving rise to repulsive forces that prevent aggregation and reduce the effectiveness of subsequent solid–liquid separation processes. Therefore, chemical coagulants are added to overcome the repulsive forces between the particles. The three main types of coagulant are inorganic electrolytes (such as alum, lime, ferric chloride and ferrous sulphate), organic polymers and synthetic polyelectrolytes with anionic or cationic functional groups. The addition of coagulants is followed by low sheer mixing in a flocculator to promote contact between the particles, allowing particle growth through the sedimentation phenomenon termed flocculant settling.

Flocculant settling refers to a rather dilute suspension of particles that coalesce, or flocculate, during the sedimentation operation. As coalescence or flocculation occurs, the particles increase in mass and settle at a faster rate. The amount of flocculation that occurs depends on the opportunity for contact, which varies with the overflow rate, the depth of the basin, the velocity gradients in the system, the concentration of particles and the range of particle sizes. The effects of these variables can only be accomplished by sedimentation tests.

Disadvantages of metals precipitation may include:

(a) The presence of multiple metal species may lead to removal difficulties as a result of the amphoteric natures of different compounds (i.e. optimization on one metal species may prevent removal of another).

(b) As discharge standards become more stringent, further treatment may be required.

(c) Reagent addition must be carefully controlled to preclude unacceptable concentrations in treatment effluents.

(d) The efficacy of the system relies on adequate solids separation techniques (e.g., clarification, flocculation and/or filtration).

(e) The process may generate toxic sludges requiring proper conditioning and disposal.

(f) The process can be costly, depending on the reagents used, the required system controls and the required operator involvement in system operation.

(g) Polymers may need to be added to the water to achieve adequate settling of solids.

(h) Treated water will often require pH adjustment.

(i) Metals held in solution by complexing agents (e.g. cyanide or EDTA) are difficult to precipitate.

11.2.6. Distillation

Distillation is a chemical separations process involving vaporization and condensation that is used to separate components of varying vapour pressures (volatilities) in a liquid or gas waste stream. Simple distillation involves a single stage operation in which heat is applied to a liquid mixture in a still, causing a portion of the liquid to vaporize. These vapours are subsequently cooled and condensed to a liquid product termed the distillate or overhead product. The distillate is enriched with the higher volatility components. Conversely, the mixture remaining in the still is enriched with the less volatile components. This mixture is termed the bottoms product. Multiple staging is utilized in most commercial distillation operations to obtain better separation of organic components than is possible in a single evaporation and condensation stage.

Most organic contaminants and certain radionuclides (^{210}Pb and ^{210}Po), heavy metals (Hg) and cyanide are volatile. The volatility increases with temperature so that such contaminants can be driven off by heating the soils concerned and recovering the gaseous contaminants. Distillation is also a side effect of the various thermal treatment methods discussed in Sections 10.3.8 and 10.4.4. Ex situ, the process can be made more efficient, if carried out in a vacuum. The variation in boiling points between various hydrocarbons and other volatile contaminants can be used to drive off and recover selectively the various compounds (fractionation distillation).

11.3. CHEMICAL AND PHYSICAL CONTAMINANT DESTRUCTION

11.3.1. Overview

Unlike radionuclides and heavy metals, many organic contaminants are amenable to natural or stimulated biodegradation, i.e. they cease to exist, rather than being transferred to a safer state. These processes can take place in situ or ex situ. A variety of engineering solutions have been developed to practicable applicability over the past two decades.

One group of methods relies on energy added in the form of light or heat to break chemical bonds on the contaminant and thus to break them down to less harmful components. A second group of methods uses strong chemical agents, typically strong oxidants, to destroy organic molecules. A third group of methods utilizes the metabolic activity of various microorganisms to break down larger molecules into components.

11.3.2. Incineration

During incineration, high temperatures, 870–1200°C, are used to volatilize and combust (in the presence of oxygen) halogenated and other refractory organic compounds from contaminated soils or wastes. Auxiliary fuels are often employed to initiate and sustain combustion. The destruction and removal efficiency for properly operated incinerators exceeds 99.99% for hazardous and toxic organic compounds. Incinerator off-gases require treatment by an air pollution control system to remove particulates and neutralize and remove acid gases (HCl, NO_x and SO_x). Baghouses, venturi scrubbers and wet electrostatic precipitators remove particulates; packed bed scrubbers and spray driers remove acid gases. The end products are CO_2, water and ash.

Typical incinerator designs include circulating bed combustors, fluidized bed combustors, infrared combustion combustors and rotary kilns:

(a) Circulating bed combustors (CBCs) use high velocity air to entrain solids and create a highly turbulent combustion zone that destroys toxic hydrocarbons. These combustors operate at lower temperatures than conventional incinerators (790–880°C). Effective mixing and the low combustion temperature of CBCs reduce operating costs and potential emissions of such gases as nitrogen oxide and carbon monoxide.

(b) Circulating fluidized beds use high velocity air to circulate and suspend the waste particles in a combustion loop, and operate at temperatures up to 880°C.

(c) The infrared combustion technology is a thermal processing system that uses electrically powered silicon carbide rods to heat organic materials and wastes to combustion temperatures. Wastes are fed into the primary chamber and exposed to infrared radiant heat (up to 1010°C) provided by silicon carbide rods above the conveyor belt. A blower delivers air to selected locations along the belt to control the oxidation rate of the waste feed. Any remaining combustible substances are incinerated in an afterburner.

(d) Commercial incinerator designs are rotary kilns, equipped with an afterburner, a quench, and an air pollution control system. The rotary kiln is a refractory lined, slightly inclined, rotating cylinder that serves as a combustion chamber and operates at temperatures up to 980°C.

Incineration is used to remediate soils contaminated with explosives and hazardous wastes, particularly chlorinated hydrocarbons, PCBs and dioxins. Factors that may limit the applicability and effectiveness of the process include:

(a) There are specific feed size and materials handling requirements that can have an impact on the applicability or cost at specific sites.

(b) Heavy metals can produce a bottom ash that requires stabilization.

(c) Volatile heavy metals and radionuclides, such as lead, cadmium, mercury and arsenic, as well as ^{210}Po and ^{137}Cs, will collect in the off-gas scrubbers and will require treatment and disposal.

(d) Metals can react with other elements in the feed stream, such as chlorine or sulphur, forming more volatile and toxic compounds than the original species. Such compounds are likely to be short lived reaction intermediates that can be destroyed in a caustic quench.

(e) Sodium and potassium form low melting point ashes that can attack the brick lining and form a sticky particulate that fouls gas ducts.

(f) Some organic compounds require rather high temperatures to be broken down completely along with careful process control in the cooling phase.

(g) The formation of dioxins and furans is a well known problem resulting from poor process control and too low temperatures during combustion. Flameless combustion in electrical furnaces with better temperature gradient control may overcome this problem [267].

These problems, together with the high energy demands and the resulting sterile material when applied to soils, have generally resulted in incineration finding disfavour in many Member States.

In addition to conventional flame or flameless incineration, interest in microwave methods for (radioactive) waste treatment is increasing [268]. With organic materials a volume reduction of 90% can be achieved, the residuals being glass-like slags or molten metals. Again, off-gas treatment for volatile constituents is needed. Owing to the absence of a hot combustion gas stream, however, the volumes to be treated are lower.

11.3.3. Pyrolysis

Pyrolysis is a form of incineration that chemically decomposes organic materials by heat in the absence of oxygen. Pyrolysis occurs under pressure and at operating temperatures above 430°C. In practice, it is not possible to achieve a completely oxygen-free atmosphere. Because some oxygen is present in any pyrolysis system, a small amount of oxidation occurs.

In pyrolysis systems, organic materials are transformed into gases, small quantities of liquid, and a solid residue containing carbon and ash. The off-gases are typically treated in a secondary thermal oxidation unit. Particulate removal equipment is also required, which can include scrubbers and HEPA filtration.

Several types of pyrolysis units are available, including rotary kilns, rotary hearth furnaces and fluidized bed furnaces. These units are similar to incinerators except that they operate at lower temperatures and with less air supply.

Pyrolysis is not effective in destroying or physically separating inorganic compounds, including radionuclides, from the contaminated medium. Volatile metals in the off-gas stream must be captured in a scrubbing unit. Residuals containing heavy metals may require chemical stabilization before final disposal. When the off-gases are cooled, liquids will condense producing an oil/tar-like residue and contaminated water. These oils and tars may be hazardous and require further treatment prior to disposal.

The target contaminant groups for pyrolysis are SVOCs and pesticides. Pyrolysis is applicable to the separation of organic compounds from refinery wastes, coal tar wastes, wood treatment wastes, soil contaminated with creosote and hydrocarbons, mixed (radioactive and hazardous) wastes, synthetic rubber processing wastes and paint wastes. Factors that may limit the applicability and effectiveness of the process include:

— There are specific feed size and materials handling requirements that affect applicability or cost at specific sites.
— Soil requires drying to achieve a low moisture content (<1%).
— Highly abrasive feed can potentially damage the processor unit.
— High moisture content increases treatment costs.
— Treated media containing heavy metals may require stabilization.

11.3.4. Thermal desorption

Thermal desorption physically removes volatile hazardous and toxic organic compounds and volatile heavy metals (cadmium, lead and mercury) and radionuclides (^{210}Pb, ^{210}Po and ^{137}Cs) from contaminated soil and wastes by application of heat. The target contaminant groups are non-halogenated VOCs, SVOCs, PAHs, PCBs, pesticides and fuels. Thermal desorbers are designed to heat soil and wastes to temperatures sufficient to cause contaminants to volatilize and desorb. Although they are not designed to decompose/destroy organic constituents, thermal desorbers can, depending upon the specific organic compounds present and the operating temperature, cause some of the constituents to completely or partially decompose. The vaporized organic compounds are generally treated in a secondary treatment unit (e.g. an after-burner, catalytic oxidation chamber, condenser or carbon adsorption unit) prior to discharge to the atmosphere. Afterburners and oxidizers destroy organic constituents. Condensers and carbon adsorption units trap organic compounds for subsequent treatment or disposal.

Some pre- and post-processing of soil and wastes is necessary when using thermal desorption. Soil must be screened to remove large (greater than 5 cm diameter) objects, which may be sized (e.g. crushed or shredded) and then reintroduced back into the feed material. Waste streams may also be ground in a homogenizer mill to a size less than 5 mm before treatment. After leaving the desorber the soil is cooled, remoistened to control dust, and stabilized (if necessary) prior to disposal or reuse.

Thermal desorption is applicable to constituents that are volatile at temperatures as high as 650°C. Most desorbers operate at temperatures of 150–540°C. They are constructed of special alloys that can operate at temperatures up to 650°C. More volatile constituents (e.g. gasoline) can be desorbed in the lower operating temperature range, while semivolatile contaminants (e.g. diesel fuel) generally require temperatures in excess of 370°C, and relatively non-volatile contaminants (e.g. lubricating oils) require even higher temperatures.

Thermal desorption systems fall into two general classes: stationary facilities and mobile units. Contaminated soil is excavated and transported to stationary facilities; mobile units are operated directly on-site. Desorption units are available in a variety of process configurations including rotary desorbers, thermal screws and conveyor furnaces.

The presence of moisture in the soil and wastes to be treated will determine the residence time required and the heating requirements for effective removal of contaminants. In order for desorption of organic constituents to occur, most of the moisture must be evaporated in the desorber. This can require significant thermal input to the desorber and excessive residence time. Soil and wastes with excessive moisture contents (>20%) must be dewatered prior to treatment. Typical dewatering methods include air drying, mixing with drier soil and mechanical dewatering.

The presence of metals can have two implications:

(1) Limitations on disposal of residual solid wastes;
(2) Limitations on metal concentrations due to air emission requirements.

However, at normal operating temperatures, heavy metals and most radionuclides are not likely to be significantly separated from soils.

Factors that may limit the applicability and effectiveness of the process include:

— There are specific particle size and material handling requirements that can have an impact on applicability or cost at specific sites.
— Dewatering may be necessary to achieve acceptable soil moisture content levels.
— Highly abrasive feed can potentially damage the processor unit.
— The presence of chlorine can affect the volatilization of some metals, such as lead.

— Heavy metals in the feed may produce a treated solid residue that requires stabilization.

— Clay, silty soils and high humic content soils increase reaction time as a result of binding of contaminants.

11.3.5. Ex situ vitrification

Ex situ vitrification is very similar to ISV (Section 9.3.4) except that it is performed inside a chamber. It can destroy or remove organic compounds and immobilize most inorganic compounds in contaminated soils, sludges or other silica bearing materials. The process has been tested on a broad range of VOCs, SVOCs and other organic compounds including dioxins and PCBs, and on heavy metals and radionuclides. Heating devices include plasma torches and electric arc furnaces.

With the plasma torch technique, the material to be treated is fed into a rotating hearth; the wastes and molten material are held against the side by centrifugal force. During the rotation, the wastes move through the plasma generated by a stationary torch. To remove the molten material from the furnace, the rotation of the hearth slows and the slag flows through an opening in the bottom. Effluent gases are generally kept in a separate container where high temperatures combust/oxidize the contents.

The arc furnace contains carbon electrodes, cooled side walls, a continuous feed system and an off-gas treatment system. In this process, wastes are fed into a chamber where they are heated to temperatures higher than 1500°C. The melt leaves the vitrification unit and cools to form a glassy solid that immobilizes inorganic compounds.

Glassy waste forms, as compared with grouted or cemented waste forms, are expected to be more stable over longer periods due to the corrosion resistance of glass. However, de-vitrification of glass can occur over periods involving thousands of years. The heat used to melt the soil can also destroy some of the harmful chemicals and cause others to evaporate. The evaporated chemicals must be captured and treated. Complete characterization of the candidate waste stream is essential before initiating ex situ vitrification to determine which glass forms are already present in the wastes and what additional glass stabilizers and fluxes need to be added.

The specific limitations to ex situ vitrification include:

(a) Vitrification does not reduce the radioactivity of a waste. Vitrified wastes containing radionuclides above regulatory limits must be managed as radioactive waste.

(b)   The initial composition of the contaminated materials may affect the strength and other properties of the vitrified material. In some cases glass making additives (e.g. sands high in borosilicate) may be needed.

(c)   Debris larger than 60 mm in diameter typically must be removed or crushed prior to the vitrification step.

(d)   Excavation of radioactively contaminated soils could cause radiation exposure to workers from fugitive gas and dust emissions, and may increase the risk to nearby populations.

(e)   Volatile heavy metals and radionuclides will accumulate in the melter off-gas system and require special treatment.

(f)   Heat loads associated with radioactive caesium loading in the glass waste form should be assessed for any applicable limits or relationships to disposal site requirements.

11.3.6.   Fluid bed steam reforming

Steam reforming destroys the hazardous organic portion of mixed wastes by exposing it to high temperature steam [269]. The process occurs in two phases. In the first phase, waste streams are exposed to steam at moderate temperatures. This volatilizes the organic components and separates them from the inorganic components of the waste stream (similar to thermal desorption). The volatilized organic compounds are transported to another reaction chamber for the second phase treatment, where the gaseous organic compounds are exposed to very high temperature steam, which destroys the organic compounds (Fig. 22). The radionuclides and non-volatile heavy metals remain in the primary reaction chamber in their solid form. Fluid bed steam reforming uses superheated steam and co-reactants in a fluidized bed to evaporate liquids, destroy organic compounds, convert nitrates, nitrites and nitric acid into nitrogen gas [270] and immobilize heavy metals, including radionuclides. To provide high nitrate and mineral conversion rates, steam reformers are operated in a strongly reducing environment. Carbon and iron based additives (reductants) are used to convert nitric acid, nitrates and nitrites directly to nitrogen gas in the reformer. Clay or other inorganic co-reactants are added to the waste feed, or bed, to convert the radionuclides, alkali metals, sulphate, chloride, fluorine, phosphate and non-volatile heavy metals into an immobilized mineral product. The final waste form is highly stable and leach resistant.

Gases and fine particulate matter entrained in the gases from the reformer are treated in a secondary unit that can also absorb metal fumes from any volatile metals in the waste stream. When treating waste that contains any

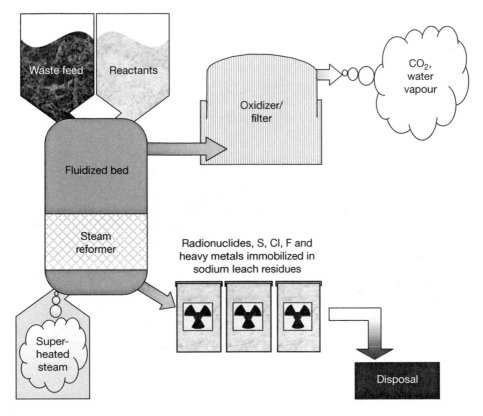

FIG. 22. Simplified flow diagram of fluidized bed steam reforming process (after Cowen et al. [270]).

radioactivity, HEPA filtration is provided. The only significant gaseous releases are carbon dioxide and water vapour emissions.

Fluid bed steam reformers are operated at 600–800°C under a small vacuum. The fluidized bed material is generally a granular product solid that accumulates in the bed during processing. Small units can be heated electrically. For production scale units, the energy is supplied by the incoming superheated steam and the introduction of oxygen with the steam to provide oxidation of the organic compounds and carbon from the wastes.

Wastes and contaminated materials that can be effectively treated by steam reforming include: radioactive waste with/without hazardous constituents, organic solvents, spent activated carbon, sludges, off-gas scrubber recycle streams, decontamination solutions, oils, PCBs, ion exchange media and resins, plastics, sodium hydroxide solutions and wastes with high concentrations of Cl,

F, S, P and heavy metals, where the final waste must be stabilized to meet heavy metal and radionuclide leach resistance and disposal site performance criteria.

During operation, the contaminated material is introduced into the system at the bottom of the fluid bed. Water in the wastes is evaporated and superheated to the bed temperature by the large mass of hot fluidized product solids. As the water in the waste feed evaporates, the temperature of dried waste solids rises to reaction temperatures. Organic compounds in the wastes are volatilized and pyrolysed upon contact with the hot bed solids. The volatile organic compounds are subjected to steam reformation in the bed. The nitric acid, nitrates and nitrites are converted to nitrogen gas when they come into contact with the reducing agents in the bed.

Alkali metals, non-volatile heavy metals, radionuclides, S, Cl, F, P and other inorganic constituents combine with co-reactants such as clay to form stable, high melting point, crystalline minerals that become the final solid product. The superheated steam, residual acid gases and fine particulates are carried into secondary units for further treatment. The accumulated product solids are semicontinuously removed from the bottom of the reformer as a fully immobilized, water insoluble, product.

The main energy requirements include: evaporation and superheating any incoming water in the waste feed, heating the organic and inorganic constituents, and supplying the heat of reaction for endothermic reformation reactions of steam with carbon and organic compounds. The main sources of energy for the reformer are the superheat of the incoming steam fluidizing gas, the reaction of nitrates with reductants to form nitrogen gas and the oxidation of organic compounds and carbon reductants in the bed.

11.3.7. Solvated electron technology (SET™)

An innovative process for treating wastes utilizes solvated electron solutions to destroy hazardous contaminants [271]. Solvated electron solutions are among the most powerful reducing agents known. Solvated electron solutions are formed by dissolving alkali or alkaline earth metals, including sodium, calcium, lithium and potassium, in anhydrous liquid ammonia. The solutions form rapidly when the metal enters the ammonia and are characterized by a deep blue coloration and an electrical conductivity approaching that of liquid metals.

In applications [272], contaminated materials are placed into a treatment cell and mixed with the solvated electron solution. In the case of halogenated contaminants, including PCBs, chemical reactions strip the halogen ions from the carbon ring. Other types of organic contaminants, such as benzene or polyaromatic hydrocarbons, are also destroyed. At the end of the reaction, ammonia in the treatment cell is recovered and recycled. The reaction products after treatment precipitate into a solid matrix as it is allowed to dry. Typically these end products are metal salts.

The system can effectively treat heterogeneous wastes and works effectively on many matrices, including:

— Soils;
— Oil waste;
— Sediments and sludge;
— Metals.

The following contaminants can be effectively treated:

— Chlorinated solvents;
— Benzene, toluene and xylenes;
— Chlorofluorocarbons;
— High energy explosives;
— Uranium hexafluoride;
— Halogenated organic compounds;
— Polyaromatic hydrocarbons;
— PCBs and pesticides;
— Chemical warfare agents;
— Dioxins and furans.

The process is non-thermal. Most reactions are performed at 5°C or below. Such low operating temperatures minimize volatile emissions. The destruction process is carried out in a totally closed system. A scrubber captures any ammonia vented when the reactor is opened. This ammonia is returned to the reactor vessel for pH adjustment.

Commodore Applied Technologies, Inc., New York, is presently the only vendor that has successfully commercialized this technology [272]. Equipment capable of treating 10 tons a day is presently in use in the field.

11.3.8. Ozonation and peroxide application

Oxidation processes including UV radiation, ozone and/or hydrogen peroxide are used to destroy organic contaminants as water flows into a treatment tank. If ozone is used as the oxidizer, an ozone destruction unit is used to treat collected off-gases from the treatment tank and downstream units where ozone gas may collect, or escape.

Ultraviolet oxidation is a destruction process that oxidizes organic and explosive constituents in water by the addition of strong oxidizers and irradiation with UV light. Oxidation of target contaminants is caused by direct reaction with the oxidizers, UV photolysis and the synergistic action of UV light, in combination with ozone (O_3) and/or hydrogen peroxide (H_2O_2). If complete mineralization is achieved, the final products of oxidation are carbon dioxide, water and salts. The main advantage of UV oxidation is that it is a destruction process, as opposed to air stripping or carbon adsorption, for which contaminants are extracted and concentrated in a separate phase. Ultraviolet oxidation processes can be configured in batch or continuous flow modes, depending on the throughput under consideration.

Ozonation relies on free oxygen radicals produced, for instance, by irradiation with a strong UV light source as an agent to break down larger organic molecules. This method is routinely applied in waterworks to disinfect raw water during the production of drinking water.

Similarly, hydrogen peroxide is a strong oxidant that has been used to disinfect water and to oxidize organic contaminants. Peroxide can also be applied to slurries or soils made into slurries. The disadvantages are relatively high costs and the fact that a considerable portion of the peroxide is consumed by the soil organic matter. An unwanted side effect is that a largely sterile soil will result due the latter effect.

Practically any organic contaminant that is reactive with the hydroxyl radical can potentially be treated by oxidation and UV oxidation. A wide variety of organic and explosive contaminants are susceptible to destruction, including petroleum hydrocarbons; chlorinated hydrocarbons used as industrial solvents and cleaners, and explosive compounds such as TNT (trinitrotoluene), RDX (cyclo-trimethylene-trinitramine) and HMX (high melting point explosive, cyclo-tetramethylene-tetranitramine). In many cases, chlorinated hydrocarbons that are resistant to biodegradation may be effectively treated by UV oxidation. Typically, easily oxidized organic compounds, such as those with double bonds (e.g. TCE, PCE and vinyl chloride), as well as simple aromatic compounds (e.g. toluene, benzene, xylene and phenol), are rapidly destroyed in UV oxidation processes.

The limitations of oxidation and UV oxidation include:

(a) The aqueous solutions to be treated must have good transmission of UV light (high turbidity causes interference). This factor can be more critical for UV/H_2O_2 than UV/O_3 (turbidity does not affect direct chemical oxidation of the contaminant by H_2O_2 or O_3).

(b) Free radical scavengers can inhibit contaminant destruction. Chemical oxidizers in excessive dosages may act as scavengers.

(c) The aqueous stream to be treated by UV oxidation should be relatively free of non-target oxidizable components, such as certain heavy metals (less than 10 mg/L) and insoluble oil or grease to minimize the potential for fouling of the process.

(d) When UV/O_3 is used on volatile organic compounds such as TCA (trichloroethane), the contaminants may be volatilized (e.g. stripped) rather than destroyed. They will then have to be removed from the off-gas by activated carbon adsorption or catalytic oxidation.

(e) Costs may be higher than those of competing technologies because of energy requirements.

(f) Pretreatment of the aqueous stream may be required to minimize cleaning and maintenance of the UV reactor.

(g) Handling and storage of oxidizers require special safety precautions.

11.3.9. Landfarming, biopiles and composting

A variety of technical solutions have been developed for ex situ soil treatment [273]. The methods have in common that biodegradation is stimulated by the addition of (lacking) essential nutrients and ensuring that sufficient electron acceptors, i.e. oxygen, reach the material. In addition, inoculation with adapted microbial strains may speed up the process. The fact that many methods are performed in a closed environment, i.e. in a bioreactor or under a tent, means that temperature control may also be critical in the colder seasons.

The main advantage of ex situ soil treatment is that it generally requires shorter time periods than in situ treatment, and there is more certainty about the uniformity of treatment because of the ability to homogenize, screen and continuously mix soils. An advantage over thermal treatment is that no volatile radionuclides need to be contained. However, ex situ treatment requires excavation of soils, leading to increased costs, equipment engineering requirements, possible permission needs, and material handling and worker exposure considerations.

This group of techniques usually involves spreading excavated contaminated soils in a thin layer on the ground surface and stimulating aerobic microbial activity within the soils through aeration and/or the addition of minerals, nutrients and moisture [274, 275] (Fig. 23). The enhanced microbial activity results in degradation of adsorbed hydrocarbons through microbial respiration. If contaminated soils are shallow (i.e. less than 1 m below the surface), it may be possible to effectively stimulate microbial activity without excavating the soils. If the contamination is deeper than 1.5 m, the soils will need to be excavated and distributed over the ground surface.

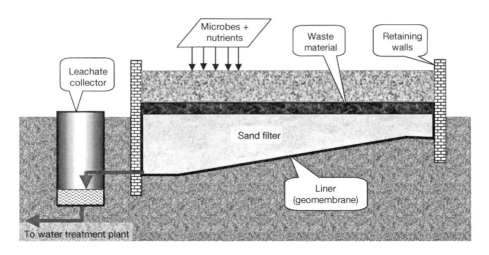

FIG. 23. Landfarming to treat organic wastes.

Landfarming has been proven effective in reducing concentrations of nearly all the constituents of petroleum products. Petroleum products generally contain constituents that possess a wide range of volatility. In general, gasoline, kerosene and diesel fuels contain constituents with sufficient volatility to evaporate from a landfarm. Lighter (more volatile) petroleum products (e.g. gasoline) tend to be removed by evaporation during landfarm aeration processes (i.e. tilling or plowing) and, to a lesser extent, to be degraded by microbial respiration. Depending upon the regulations for air emissions of VOCs, these emissions may need to be controlled, for example by putting the landfarm under a tent. The midrange hydrocarbon products (e.g. diesel fuel and kerosene) contain lower percentages of lighter (more volatile) constituents than does gasoline. Biodegradation of these petroleum products is more significant than evaporation. Heavier (non-volatile) petroleum products (e.g. heating oil and lubricating oils) do not evaporate during landfarm aeration; the dominant mechanism that breaks down these petroleum products is biodegradation. However, higher molecular weight petroleum constituents, such as those found in heating and lubricating oils, and, to a lesser extent, in diesel fuel and kerosene, require a longer period of time to degrade than do the constituents in gasoline.

While the technological and process control requirements are not very sophisticated, a large land area may be required for larger quantities of contaminated soil. Typical landfarms are uncovered and, therefore, exposed to climatic factors including rainfall, snow and wind, as well as ambient temperatures.

Rainwater that falls directly onto, or runs onto, the landfarm area will increase the moisture content of the soil and may cause erosion. During and following a significant precipitation event, the moisture content of the soils may be temporarily in excess of that required for effective bacterial activity. On the other hand, during periods of drought, the moisture content may be below the effective range and additional moisture may need to be added. Erosion of landfarm soils can occur during windy periods and particularly during tilling or plowing operations. Wind erosion can be limited by plowing soils into windrows and applying moisture periodically. In colder regions the length of the landfarming season typically ranges from 7 to 9 months. In very cold climates, special precautions can be taken, including enclosing the landfarm within a greenhouse type structure or introducing special bacteria (psychrophiles) that are capable of activity at lower temperatures. In warm regions, the landfarming season can last all year.

The technical arrangements for landfarming or biopiles may include the construction of leachate capture and treatment systems as well as vapour and odour control (Figs 23 and 24). Control of soil moisture, for example by drainage, may also be required to provide optimum growth conditions. Soils may need to be pretreated to adjust pH to the optimum, circum-neutral, range for most organisms. Growth can be stimulated by addition of nutrients, for example nitrogen and phosphorus, or essential elements, if respective deficiencies exist in the soils to be treated. Cattle or chicken manure is a typical additive, which also introduces additional microorganisms. Microbial strains specialized to particular contaminants may be obtained as inoculants from commercial suppliers.

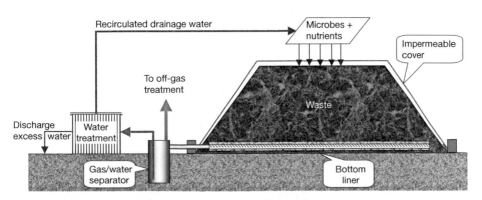

FIG. 24. The principle of biopile arrangements.

11.3.10. Bioreactors

The principles of the treatment process in bioreactors are rather similar to those of landfarming except that the process takes place in a closed vessel and is, therefore, amenable to tighter process control.

Slurry phase biological treatment involves the controlled treatment of excavated soil in a bioreactor [276] (Fig. 25). The excavated soil is first processed to physically separate stones and rubble. The soil is then mixed with water to a predetermined concentration dependent upon the concentration of the contaminants, the rate of biodegradation and the physical nature of the soils. Some processes prewash the soil to concentrate the contaminants. Clean sand may then be discharged, leaving only contaminated fines and washwater to biotreat. Typically, a slurry contains from 10 to 30% solids by weight.

The solids in a reactor vessel are maintained in suspension and mixed with nutrients and oxygen. If necessary, an acid or alkali may be added to control pH. Microorganisms also may be added if a suitable population is not present. When biodegradation is complete, the soil slurry is dewatered. Dewatering devices that may be used include clarifiers, pressure filters, vacuum filters, sand drying beds and centrifuges. Slurry phase bioreactors may be classified as short to medium term technologies.

A variety of bioremediation methods have been developed for ex situ metal recovery. These methods may range from complex, process controlled sets of bioreactors [277] to relatively simple heap leaching arrangements (see

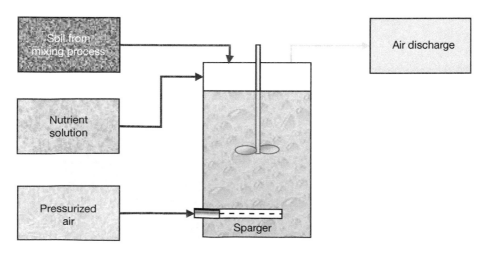

FIG. 25. A typical bioreactor arrangement.

also Ref. [17]). Such methods can have the added value of recovering metals in relatively high purity making them a marketable commodity that would help to pay for the treatment.

Factors that may limit the applicability and effectiveness of the slurry phase biotreatment process include [276]:

(a) Excavation of contaminated media is required, except for lagoon implementation.
(b) Sizing of materials prior to putting them into the reactor can be difficult and expensive. Non-homogeneous soils and clayey soils can create serious material handling problems.
(c) Dewatering soil fines after treatment can be expensive.
(d) An acceptable method for treating and disposing of non-recycled wastewater is required.

11.4. EX SITU WATER TREATMENT

11.4.1. Principles

Biological (waste)water treatment relies on microorganisms to break down organic molecules and gain energy from it. Today, almost all advanced wastewater treatment plants involve a third, biological, step in treatment. Many arrangements (bioreactors) have been developed over the decades that are capable of processing large quantities of liquid effluents. These arrangements are intended to bring the microorganisms (aerobic, anaerobic and facultative bacteria; fungi; algae; and protozoa) into contact with fresh contaminated solution and other nutrients and to remove the degradation products. In attached growth systems, such as upflow fixed film bioreactors, rotating biological contactors (RBCs) and trickling filters, microorganisms are established on an inert support matrix to aerobically degrade water contaminants. However, a comprehensive review of all the technical arrangements for biological (waste) water treatment is beyond the scope of this publication and only the principles of a few arrangements are presented here.

Nevertheless, it should be noted that the biomass involved in the processes is likely to accumulate heavy metals and radionuclides. Two problems may arise from this:

(1) The inorganic contaminants may eventually poison the system, thus reducing the efficiency of organic contaminant removal.

(2) The microorganisms are constantly dying off and may be washed out of the system together with their inorganic contaminant load.

Depending on the sequence of process steps, a step to catch the contaminated biomass may be needed, resulting in secondary wastes.

11.4.2. Trickling filters

The trickling filter consists of a bed of highly permeable media, a water distributor and a bottom drain system (Fig. 26). Wastewater is distributed over the top of the filter bed through which wastewater is trickled. The organic contaminants in wastewater are degraded by the microorganisms attached to the filter medium. The filter media may be rocks, slag, plastic or wood. The filter bed is normally round with depth varying from 1.0 to 2.5 m with an average of 1.8 m. As wastewater flows over the solid filter media, it is aerated and the organic contaminants are degraded by the microorganisms attached to

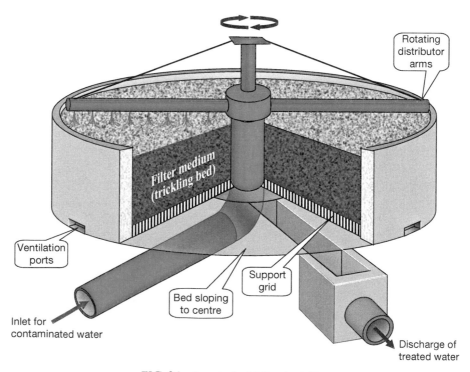

FIG. 26. A typical trickling bed filter.

the media surface. The drainage system is used to collect the treated water and any biomass detached from the filter media. It is also important as a porous structure through which air can circulate. The duration of operation and maintenance of sprinkler irrigation depends on the amount of time needed to capture and treat the contaminated wastes, to monitor the treated water and to monitor potential metal accumulation. Owing to their widespread application in the treatment of domestic and industrial effluents, a vast amount of operating experience exists. The problems in a remediation context are finding a suitable microorganism population and the potential toxicity of certain organic contaminants. Performance very much depends on the ambient conditions and, therefore, a drop is observed during the cold winter months.

11.4.3. Rotating biological contactors

An RBC is an aeration device for reducing the biological oxygen demand (BOD) value of a liquid effluent (Fig. 27). A fixed film of microorganisms is established on a contactor that is constructed from sets of discs made of corrugated glass reinforced plastic (GRP), high density polyethylene or

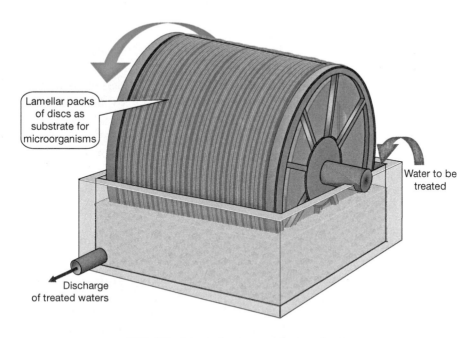

FIG. 27. A typical rotary contactor wheel.

177

polypropylene fixed to a central horizontal shaft. The shaft may be 3–7 m long and is supported on bearings in a semicircular steel, GRP or concrete tank so that about 40% of the contactor lies below the surface of the effluent to be treated. The shaft is turned slowly and the attached biomass is alternately submerged in the effluent, where it absorbs BOD, and raised out of the liquid so that the microorganisms absorb oxygen. Such systems are available commercially as self-contained units.

11.4.4. Fluidized bed reactors

In contrast to these fixed bed reactors, the active microorganisms might also be suspended in the solutions (fluidized bed reactors), either forming floating entities themselves, or being affixed to or in a floating substrate. The means to separate or strain out the microorganism from the solution are provided for.

One promising methodology includes the use of active supports (such as activated carbon, which adsorbs the contaminant and slowly releases it to the microorganisms for degradation). The microbial population may be derived either from the contaminant source or from an inoculum of organisms specific to the contaminant. Other applications include wetland ecosystems and column reactors.

11.5. IMMOBILIZATION AND SOLIDIFICATION FOR SOILS

As for immobilization and solidification (Section 9.3.3), contaminants are physically bound in or encapsulated within a stabilizing mass, or are chemically bound to a cementing matrix. The intention is to prevent access of pore waters by physical encapsulation, to reduce the porosity and permeability by filling the pore spaces, thus reducing the exchange rates between the solid and any mobile aqueous phase, or to take up the contaminants in the mineralogical matrix, thus reducing their leachability. The body of information on waste conditioning and waste treatment methods is extensive [278], and some of the techniques will also pertain to excavated materials.

There have been many innovations in the area of immobilization and solidification technology. A wide variety of agents have been used, or proposed for use, for the solidification of excavated materials [181]. Most of the innovations are modifications of proven processes and are directed towards encapsulation or immobilization of harmful constituents and involve processing of the wastes or contaminated soil. Ex situ immobilization and solid-ification processes include:

(a) *Hot bituminization*: In the bituminization process, wastes are embedded in molten bitumen and encapsulated when the bitumen cools [279]. The process screw-mixes heated bitumen and a concentrate of the waste material, usually in slurry form, in a heated extruder. Water is evaporated from the mixture to about 0.5% moisture. The final product is a homogeneous mixture of extruded bitumen and solids.

(b) *Emulsified asphalt*: Asphalt emulsions are very fine droplets of asphalt dispersed in water that are stabilized by chemical emulsifying agents. The emulsions are available in either cationic or anionic forms. The conditioning process involves adding emulsified asphalts having the appropriate charge to hydrophilic liquid or semiliquid wastes at ambient temperature. After mixing, the emulsion breaks down, the water in the wastes is released, and the organic phase forms a continuous matrix of hydrophobic asphalt around the waste solids. In some cases, additional neutralizing agents, such as lime or gypsum, may be required. After being given sufficient time to set and cure, the resulting solid asphalt has the wastes uniformly distributed throughout it and is impenetrable to water.

(c) *Modified sulphur cement*: Modified sulphur cement is a commercially available thermoplastic material. It is easily melted (125–150°C) and then mixed with the wastes to form a homogeneous molten slurry that is poured into suitable containers for cooling, storage and disposal [280]. A variety of common mixing devices, such as paddle mixers and pug mills, can be used. The relatively low process temperatures limit emissions of sulphur dioxide and hydrogen sulphide to allowable threshold values.

(d) *Polyethylene extrusion*: This process involves the mixing of granular polyethylene binders with the dry waste materials using a heated extruder containing a mixing/transport screw. The hot homogenized mixture is extruded through a die into a mold, where it cools and solidifies. The properties of polyethylene make for a chemically quite stable solidified product. The process has been tested on nitrate salt wastes at plant scale, thereby establishing its viability, and on various other wastes at the bench and pilot scale.

(e) *Pozzolan/Portland cement*: Pozzolan or OPC [281] and similar hydraulic materials like fly ash, kiln dust, pumice or blast furnace slag can be used as binders. These materials chemically react with water to form a solid matrix that improves the handling and physical characteristics of the wastes. Hydrolysing cement results in pore waters with high pH in which the solubilities of heavy metals and radionuclides are very low. Metal ions are built into the cementitious matrix. For this reason it has been extensively studied in the context of conditioning and deep geological disposal of radioactive wastes. Such cements have been proven effective with inorganic contaminants, but the effect of specific organic compounds may need to be studied. High sulphate concentrations in wastes tend to be detrimental unless special cements resistant to sulphate are used.

(f) *Various inorganic additives*: A range of additives to waste materials has been proposed or already tested in practice. Materials of interest include gypsum, phosphates and silicate gels (water glass). The desired effect is either cementation or (co-)precipitation of contaminants in insoluble minerals. Plaster of Paris ($CaSO_4 \times \frac{1}{2}H_2O$) acts as both a solidifying cement by forming gypsum ($CaSO_4 \times 2H_2O$) and as a co-precipitating agent, primarily for divalent ions. Metals sequestered in apatite (phosphate) minerals have great durability and leach resistance, significantly exceeding those of many other chemically stabilized forms [282, 283]. This is because the apatite mineral structure is very stable over a wide range of environmental conditions and the contaminant metals are built into their structure. Apatites for this purpose are available commercially. Water glass (alkali silicate gels) is used as a chemical grout [284] in the mining and waste disposal industry for various sealing and waterproofing purposes, to stabilize dirt roads and airfield surfaces [285, 286], and also in environmental remediation [287]. Adding water glass to OPC reduces its water permeability.

(g) *Various organic additives*: Organic polymers, particularly acrylic and epoxy resins, and co-polymers are used in the geotechnical industry [284], environmental remediation [186] and radioactive waste management [288] to stabilize soils and wastes [289].

The target contaminant group for ex situ immobilization and solidification is inorganic compounds, including radionuclides. Many immobilization and solidification technologies, particularly those techniques that rely on inorganic binders, have limited effectiveness against organic compounds and pesticides. Factors that may limit the applicability and effectiveness of the process include:

— Environmental conditions may affect the long term immobilization of contaminants.
— Some processes result in a significant increase in volume (up to double the original volume).
— Certain wastes are incompatible with different processes.
— Organic compounds are generally not immobilized.
— Long term effectiveness has not been demonstrated for many contaminant–process combinations.

In any case, the resulting waste mass has to meet the waste acceptance criteria of the waste management facility for which they are destined.

Often the objectives are not only to immobilize contaminants but to add value to the waste material by converting it into a useful product, for example for construction purposes. The use in general construction as a substitute for valuable raw materials requires special testing and licensing procedures to ensure environmental compatibility and compliance with quality criteria, such as compressive strength, freeze–thaw cycle stability and capability to be leached. Solidified wastes may also be used in the construction of cappings for (hazardous wastes) landfills. In cases where no further use is envisaged, minimization of the volume increase by the solidification agents is desirable to save valuable raw materials and repository space. If only small volumes arise, the material may be combined with material from other waste streams requiring a similar immobilizing treatment. The combining of waste streams can make the process more economically viable as products in marketable quantities are produced.

The treatment may be undertaken on-site or off-site at dedicated facilities. In the case of off-site treatment, the material has to comply with the applicable transport regulations and has to meet the appropriate safety criteria while being handled. The additional risk element from transporting materials has to be worked into the respective safety and cost–benefit analyses.

12. SUMMARY AND CONCLUSIONS

12.1. OVERVIEW

Radiologically contaminated sites often include non-radiological co-contaminants, such as heavy metals, organic compounds, such as solvents and greases, as well as explosives residues. These co-contaminants may or may not reside in the same media on the site, including soils, groundwater, surface water, lakes, streams and marine sediments, or in the air. At such contaminated sites, the radiological and non-radiological components may be isolated from each other, such that they can be remediated separately; or they may be co-mingled, requiring a more complex approach. Remediating such sites, in either setting, provides significant challenges related to understanding their contaminant setting, developing a remediation approach, addressing regulatory requirements, conducting sampling and analysis, and choosing an adequate remediation technology.

12.2. SOURCES OF CONTAMINATION

Mixed contaminated sites may result from a variety of activities, including nuclear weapons production, assembly and testing, military bases, research and commercial reactors, mining ventures, hospital wastes, research facilities, industrial complexes and accidents. Common radiological contaminants may include the respective radioisotopes of americium, caesium, cobalt, iodine, plutonium, radium, radon, strontium, technetium, thorium, tritium and uranium. Non-radiological components may include heavy metals, organic solvents, pesticides, explosives and biological wastes. These contaminants may exist in a wide variety of chemical forms and even in different physical phases within the various environment media. The behaviour of these contaminants in the environment will be determined by their specific characteristics; however, one may also expect that variations in behaviour will arise as a result of their interactions with each other. For example, the presence of a certain non-radiological co-contaminant may actually retard or enhance the radionuclide mobility in the environment.

12.3. REGULATORY IMPLICATIONS

It is typical for radioactive and non-radioactive contaminated sites to be dealt with by different regulatory authorities within a Member State. Therefore, addressing a mixed contaminated site incurs added regulatory complexity. Thus, regulatory requirements have an impact on several different aspects of the remediation of a mixed contaminant site including jurisdiction, assessments of environmental impacts, remediation cleanup targets, limits on worker and public exposures, waste management, mixed waste transportation, worker training, health and safety jurisdiction, waste handling and classification, and permitting a treatment process.

12.4. IMPLICATIONS FOR WORKER HEALTH AND SAFETY

Remediation of a mixed contaminant site requires additional considerations for on-site worker health and safety. Health and safety professionals who have proper training in both radiological and non-radiological contamination situations, as well as industrial safety, would need to be assigned to the remediation project. Proper health and safety analyses need to be conducted and results incorporated into a robust health and safety plan. Additional steps are typically taken in controlling and monitoring the site, including the use of hand-held monitoring detectors for both the non-radiological and radiological components. Personal protective clothing may be required to address chemical or biological hazards. Contingency and emergency planning would include medical surveillance and provisions for decontamination.

12.5. IMPLICATIONS FOR SAMPLING AND ANALYSIS

Another major component of any mixed contamination remediation project is a strong sampling and analysis programme that is typically conducted in support of:

(a) Site assessment;
(b) Monitoring of worker health and safety;
(c) Compliance monitoring associated with the remediation treatment process;
(d) Measuring the performance of the treatment process.

Such programmes need to anticipate the complexities associated with the presence of a variety of contaminants. There are numerous sampling and analysis methods. It is important to select the appropriate laboratories that are aware of health and safety implications, and that have a strong QA/QC programme.

12.6. REMEDIATION OPTIONS

In general, remediation approaches are more complex where the non-radiological component is co-mingled with the radiological component. Three basic options are available to deal with a contaminated site or parts thereof:

(1) Leave the site undisturbed;
(2) Contain or restrict contaminants;
(3) Remove or destroy contaminants.

Leaving a site undisturbed is the baseline option but is not equivalent to 'doing nothing', as a thorough site investigation is the basis for what is often termed monitored natural attenuation. Improving the attenuation and retention properties of the natural environment gradually leads to strategies in which the contaminants are contained in situ or are restricted in their mobility. Respective techniques are either applied to the contaminated environmental medium itself, such as in situ solidification techniques, or create a physical or chemical barrier around the contaminated zone. Removal of contaminated material, be it groundwater or soil, is a classical strategy, but one has to be aware that in cases in which contaminants cannot be destroyed subsequently, as for heavy metals and radionuclides, the problem in fact is transferred to another location. The rationale here is that such disposal locations can be properly engineered for containment. Disposal is usually preceded by suitable ex situ conditioning in order to improve the handling properties and reduce the leachability of contaminants. In the case of contaminants that are amenable to destruction, as is the case for most organic compounds, the removed material would be subject to a suitable process. Destruction can also be initiated in situ — so-called in situ biodegradation.

12.7. MONITORED NON-INTERVENTION

Monitored non-intervention, relying on natural processes for the retardation and attenuation of contaminants, is receiving increasing attention. One reason for this is the seemingly lower cost associated with it, notwithstanding the fact that an extensive and sustained monitoring programme over very long periods of time may be required. There are also substantive scientific and technical reasons for choosing such an option:

(a)   Minimization of interference with, and hence, collateral damage to, the site;
(b)   No generation of additional waste streams, apart from sampling wastes;
(c)   Little exposure of workers.

An indispensable precondition, however, is a thorough understanding of the site, based on a comprehensive site assessment and a (conceptual) site model.

Nevertheless, it should be remembered that heavy metals are persistent for eternity and that many radionuclides only decay over very long timescales. It is only organic contamination that is truly amenable to attenuation by degradation.

12.8. BLOCKING OF PATHWAYS

The first classical approach to dealing with contamination is isolation from potential receptors and certain environmental compartments. Respective steps can be undertaken to isolate contamination in situ or in engineered facilities. In both cases the strategy usually involves minimizing the flow of (pore) water into and through the contaminated zone and to reduce the contact of the contaminated material with this water. The first objective is achieved by various types of cappings, covers and barriers. The second objective is achieved by conditioning the material to make the contaminants less soluble or to reduce their permeability. In recent years many variants and combinations of these basic strategies have been developed. Most notable is the development of reactive permeable barriers that aim to block pathways by turning mobile species of contaminants into less mobile ones. In the case of organic compounds these may also be more or less completely attenuated. Larger areas to be treated are still a challenge to techniques such as in situ vitrification and other in situ solidification techniques. The treatment of larger aquifer volumes by reductants (mainly for metals) or oxidants (mainly for organic compounds) appears to be promising, but is still an emerging technology.

12.9. SOURCE TERM REMOVAL

The second classical approach to remediation is the removal of the source term by excavation, pumping or (in situ) destruction in the case of organic compounds. Excavation or pumping, however, requires as a second step the conditioning and disposal of inorganic contaminants or, conversely, the destruction of organic contaminants.

Excavation is an obvious way to remove contaminated soil and buried wastes but has its limitations with respect to the volumes that can be handled. A waste stream is generated that needs to be treated and that requires a suitable disposal option. In fact, the contamination is removed from one location to another, albeit a more manageable one. It should be noted in this context that engineered facilities have only a limited lifetime and will need periodic maintenance, raising the issue of long term stewardship. Excavation also causes significant surface disturbance.

Pump and treat was considered for many years the baseline technology against which all other groundwater related techniques were compared. It is, however, only effective against those contaminants that can be removed by the physical force of flowing water. If the major part of the contaminant is bound to the sediment surface, it cannot be removed at all or results in protracted tailing, i.e. in very long (sometimes in excess of decades) pumping times. For hydraulic reasons some parts of an aquifer may not be accessible to pumping at all. For these reasons, pumping is now considered primarily a containment method, by which the further spread of contamination is prevented. Different methods to improve on the recovery rates have been developed. For instance, permeabilities can be increased by physical methods, such as hydrofracturing. Other methods are intended to increase the solubilities of contaminants by changing the redox conditions, by introducing complexing agents, solvents or surfactants, or by biological means. Reducing the viscosities or increasing the vapour pressure enhances the recovery of organic compounds, and can be achieved by resistance or steam heating. Thermal methods are also applied in situ to destroy organic contaminants. Biological methods have found increasing interest in recent years, not least because they appear to be less invasive.

In all cases, a considerable technical infrastructure is required and there is a significant environmental impact caused by remediation.

12.10. EX SITU TREATMENT METHODS

Many treatment and condition processes can be applied ex situ as well as in situ. While in situ application typically causes less surface disturbance, ex situ application is generally more controllable with respect to process conditions. After excavation, the material can be separated into fractions that are more or less contaminated, allowing the application of targeted treatment techniques and reducing the volume that needs treatment. A variety of physical separation techniques are available, mainly borrowed from the minerals processing industry.

Contaminated solids then may be subject to a chemical separation process, such as washing (for metals and organic compounds) or heating (for semivolatile and volatile organic compounds). Depending on the process conditions and lixiviants used, heating and washing processes may also lead to the destruction of organic compounds. Outright incineration of soils, however, also destroys the soil organic matter and microorganisms, resulting in a sterile product of limited reusability. Various bioremediation techniques, such as landfarming or composting, are increasingly being used to degrade organic compounds.

Pumped groundwater is typically treated on the surface to remove contaminants by adsorption (organic compounds and inorganic compounds), ion exchange (metals) or (co-)precipitation (metals). More esoteric techniques include membrane pervaporation and reverse osmosis. Volatile organic compounds can be driven off in the vacuum or by heating and collected in the headspace; they require further treatment such as incineration. Non-volatile organic compounds are treated using classical techniques borrowed from wastewater technology, such as trickling filters.

Mixed contamination residues may pose particular challenges as a selected treatment method may not be compatible with certain contaminants. For instance, heavy metals or radionuclides may poison biological treatment systems, while volatile heavy metals (e.g. Hg) or radionuclides (e.g. ^{210}Po) may cause problems in thermal treatment systems.

12.11. CONCLUSIONS

Cases of mixed contamination pose a variety of challenges from both the technical and the managerial points of view. Each contaminated site requires careful assessment in order to understand its properties and the contaminant behaviour. The possible interactions between different groups of contaminants — radionuclides, heavy metals and organic compounds — at the site under natural conditions and during remediation need to be thoroughly understood. No single technique is likely to solve the problem, so a combination of techniques may be required. Notwithstanding the limitations of the individual techniques discussed in this report, it appears that there is an arsenal of techniques at our disposal that is capable of handling even complex instances of contamination.

It is important to remember nevertheless, that, with the exception of organic contaminants, which can be completely destroyed in many instances, heavy metals and radionuclides will persist and that any remedial solution will require some form of attention (stewardship) for very long periods of time.

REFERENCES

[1]   INTERNATIONAL ATOMIC ENERGY AGENCY, Management of Radioactive Waste from the Mining and Milling of Ores, IAEA Safety Standards Series No. WS-G-1.2, IAEA, Vienna (2002).

[2]   INTERNATIONAL ATOMIC ENERGY AGENCY, Factors for Formulating Strategies for Environmental Restoration, IAEA-TECDOC-1032, IAEA, Vienna (1998).

[3]   INTERNATIONAL ATOMIC ENERGY AGENCY, A Directory of Information Resources on Radioactive Waste Management, Decontamination and Decommissioning, and Environmental Restoration, Data as of June 1995, IAEA-TECDOC-841, IAEA, Vienna (1995).

[4]   INTERNATIONAL ATOMIC ENERGY AGENCY, Technologies for Remediation of Radioactively Contaminated Sites, IAEA-TECDOC-1086, IAEA, Vienna (1999).

[5]   INTERNATIONAL ATOMIC ENERGY AGENCY, Extent of Environmental Contamination by Naturally Occurring Radioactive Material (NORM) and Technological Options for Mitigation, Technical Reports Series No. 419, IAEA, Vienna (2003).

[6]   INTERNATIONAL ATOMIC ENERGY AGENCY, Monitoring and Surveillance of Residues from the Mining and Milling of Uranium and Thorium, Safety Reports Series No. 27, IAEA, Vienna (2002).

[7]   INTERNATIONAL ATOMIC ENERGY AGENCY, Characterization of Radioactively Contaminated Sites for Remediation Purposes, IAEA-TECDOC-1017, IAEA, Vienna (1998).

[8]   INTERNATIONAL ATOMIC ENERGY AGENCY, Design Criteria for a Worldwide Directory of Radioactively Contaminated Sites (DRCS), IAEA-TECDOC-1251, IAEA, Vienna (2001).

[9]   INTERNATIONAL ATOMIC ENERGY AGENCY, Technical Options for the Remediation of Contaminated Groundwater, IAEA-TECDOC-1088, IAEA, Vienna (1999).

[10] INTERNATIONAL ATOMIC ENERGY AGENCY, The Long-term Stabilization of Uranium Mill Tailings, Final Report on the Co-ordinated Research Project 2000–2004, IAEA-TECDOC-1403, IAEA, Vienna (2004).

[11] INTERNATIONAL ATOMIC ENERGY AGENCY, Remediation of Areas Contaminated by Past Activities and Accidents, IAEA Safety Standards Series No. WS-R-3, IAEA, Vienna (2003).

[12] INTERNATIONAL ATOMIC ENERGY AGENCY, Compliance Monitoring for Remediated Sites, IAEA-TECDOC-1118, IAEA, Vienna (1999).

[13] INTERNATIONAL ATOMIC ENERGY AGENCY, A Worldwide Directory of Radioactively Contaminated Sites (DRCS), IAEA, Vienna, www-drcs.iaea.org/

[14] INTERNATIONAL ATOMIC ENERGY AGENCY, Site Characterization Techniques Used in Environmental Restoration Activities, Final Report of a Co-ordinated Research Project 1995–1999, IAEA-TECDOC-1148, IAEA, Vienna (2000).

[15] INTERNATIONAL ATOMIC ENERGY AGENCY, The Removal of Sites and Buildings from Regulatory Control upon the Termination of Practices, IAEA Safety Standards Series, Vienna (in preparation).

[16] INTERNATIONAL ATOMIC ENERGY AGENCY, Non-technical Factors Impacting on the Decision Making Processes in Environmental Remediation, IAEA-TECDOC-1279, IAEA, Vienna (2002).

[17] INTERNATIONAL ATOMIC ENERGY AGENCY, Remediation of Sites with Dispersed Radioactive Contamination, Technical Reports Series No. 424, IAEA, Vienna (2004).

[18] INTERNATIONAL ATOMIC ENERGY AGENCY, Applicability of Monitored Natural Attenuation at Radioactively Contaminated Sites, Technical Reports Series No. 445, IAEA, Vienna (2006).

[19] INTERNATIONAL ATOMIC ENERGY AGENCY, Planning for Environmental Restoration of Uranium Mining and Milling Sites in Central and Eastern Europe, IAEA-TECDOC-982, IAEA, Vienna (1997).

[20] INTERNATIONAL ATOMIC ENERGY AGENCY, Planning for Cleanup of Large Areas Contaminated as a Result of a Nuclear Accident, Technical Reports Series No. 327, IAEA, Vienna (1991).

[21] INTERNATIONAL ATOMIC ENERGY AGENCY, International Basic Safety Standards for Protection Against Ionizing Radiation and for the Safety of Radiation Sources, Safety Series No. 115, IAEA, Vienna (1996).

[22] UNITED NATIONS ENVIRONMENT PROGRAMME, Persistent Organic Pollutants, UNEP, Geneva,
http://www.chem.unep.ch/pops/default.html

[23] UNITED STATES ENVIRONMENTAL PROTECTION AGENCY, Fact Sheet: Notice of Draft Ambient Water Quality Criteria Document for Tributyltin (TBT), EPA-822-F-02-003, USEPA, Washington, DC (2002),
http://www.epa.gov/waterscience/criteria/tributyltin/draftfs.htm

[24] EUROPEAN UNION, Council Directive 98/83/EC of 3 November 1998 on the Quality of Water Intended for Human Consumption, Official Journal L 330, 05/12/1998, EU, Luxembourg (1998) 32–54,
http://www.europa.eu.int/eur-lex/en/consleg/main/1998/en_1998L0083_index.html

[25] UNITED STATES ENVIRONMENTAL PROTECTION AGENCY, National Primary Drinking Water Standards, USEPA, Washington, DC (2003),
http://www.epa.gov/safewater/consumer/mcl.pdf

[26] FETTER, C.W., Contaminant Hydrogeology, Prentice-Hall, Englewood Cliffs, NJ (1999).

[27] IVANOVICH, M., HARMON, R.S. (Eds), Uranium-Series Disequilibrium: Applications to Earth, Marine and Environmental Sciences, Clarendon Press, Oxford (1992).

[28] WARING, C.L., TAYLOR, J.R., "A new technique for building in-situ subsurface hydrologic barriers: NBT", Mine, Water and Environment (Proc. Conf. Seville, 1999), (RUBIO, R.F., Ed.), International Mine Water Association (1999) 663–665.

[29] ZIEGENBALG, G., "In-situ remediation of heavy metal contaminated soil or rock formations and sealing of water inflows by directed and controlled crystallization of natural occurring minerals", ibid., pp. 667–672.

[30] WAGH, A.S., SING, D., JEONG, S.-Y., Chemically Bonded Phosphate Ceramics for Stabilization and Solidification of Mixed Waste, Argonne Natl Lab., IL, http://www.techtransfer.anl.gov/docs/ CRC5.pdf

[31] STUMM, W. (Ed.), Aquatic Surface Chemistry: Chemical Processes at the Particle–Water Interface, Wiley, New York (1987).

[32] HODGES, F.N., Results of Phase I Groundwater Quality Assessment for Single-Shell Tank Waste Management Areas T and TX-TY at the Hanford Site, Draft Report, Pacific Northwest Natl Lab., Richland, WA (1997).

[33] JOHNSON, V.G., CHOU, C.J., Results of Phase I Groundwater Quality Assessment for Single-Shell Tank Waste Management Areas S-SX at the Hanford Site, Rep. PNNL-11810, Pacific Northwest Natl Lab., Richland, WA (1998).

[34] SERNE, R.J., ZACHARA, J.M., BURKE, D.S., Chemical Information on Tank Supernatants, Cs Adsorption from Tank Liquids onto Hanford Sediments, and Field Observations of Cs Migration from Past Tank Leaks, Rep. PNNL-11495, Pacific Northwest Natl Lab., Richland, WA (1997).

[35] SMITH, R.M., 216-B-5 Reverse Well Characterization Study, Rep. RHO-ST-37, Rockwell Hanford Operations, Richland, WA (1980).

[36] URBAN, N.R., EISENREICH, S.J., GRIGAL, D.F., SCHURR, K.T., Mobility and diagenesis of Pb and ^{210}Pb in peat, Geochim. Cosmochim. Acta **54** (1990) 3329.

[37] FIRSOVA, E.V., GERMAN, K.E., PERETROUKHIN, V.F., KHIJNYAK, T.V., "Bioaccumulation of long-lived radionuclides by fresh-water silt", Environmental Contamination in Central and Eastern Europe (Proc. 4th Int. Symp. Warsaw, 1998), Florida State University, Tallahassee (1998) CD-ROM, http://iicer.fsu.edu/SymposiumSeries.cfm

[38] HAIGH, D., et al., The Effect of Organics on the Sorption of Strontium, Caesium, Iodine, Neptunium, Uranium and Europium by Glacial Sand, Rep. WE/89/16, Fluid Processes Research Group, British Geological Survey, Keyworth (1989).

[39] READ, D., FALCK, W.E., "Long-term uranium migration behaviour — an overview of the 'natural analogue' studies carried out on the British Isles", Uranium Mining and Hydrogeology (Proc. Int. Symp. Freiberg, 1995), Sven von Loga, Cologne (1995) 473–482.

[40] WEBB, A.B., et al., Preliminary Safety Criteria for Organic Watch List Tanks at the Hanford Site, Rep. WHC-SD-WM-SARR-033 Rev. 0, Westinghouse Hanford Company, Richland, WA (1995).

[41] FRANCIS, A.J., Microbial dissolution and stabilization of toxic metals and radionuclides in mixed wastes, Experientia **46** (1990) 840–851.

[42]   CHANMUGATHAS, P., BOLLAG, J.M., Microbial mobilization of cadmium in soil under aerobic and anaerobic conditions, J. Environ. Qual. **16** (1987) 161–167.

[43]   GERRINGA, L., Aerobic degradation of organic matter and the mobility of Cu, Cd, Ni, Pb, Zn and Fe in marine sediment slurries, Mar. Chem. **29** (1990) 355–374.

[44]   BURKE, B.E., WING TSANG, K., PFISTER, R.M., Cadmium sorption by bacteria and freshwater sediment, J. Ind. Microbiol. Biotechnol. **8** 3 (1991) 201–208.

[45]   UNITED STATES DEPARTMENT OF ENERGY, Report on the Joint Convention on the Safety of Spent Fuel Management and on the Safety of Radioactive Waste Management, Rep. DOE/EM-0654, USDOE, Washington, DC (2003).

[46]   CIRIA, SAFEGROUNDS (Safety and Environmental Guidance for the Remediation of Nuclear and Defense Sites) Learning Network (2004),
http://www.safegrounds.com/

[47]   GERMAN FEDERAL GOVERNMENT, Gesetz zum Schutz vor Schädlichen Bodenveränderungen und zur Sanierung von Altlasten – BBodSchG – Bundes-Bodenschutzgesetz vom 17 März 1998, Bundesgesetzblatt I, Bundesanzeiger Verlag, Berlin (1998) 502,
http://www.bundesanzeiger.de/

[48]   GERMAN FEDERAL GOVERNMENT, ibid. (2001) 2331.

[49]   WORLD HEALTH ORGANIZATION, Guidelines for Drinking Water Quality, (2003),
http://www.who.int/water_sanitation_health/dwq/GDWQ2004web.pdf

[50]   MINISTRY OF HOUSING, REGIONAL PLANNING AND THE ENVIRONMENT, Leidraad Bodensanering, MVROM, The Hague (1986).

[51]   INTERNATIONAL COMMISSION ON RADIOLOGICAL PROTECTION, Protection of the Public in Situations of Prolonged Radiation Exposure, ICRP Publication 82, Elsevier, Amsterdam and New York (2000),
http://www.icrp.org/icrp82.htm

[52]   INTERNATIONAL COMMISSION ON RADIOLOGICAL PROTECTION, Recommendations of the International Commission on Radiological Protection, ICRP Publication 60, Elsevier, Amsterdam and New York (1990),
http://www.elsevier.com/inca/publications/store/2/9/0/8/3/

[53]   NATIONAL INSTITUTE FOR OCCUPATIONAL HEALTH AND SAFETY, NIOSH, Washington, DC, USA,
http://www.cdc.gov/niosh/homepage.html

[54]   HEALTH AND SAFETY EXECUTIVE, Occupational Exposure Limits, Publication EH40, Hazardous Installations Inspectorate, HMSO, Norwich (2002),
http://www.hse.gov.uk

[55]   EUROPEAN COMMISSION, Waste, Directive 75/442/EEC, Off. J. Eur. Commun. L **194** (1975) 39–41,
http://europa.eu.int/eur-ex/lex/LexUriServ/
LexUriServ.do?uri=CELEX:31975L0442:EN:HTML

[56] EUROPEAN COMMISSION, Hazardous Waste, Directive 91/689/EEC, Off. J. Eur. Commun. L **377** (1991) 20–27,
http://europa.eu.int/eur-ex/lex/LexUriServ/
LexUriServ.do?uri=CELEX:31991L0689:EN:HTML

[57] EUROPEAN COMMISSION, Supervision and Control of Shipments of Waste into and out of the European Communities, Directive 259/93/EEC, EC, Brussels (1993).

[58] EUROPEAN COMMISSION, Prevention of Air Pollution from New Municipal Waste Incineration Plants, Directive 89/369/EEC, EC, Brussels (1989).

[59] EUROPEAN COMMISSION, Reduction of Pollution from Existing Waste-Incineration Plants, Directive 89/429/EEC, EC, Brussels (1989).

[60] EUROPEAN COMMISSION, Incineration of Hazardous Waste, Directive 94/67/EEC, Off. J. Eur. Commun. L **365** (1994) 34–45,
http://europa.eu.int/smartapi/cgi/sga_doc?smartapi!celexapi!prod!
CELEXnumdoc&ig=en&numdoc=31994L0067

[61] EUROPEAN COMMISSION, Integrated Prevention and Control, Directive 96/61/EC, Off. J. Eur. Commun. L **267** (1996) 26–40.

[62] EUROPEAN COMMISSION, Landfill of Waste, Directive 1999/31/EC, Off. J. Eur. Commun. L **182** (1999) 1–19,
http://europa.eu.int/eur-lex/pri/en/oj/dat/1999/l_182/
l_18219990716en00010019.pdf

[63] EUROPEAN COMMISSION, Incineration of Waste, Directive 2000/76/EC, Off. J. Eur. Commun. L **332/91** (2000) 91–111,
http://europa.eu.int/comm/environment/wasteinc/newdir/2000-76_en.pdf

[64] EUROPEAN COMMISSION, Disposal of Waste Oils, Directive 75/439/EEC, Off. J. Eur. Commun. L **194** (1975) 23–25,
http://europa.eu.int/smartapi/cgi/sga_doc?smartapi!celexplus!prod!
DocNumber&ig=en&type_doc=Directive&an_doc=1975&nu_doc=439

[65] EUROPEAN COMMISSION, Waste from the Titanium Dioxide Industry, Directive 78/176/EEC, EC, Brussels (1978),
http://rod.eionet.eu.int/show.jsv?id=209&mode=S

[66] EUROPEAN COMMISSION, Sludges, Directive 86/278/EEC, EC, Brussels (1986),
http://rod.eionet.eu.int/show.jsv?id=514&mode=S

[67] EUROPEAN COMMISSION, Batteries and Accumulators Containing Certain Dangerous Substances, Directive 91/157/EEC, Off. J. Eur. Commun. L **078** (1991) 38–41,
http://europa.eu.int/smartapi/cgi/sga_doc?smartapi!celexdoc!prod!
CELEXnumdoc&ig=EN&numdoc=31991L0157&model=guicheti

[68] EUROPEAN COMMISSION, Packaging and Packaging Waste, Directive 94/62/EEC, Off. J. Eur. Commun. L **365** (1994) 10–23,
http://europa.eu.int/smartapi/cgi/sga_doc?smartapi!celexapi!prod!
CELEXnumdoc&lg=EN&numdoc=31994L0062&model=guichett

[69]   EUROPEAN COMMISSION, Disposal of PCBs and PCTs, Directive 96/59/EC,
        Off. J. Eur. Commun. L **243** (1996) 31–35,
        http://europa.eu.int/smartapi/cgi/sga_doc?smartapi!celexplus!prod!DocNumber
        &lg=en&type_doc=Directive&an_doc=1996&nu_doc=59
[70]   INTERNATIONAL ATOMIC ENERGY AGENCY, Regulations for the Safe
        Transport of Radioactive Material, IAEA Safety Standards Series No. TS-R-1
        (ST-1, Rev.), IAEA, Vienna (1996).
[71]   UNITED NATIONS ECONOMIC COMMISSION FOR EUROPE, UN
        Recommendations on the Transport of Dangerous Goods: Model Regulations,
        Rep. ST/SG/AC.10/1/Rev.13, UNECE, Geneva (2002).
[72]   INTERNATIONAL MARITIME ORGANISATION, International Maritime
        Dangerous Goods (IMDG) Code, 2002 Edition, IMO, London (2002).
[73]   COATES, R., Experience on the application of the ALARP principle, J. Radiol.
        Prot. **10** (1990) 39–42.
[74]   UK HEALTH AND SAFETY EXECUTIVE, Policy and Guidance on Reducing
        Risks as Low as Reasonably Practicable in Design, HSE, London (2003),
        http://www.hse.gov.uk/risk/theory/alarp3.htm
[75]   INTERNATIONAL ATOMIC ENERGY AGENCY, Long-Term Stewardship
        for Radioactively Contaminated Sites, Technical Reports Series (in press).
[76]   UNITED STATES DEPARTMENT OF ENERGY, Handbook for Occupational
        Health and Safety During Hazardous Waste Activities, USDOE, Washington, DC
        (1996).
[77]   WATSON, D.D., JOHNSON, C.E., Jr., HYLKO, J.M., WALTER, J.F., WAGNER,
        C.T., "Experiences using Level A and B personal protective equipment to remove
        high-hazard radioactive and hazardous constituents from a USDOE material
        storage area", Waste Management 2001 (Proc. Int. Conf. Tucson, 2001),
        http://www.wmsym.org/Abstracts/2001/21A/ 21A-5.pdf
[78]   INTERNATIONAL ORGANIZATION FOR STANDARDIZATION, Interna-
        tional Classification for Standards (ICS) Field 13: Environment. Health Protec-
        tion. Safety, ISO, Geneva,
        http://www.iso.ch/iso/en/CatalogueListPage.CatalogueList?ICS1=13
[79]   BYRNES, M.E., KING, D.A., Sampling and Surveying Radiological Environ-
        ments, Lewis Publishers, Boca Raton, FL (2000).
[80]   INTERNATIONAL ORGANIZATION FOR STANDARDIZATION, The ISO
        9000 Family (Quality Management), ISO, Geneva,
        http://www.iso.ch/iso/en/iso9000-14000/iso9000/iso9000index.html
[81]   JOHNSON, G.L., "Overview of the ISO 14000 environmental management
        standards and their impact on waste management and remediation", Waste
        Management and Environmental Remediation (Proc. 6th Int. Conf. Singapore,
        1997) 147–152,
        http://members.asme.org/catalog/ItemView.cfm?ItemNumber=I00405

[82] DYER, R.S., "Bench scale studies and pilot scale design of a modified volume reduction-chemical extraction system for radiation contaminated soils", Residual Radioactivity and Recycling Criteria (Proc. Workshop St. Michaels, 1989), Rep. EPA 520/1-90-013, US Environmental Protection Agency, Washington, DC (1990) 122–131.

[83] VANDENHOVE, H., et al., Investigation of a Possible Basis for a Common Approach with Regard to the Restoration of Areas Affected by Lasting Radiation Exposure as a Result of Past or Old Practice or Work Activity — CARE, Final Report to the European Commission, Radiation Protection 115, EC, Brussels (1999).

[84] JOHNSON, R., SMITH, K.P., QUINN, J., The Application of Adaptive Sampling and Analysis Program (ASAP) Techniques to NORM Sites", Rep. DOE/BC/W-31-109-ENG-38-9, OSTI No. 14169, United States Department of Energy, Washington, DC (1999).

[85] FELLOWS, R.L., SINGH, S.P.N., "Technology logic diagrams: Their use in nuclear and hazardous waste management", Nuclear and Hazardous Waste Management (Proc. Int. Top. Mtg Atlanta, 1994), American Nuclear Society, Washington, DC (1994) 893–897.

[86] FEDERAL REMEDIATION TECHNOLOGY ROUNDTABLE, Remediation Technologies Screening Matrix and Reference Guide, Version 4.0 (2002), http://www.frtr.gov/matrix2/top_page.html

[87] CLARINET, The Contaminated Land Rehabilitation Network for Environmental Technologies in Europe (2002), http://www.clarinet.at/

[88] ENVIROTOOLS, Hazardous Substances Research Center, Michigan State University, East Lansing, MI (2002), www.envirotools.org

[89] HEIDEN, S. (Ed.), Innovative Techniken der Bodensanierung — ein Beitrag zur Nachhaltigkeit, Spektrum Akademischer Verlag, Heidelberg (1999).

[90] GOVINDARAJU, R.S., BANKS, M.K., SCHWAB, A.P., "Use of geostatistics in designing and analyzing treatment effects at the field scale", Hazardous Waste Research (Proc. 10th Annu. Conf. Manhattan, KS, 1995) (ERICKSON L.E., TILLISON, D.L., GRANT, S.C., McDONALD, J.P., Eds), Kansas State University, Manhattan, KS (1996), http://www.engg.ksu.edu/HSRC/95Proceed/home.html

[91] GUNN, R.D., ORR, C.H., "New approaches to monitoring and characterization in the remediation of nuclear sites", Radioactive Waste Management and Environmental Remediation (Proc. 6th Int. Conf. Singapore, 1997), American Society of Mechanical Engineers, New York (1997) 761–764.

[92] ENVIRONMENTAL COST ENGINEERING COMMITTEE, Historical Cost Assessment System (HCAS), Remedial Action Breakdown Structure (2000), http://www.environmental.usace.army.mil/ec2/index.html

[93] BOARDMAN, C., HOLMES, R., ROBBINS, R., FOX, R., MINCHER, B., "Remediation of soil at nuclear sites", Waste Management 2000 (Proc. Conf. Tucson, 2000),
http://www.wmsym.org/archive_proceedings.asp

[94] CHAN HILTON, A., IYER, S.K., "Optimization of natural attenuation with active remediation under uncertainty", In Situ and On-Site Bioremediation (Proc. 7th Int. Symp. Orlando, 2003), Battelle Press, Columbus, OH (2003) CD-ROM, abstract.

[95] SEMPRINI, L., "In-situ transformation of halogenated aliphatic compounds under anaerobic conditions", Subsurface Restoration (WARD, H., CHERRY, J.A., SCALF, M.R., Eds), Ann Arbor Press, Chelsea, MI (1997) 429–449.

[96] SEMPRINI, L., ELY, R.L., LANG, M.M., "Modeling of cometabolism for the in situ biodegradation of trichloroethylene and other chlorinated aliphatic hydrocarbons", Bioremediation: Principles and Practice 1, Fundamentals and Applications (SIKDAR, K., IRVINE, R.L., Eds), Technomic Publishing Co., Lancaster, PA (1997) 89–134.

[97] THOMSON, M.M., VIDUMSKY, J.E., "Field evidence for natural attenuation of 1, 2-dichloroethane and 1, 2-dibromoethane", In Situ and On-Site Bioremediation (Proc. 7th Int. Symp. Orlando, 2003), Battelle Press, Columbus, OH (2003), CD-ROM, abstract.

[98] UNITED STATES ENVIRONMENTAL PROTECTION AGENCY, Technical Protocol for Evaluating Natural Attenuation of Chlorinated Solvents in Ground Water, Rep. EPA/600/R-98/128, USEPA, Washington, DC (1998).

[99] KENNEDY, L., EVERETT, J.W., GONZALES, J., "Geomicrobiological treatment for engineered and natural attenuation of chlorinated solvents", In Situ and On-Site Bioremediation (Proc. 7th Int. Symp. Orlando, 2003), Battelle Press, Columbus, OH (2003) CD-ROM, abstract.

[100] FALCK, W.E, A Review of Modelling the Interaction between Natural Organic Matter and Metal Cations, Rep. EUR 12531, European Commission, Brussels (1988).

[101] McALLISTER, P.M., CHIANG, C.Y., A practical approach to evaluating natural attenuation of contaminants in groundwater, Ground Water Monit. Rev. **14** 2 (1994) 161–173.

[102] LAHVIS, M.A., BAEHR, A.L., Estimation of rates of aerobic hydrocarbon biodegradation by simulation of gas transport in the unsaturated zone, Water Resour. Res. **32** (1996) 2231–2249.

[103] GEMOETS, J., et al., "Evaluation of the potential for natural attenuation and in situ bioprecipitation of hexavalent chromium", In Situ and On-Site Bioremediation (Proc. 7th Int. Symp. Orlando, 2003), Battelle Press, Columbus, OH (2004) CD-ROM, paper L-07.

[104] DETHLEFSEN, F., "Comparison of methods to evaluate the sedimentary oxidation capacity", ibid., paper H-29.

195

[105] REGENESIS BIOREMEDIATION PRODUCTS INC., Sales Brochure on Hydrogen Release Compound (HRC®), Regenesis, San Clemente, CA (2003), http://www.regenesis.com

[106] REGENESIS BIOREMEDIATION PRODUCTS INC., Sales Brochure on Oxygen Release Compound (ORC®), Regenesis, San Clemente, CA (2003), http://www.regenesis.com

[107] REGENESIS BIOREMEDIATION PRODUCTS Inc., Sales Brochure on Metals Remediation Compound (MRC®), Regenesis, San Clemente, CA (2003), http://www.regenesis.com

[108] FMC INDUSTRIAL CHEMICALS, Product PermeOx® Plus: Slow Release of Oxygen for Enhanced Natural Attenuation, FMC, Philadelphia, PA (2003), http://www.fmcchemicals.com/

[109] SONGKASIRI, W., RITTMANN, B.E., REED, D.T., WILLETT, A., KOENIGS-BERG, S., "Bioremediation of neptunium(V) using lactate, hydrogen (H_2), or Hydrogen Release Compound (HRC®)", In Situ and On-Site Bioremediation (Proc. 7th Int. Symp. Orlando, 2003), Battelle Press, Columbus, OH (2004), CD-ROM, paper L-09.

[110] SONGKASIRI, W., RITTMANN, B.E., REED, D.T., "Bio-reduction of neptunium(V) by *Shewanella* alga with lactate or Hydrogen Release Compound (HRC®) as an electron donor", paper presented at Am. Nucl. Soc. Int. Conf. on Nuclear and Hazardous Waste Management, Reno, NV (2002).

[111] SPERRY, K.L., et al., "O_2 delivery: A comparative analysis of in situ oxygen delivery methods", In Situ and On-Site Bioremediation (Proc. 7th Int. Symp. Orlando, 2003), Battelle Press, Columbus, OH (2003) CD-ROM, abstract.

[112] PHIFER, M.A., et al., "Sulfate reduction remediation of a metals plume through organics injection", ibid., paper L-04.

[113] BENDA, G.A., WILLIAMS, C.A., "New developments in stabilization of heavy metals in mixed waste using inorganic sulfides", Waste Management 2000 (Proc. Int. Conf. Tucson, 2001), WM Symposia, Inc., Tucson, AZ (2000) CD-ROM, paper 31-14, http://www.wmsym.org/

[114] COULIBALY, K.M., BORDEN, R.C., "Distribution of edible oil emulsions and permeability loss in sandy sediments", In Situ and On-Site Bioremediation (Proc. 7th Int. Symp. Orlando, 2003), Battelle Press, Columbus, OH (2004) CD-ROM, paper B-10.

[115] VIAMAJALA, S., et al., "Cr(VI) reduction by *Cellulomonas spp.* — Batch kinetics and meso-scale tests", ibid., abstract.

[116] INTERNATIONAL ASSOCIATION OF GEOSYNTHETIC INSTALLERS, IAGI White Paper on Improving Geomembrane Installations, IAGI White Paper, St. Paul, MN (2004), http://www.iagi.org/Source%20Documents/White_Paper.pdf

[117] RINCK, G., RISLER, J.J., Mise en tombeau étanche de terres polluées par de l'hexachlorocyclohexane, Hydrogéologie **2** (1985) 143–147.

[118] RUMER, R.R., MITCHELL, J.K. (Eds), "Assessment of barrier containment technologies. A comprehensive treatment for environmental remedial application", International Containment Technology Workshop, Rep. PB96-180583, National Technical Information Service, Springfield, VA (1996).

[119] SULLIVAN, T.M., HEISER, J., GARD, A., SENUM, G., Monitoring subsurface barrier integrity using perfluorocarbon tracers, J. Environ. Eng. **124** 6 (1998) 490–497.

[120] SAYLES, F.N., ISKANDAR, I.K., "Ground freezing for containment of hazardous waste", paper presented at Int. Containment Tech. Workshop, Baltimore, MD, 1995.

[121] UNITED STATES DEPARTMENT OF ENERGY, Frozen Soil Barrier, SCFA Factsheet 51, USDOE, Washington, DC (1999),
www.envnet.org/scfa/prodlines/stcr/factsheets/tms51.pdf

[122] SOPKO, J.A., ALUCE, G.F., Artificial Ground Freezing for Environmental Remediation, Layne Christensen Co.,
http://www.groundfreezing.com/artificial_ground_freezing.html

[123] THIMUS, J.-F. (Ed.), Ground Freezing 2000: Frost Action in Soils (Proc. 9th Int. Symp. Louvain-la-Neuve, 2000), A.A. Balkema, Lisse, Netherlands (2000).

[124] UNITED STATES DEPARTMENT OF ENERGY, Frozen Soil Barrier: Innovative Technology, Rep. DOE/EM-0483, USDOE, Washington, DC (1999),
http://apps.em.doe.gov/ost/pubs/itsrs/itsr51.pdf

[125] OAK RIDGE NATIONAL LABORATORY, Soil Freezing Technology Demonstrated at Oak Ridge, ORNL, Oak Ridge, TN (1997),
http://www.oakridge.doe.gov/media_releases/1997/r-97-016.htm

[126] BLOWES, D.W., PTACEK, C.J., "Geochemical remediation of groundwater by permeable reactive walls: Removal of chromate by reaction with iron-bearing solids", Subsurface Restoration (Proc. 3rd Int. Conf. Dallas, 1992), Rice Univ., Houston, TX (1992) 214–216.

[127] UNITED STATES ENVIRONMENTAL PROTECTION AGENCY, Field Applications of In Situ Remediation Technologies: Permeable Reactive Barriers, USEPA, Washington, DC (2002),
http://clu-in.org/download/rtdf/fieldapp_prb.pdf

[128] UNITED STATES DEPARTMENT OF ENERGY, Passive Reactive Barrier, SCFA Factsheet 46, USDOE, Washington, DC (1999),
http://apps.em.doe.gov/ost/pubs/itsrs/itsr46.pdf

[129] BLOWES, D.W., et al., Treatment of inorganic contaminants using permeable reactive barriers, J. Contam. Hydrol. **45** (2000) 123–137.

[130] POWELL, R.M., PULS, R.W., HIGHTOWER, S.K., SABATINI, D.A., Coupled iron corrosion and chromate reduction: mechanisms for subsurface remediation, Environ. Sci. Technol. **29** (1995) 1913–1922.

[131] BLOWES, D.W., PTACEK, C.J., JAMBOR, J.L., In situ remediation of chromate contaminated groundwater using permeable reactive walls, Environ. Sci. Technol. **31** (1997) 3348–3357.

[132] WAYBRANT, K.R., BLOWES, D.W., PTACEK, C.J., Selection of reactive mixtures for use in permeable reactive walls for treatment of mine drainage, Environ. Sci. Technol. **32** (1998) 1972–1979.

[133] BENNER, S.G., HERBERT, R.B., Jr., BLOWES, D.W., PTACEK, C.J., GOULD, W.D., Geochemistry and microbiology of a permeable reactive barrier for acid mine drainage, Environ. Sci. Technol. **33** (1999) 2793–2799.

[134] LUDWIG, R., McGREGOR, R.G., BLOWES, D.W., BENNER, S.G., MOUNTJOY, K., A permeable reactive barrier for treatment of heavy metals, Ground Water **40** (2002) 59–66.

[135] CANTRELL, K.J., KAPLAN, D.I., WIETSMA, T.W., Zero-valent iron for the in situ remediation of selected metals in groundwater, J. Hazard. Mater. **42** (1995) 201–212.

[136] GU, B., LIANG, L., DICKEY, M.J., YIN, X., DAI, S., Reductive precipitation of uranium(VI) by zero-valent iron, Environ. Sci. Technol. **32** (1998) 3366–3373.

[137] MORRISON, S.J., METZLER, D.R., CARPENTER, C.E., Uranium precipitation in a permeable reactive barrier by progressive irreversible dissolution of zerovalent iron, Environ. Sci. Technol. **35** (2001) 385–390.

[138] FULLER, C.C., PIANA, M.J., BARGAR, J.R., DAVIS, J.A., KOHLER, M., "Evaluation of apatite materials for use in permeable reactive barriers for the remediation of uranium-contaminated groundwater", Handbook of Groundwater Remediation Using Permeable Reactive Barriers (MORRISON, S.J., NAFTZ, D.L., DAVIS, J.A., FULLER, C.C., Eds), Academic Press, San Diego, CA (2002) 256–280.

[139] ROBERTSON, R.D., CHERRY, J.A., In situ denitrification of septic system nitrate using reactive porous medium barriers: Field trials, Ground Water **33** (1995) 99–111.

[140] BAKER, M.J., BLOWES, D.W., PTACEK, C.J., Laboratory development of permeable reactive mixtures for the removal of phosphorus from onsite wastewater disposal systems, Environ. Sci. Technol. **32** (1998) 2308–2316.

[141] SCHIPPER, L., VOJVODIĆ-VUKOVIĆ, M., Nitrate removal from groundwater using a denitrification wall amended with sawdust: Field trial, J. Environ. Qual. **27** (1998) 664–668.

[142] GRUBE, W.E., "Soil barrier alternatives", Remedial Action, Treatment, and Disposal of Hazardous Wastes (Proc. 7th Annu. Symp. Cincinnati, 1991), Rep. EPA/600/9-91/002, United States Environmental Protection Agency, Washington, DC (1991).

[143] HANSEN, W., et al., Barriers and Post-Closure Monitoring, Briefing Chart, Rep. TTP AL-1212-25, Los Alamos Natl Lab., NM (1992).

[144] THOMSON, B.M., HENRY, E.J., THOMBRE, M.S., "Applications of permeable barrier technology to ground water contamination at the Shiprock, NM, UMTRA site", Hazardous Waste Research (Proc. 10th Annu. Conf. Manhattan, 1995), Kansas State University, Manhattan, KS (1996), www.engg.ksu.edu/HSRC/96Proceed/thomson.pdf

[145] MORRISON, S.J., SPANGLER, R.R., Chemical barriers for controlling groundwater contamination, Environ. Prog. **12** (1993) 175–181.

[146] LEE, D.R., HARTWIG, D.J., "Wall-and-curtain for subsurface treatment of contaminated groundwater", Containment & Remediation Technology (Proc. Int. Conf. and Exhibition, Orlando, 2001), Florida State University, Orlando (2001).

[147] McMURTY, D., ELTON, R.O., New approach to in-situ treatment of contaminated groundwater, Environ. Prog. **4** (1985) 168–170.

[148] VICTOR, E.A., "Landfill barrier design: A case study on accelerated natural attenuation", In Situ and On-Site Bioremediation (Proc. 7th Int. Symp. Orlando, 2003), Battelle Press, Columbus, OH (2004) CD-ROM, paper M-06.

[149] BOSTICK, W.D., SHOEMAKER, J.L., OSBORNE, P.E., EVANS-BROWN, B., "Treatment and disposal options for a heavy metals waste containing soluble technetium-99", Emerging Technologies in Hazardous Waste Management II (TEDDER, D.W., POHLAND, F.G., Eds), Am. Chem. Soc. Symp. Ser. **422** (1990) 345–367.

[150] DEL CUL, G.D., BOSTICK, W.D., TROTTER, D.R., OSBORNE, P.E., Technetium-99 removal from process solutions and contaminated groundwater, Sep. Sci. Technol. **28** (1993) 551–564.

[151] UNIVERSITY OF WATERLOO, Permeable Reactive Barrier for Treatment of Cr and TCE, Ontario, Canada,
www.science.uwaterloo.ca/research/ggr/PermeableReactiveBarriers/
Cr-TCE_Treatment/Cr-TCE_Treatment.html

[152] FERRIS, F.G., Microbial Mineral Transformations at the Fe(II)/Fe(III) Redox Boundary for Solid Phase Capture of Strontium and Other Metal/Radionuclide Contaminants 1998: Annual Progress Report, Rep. EMSP-54790-98, United States Department of Energy, Washington, DC (1998),
www.osti.gov/bridge/servlets/purl/13471-F4YTMz/webviewable/13471.pdf

[153] RODEN, E.E., URRUTIA, M.M., Advanced Experimental Analysis of Controls on Microbial Fe(III) Oxide Reduction: 1998 Annual Progress Report, Rep. EMSP-55164-98, United States Department of Energy, Washington, DC (1998),
www.osti.gov/bridge/servlets/purl/13478-5aJwS2/webviewable/13478.pdf

[154] MORRISON, S.J., NAFTZ, D.L., DAVIS, J.A., FULLER, C.C. (Eds), Handbook of Groundwater Remediation Using Permeable Reactive Barriers, Academic Press, San Diego, CA (2002) 222–252.

[155] ALOWITZ, M.J., GETTLER, R., SCHERER, M.M., "Reduction kinetics of inorganic contaminants by iron metal", Hazardous Waste Research (Proc. Conf. Denver, 2000), Kansas State University, Manhattan, KS (2000),
http://www.engg.ksu.edu/HSRC/abs43.doc

[156] FELTCORN, E., NAFTZ, D.L., FULLER, C.C., MORRISON, S.J., "Field demonstration of permeable reactive barriers to control uranium contamination in ground water", Waste Management 2001 (Proc. Conf. Tucson, 2001),
www.wmsym.org/Abstracts/2001/43A/43A-7.pdf

[157] MORRISON, S.J., CARPENTER, C.E., METZLER, D.R., BARTLETT, T.R., MORRIS, S.A., "Design and performance of a permeable reactive barrier for containment of uranium, arsenic, selenium, vanadium, molybdenum, and nitrate at Monticello, Utah", Handbook of Groundwater Remediation Using Permeable Reactive Barriers (MORRISON, S.J., NAFTZ, D.L., DAVIS, J.A., FULLER, C.C., Eds), Academic Press, San Diego, CA (2002) 371–399.

[158] MATHESON, L.J., GOLDBERG, W.C., BOSTICK, W.D., HARRIS, L., "Analysis of uranium-contaminated zero valent iron media sampled from permeable reactive barriers installed at U.S. Department of Energy Sites in Oak Ridge, Tennessee, and Durango, Colorado", ibid., pp. 343–367.

[159] TAWACHSUPA, S., ISLEYEN, M., RAMASWAMI, A., "Batch-mixed iron treatment of high arsenic waters", Water Res. **35** 18 (2001) 4474–4479.

[160] TÄLJEMARK, K., ÖBERG, K., ENELL, A., HANSSON, H., "Heavy metal and PAH sorption by pine bark", In Situ and On-Site Bioremediation (Proc. 7th Int. Symp. Orlando, 2003), Battelle Press, Columbus, OH (2004) CD-ROM, paper O-15.

[161] PRIMROSE, A., "Operational status of reactive barriers for treatment of groundwater at Rocky Flats environmental technology site", TIE Quarterly, Winter 2001, Vol. 9, United States Department of Energy, Washington, DC (2001).

[162] LEE, D.R., et al., "Wall-and-curtain for passive collection/treatment of contaminant plumes", Remediation of Chlorinated and Recalcitrant Compounds (Proc. 1st Int. Conf. Monterey, 1998), Battelle Press, Columbus, OH (1998) 77–84.

[163] CONCA, J., et al., "Treatability study of reactive materials to remediate groundwater contaminated with radionuclides, metals, and nitrates, in a four-component permeable reactive barrier", Handbook of Groundwater Remediation Using Permeable Reactive Barriers (MORRISON, S.J., NAFTZ, D.L., DAVIS, J.A., FULLER, C.C., Eds), Academic Press, San Diego, CA (2002) 222–252.

[164] LIANG, L., et al., Byproduct formation during the reduction of TCE by zero-valent iron and palladized iron, Ground Water Monit. Remed. **17** 1 (1997) 122–127.

[165] VIKESLAND, P.J., "Granular iron and bioaugmented granular iron system: Effects of co-solutes", In Situ and On-Site Bioremediation (Proc. 7th Int. Symp. Orlando, 2003), Battelle Press, Columbus, OH (2003) CD-ROM, abstract.

[166] CHARLET, L., LIGER, E., GERASIMO, P., Decontamination of TCE- and U-rich waters by granular iron: Role of sorbed Fe(II), J. Environ. Eng. (N.Y.) **124** 1 (1998) 25–30.

[167] GREGORY, K.B., et al., "RDX transformation in the presence of ferrihydrite and *Geobacter metallireducens* GS-15", In Situ and On-Site Bioremediation (Proc. 7th Int. Symp. Orlando, 2003), Battelle Press, Columbus, OH (2003) CD-ROM, abstract.

[168] DRIES, J., BASTIAENS, L., SPRINGAEL, D., AGATHOS, S.N., DIELS, L., "Multibarrier, a technology concept for the in-situ remediation of mixed groundwater pollution", ibid., paper K-04.

[169] UNITED STATES ENVIRONMENTAL PROTECTION AGENCY, Slurry Walls, Engineering Bulletin, Rep. EPA/540/2-92/0038, USEPA, Washington, DC, (1991).

[170] MORONEY, K., MORONEY, J., TURNEY, J., JOHNSON, N., "Remediation of transuranic-contaminated coral soil at Johnston Atoll using the segmented gate system", Waste Management 1993 (Proc. Conf. Tucson, 1993), WM Symposia, Inc., Tucson, AZ (1993) 845–848,
http://www.wmsym.org/

[171] UNITED STATES DEPARTMENT OF ENERGY, Segmented Gate System, SCFA Factsheet, USDOE, Washington, DC (2001).

[172] UNITED STATES DEPARTMENT OF ENERGY, Directional Boring and Thrusting with Hybrid Underground Utility Industry Equipment, ProTech Database, TTP Reps AL2211-16 and AL2211-03, USDOE, Washington, DC (1993).

[173] HOCKING, G., WELLS, S.L., OSPINA R.I., "Design and construction of vertical hydraulic fracture placed iron reactive walls", Designing and Applying Treatment Technologies (Proc. 1st Int. Conf. Monterey, 1998), (WICKRAMANAYAKE, G.B., HINCHEE, R.E., Eds), Battelle Press, Columbus, OH (1998).

[174] LANDIS, R.C., "The innovative use of high pressure jetting of thin diaphragm walls to construct hydraulic control barriers", Containment & Remediation Technology (Proc. Int. Conf. Orlando, 2001), Florida State University, Orlando (2001), http://iicer.fsu.edu/SymposiumSeries.cfm

[175] GARDNER, K.H., MILLER, C.M., KONG, L., "Placement of a colloidal-catalyst in situ reactive treatment wall", Remediation of Chlorinated and Recalcitrant Compounds (Proc. 2nd Int. Conf. Monterey, 2000), (WICKRAMANAYAKE, G.B., GIBBS, J.T., MEANS, J.L., Eds), Battelle Press, Columbus, OH (2000).

[176] HAAS, R.F., "The EnviroWall™ barrier system", Nuclear and Hazardous Waste Management (Proc. Int. Top. Mtg Atlanta, 1994), American Nuclear Society, Washington, DC (1994) 2368–2370.

[177] UNIVERSITY OF WATERLOO, Technology Transfer and Licensing Office (TTLO),
http://www.research.uwaterloo.ca/ttlo/

[178] ROSS, N., et al., "Initiating a field demonstration of the development of a biological barrier in a fractured shale", In Situ and On-Site Bioremediation (Proc. 7th Int. Symp. Orlando, 2003), Battelle Press, Columbus, OH (2004) CD-ROM, paper K-06.

[179] CHEVRON, P., et al., "Restoration of a nitrogen-polluted aquifer by biotransformation in-situ", In Situ and On-Site Bioremediation (Proc. 4th Int. Symp. New Orleans, 1997), Battelle Press, Columbus, OH (1997) 405–409.

[180] UNITED STATES ENVIRONMENTAL PROTECTION AGENCY, Solidification/Stabilization and Its Application to Waste Materials, Rep. EPA/530/R-93/012 EPA, USEPA, Washington, DC (1993).

[181] UNITED STATES ENVIRONMENTAL PROTECTION AGENCY, Solidification/Stabilization of Organics and Inorganics, Rep. EPA/540/S-92/015, USEPA, Washington, DC (1993).

[182] FINNERAN, K.T., LOVLEY, D.R., "The role of Fe(III) and humic substances in bioremediation of organic and metal contaminants", In Situ and On-Site Bioremediation (Proc. 7th Int. Symp. Orlando, 2003), Battelle Press, Columbus, OH (2003) CD-ROM, abstract.

[183] EVANS, P., LEBRÓN, C., "In situ bioremediation with electron shuttles", ibid., abstract.

[184] BRITTON, L., MEHLHORN, R.J., TOROK, T., "Bioreduction of metal ions using synthetic electron shuttles", ibid., paper K-13.

[185] MIKHEYKIN, S.V., et al., "Interpolyelectrolyte complexes for contaminated soil immobilization and remediation", Waste Management 2002 (Proc Int. Conf. Tucson, 2002), WM Symposia, Inc., Tucson, AZ (2000) CD-ROM, http://www.wmsym.org

[186] MIKHEYKIN, S.V., "Polymeric coats for the stabilization of contaminated surfaces", IAEA-TECDOC-1403, International Atomic Energy Agency, Vienna (2004) Annex XI.

[187] UNITED STATES DEPARTMENT OF ENERGY, In Situ Vitrification Bottoms Up, SCFA Factsheet, USDOE, Washington, DC (2001).

[188] TIXIER, J.S., THOMPSON, L.E., "In situ vitrification: Providing a comprehensive solution for remediation of contaminated soils", Nuclear Waste Management and Environmental Remediation (Proc. Int. Conf. Prague, 1993), American Society of Mechanical Engineers, New York (1993) 47–58.

[189] GEOMELT™, Vitrification, GM, Washington, DC, http://www.geomelt.com/

[190] SIEGRIST, R.L., URYNOWICZ, M.A., WEST, O.R., CRIMI, M.L., LOWE, K.S., Principles and Practices of In Situ Chemical Oxidation using Permanganate, Battelle Press, Columbus, OH (2001).

[191] SCHNARR, M. et al., Laboratory and controlled field experimentation using potassium permanganate to remediate trichloroethylene and perchloroethylene DNAPLs in porous media, J. Contaminant Hydrol. **29** 3 (1998) 205–224.

[192] SYKES, K., Evaluation of Soil and Buried Waste Retrieval Technologies for Operable Unit, Rep. 7-13/14, INEEL/EXT-01-000281, Rev. 0, Idaho National Engineering and Environmental Laboratory, Idaho Falls, ID (2002).

[193] UNITED STATES ENVIRONMENTAL PROTECTION AGENCY, Survey of Materials-Handling Technologies Used at Hazardous Waste Sites, Rep. EPA/540/2-91/010, USEPA, Washington, DC (1991).

[194] IDAHO NATIONAL ENGINEERING AND ENVIRONMENTAL LABORATORY, Hot Spot Removal System: System Description, Rep. INEEL/EXT-970666, INEEL, Idaho Falls, ID (1997).

[195] BECHTEL HANFORD INC., Technical Alternatives Baseline Report, Bechtel Hanford Inc., Hanford, WA (2000).

[196] UNITED STATES ENVIRONMENTAL PROTECTION AGENCY, Pump and Treat Ground-Water Remediation: A Guide for Decision Makers and Practitioners, Rep. EPA/625/R-95/005, USEPA, Washington, DC (1996).

[197] UNITED STATES ENVIRONMENTAL PROTECTION AGENCY, Methods for Monitoring Pump-And-Treat Performance, Rep. EPA/600/R-94/123, USEPA, Washington, DC (1994).

[198] BUCKLEY, L.P., VIJAYAN, S., WONG, P.C., "Remediation process technology for ground water", Nuclear Waste Management and Environmental Remediation (Proc. Int. Conf. Prague, 1993), American Society of Mechanical Engineers, New York (1993) 33–39.

[199] DOILNITSYN, V.A., NECHAEV, A.F., VOLKOV, A.S., SHIBKOV, S.N., "Purification of slightly contaminated low-salt water from the long-lived radionuclides", Radioactive Waste Management and Environmental Remediation (Proc. 6th Int. Conf. Singapore, 1997), American Society of Mechanical Engineers, New York (1997) 527–528.

[200] LAUL, J.C., et al., "Removal of uranium, plutonium and americium from Rocky Flats waste water", Nuclear and Hazardous Waste Management (Proc. Int. Top. Mtg Boise, 1992), La Grange Park, IL (1992) 637–642.

[201] UNITED STATES DEPARTMENT OF ENERGY, A Process for Contaminant Removal and Waste Volume Reduction to Remediate Groundwater Containing Certain Radionuclides, Toxic Metals, and Organics, Rep. DOE/CH-9201, USDOE, Washington, DC (1992).

[202] MACKAY, D., CHERRY, J.A., Groundwater contamination: Pump-and-treat remediation, Environ. Sci. Technol. **23** (1989) 7–13.

[203] UNITED STATES NATIONAL ACADEMY OF SCIENCES, Alternatives for Ground Water Cleanup, National Academy Press, Washington, DC (1994), www.nap.edu/books/0309049946/html/R1.html

[204] KORTE, N., et al., Field Evaluation of a Horizontal Well Recirculation System for Groundwater Treatment: Field Demonstration at X-701B Portsmouth Gaseous Diffusion Plant, Piketon, Ohio, Rep. ORNL/TM-13529, Oak Ridge Natl Lab., TN (1998),
www.osti.gov/bridge/servlets/purl/296857-ObDJpt/webviewable/296857.pdf

[205] QUARANTA, J.D., GABR, M.A., "Prefabricated vertical drain enhanced soil flushing field demonstration for remediation of a low-level mixed waste plume in glacial till soil", paper presented at 4th Int. Symp. on Environmental Contamination in Central and Eastern Europe, Warsaw, 1998.

[206] UNITED STATES ENVIRONMENTAL PROTECTION AGENCY, In Situ Remediation Technology Status Report: Electrokinetics, Rep. EPA/542/K-94/007, USEPA, Washington, DC (1994).

[207] UNITED STATES ENVIRONMENTAL PROTECTION AGENCY, Chemical Enhancements to Pump-and-Treat Remediation, Rep. EPA/540/S-92/001, USEPA, Washington, DC (1992).

[208] MITCHELL, P., ANDERSON, A.L, "Silica micro encapsulation: ARD treatment and beyond", Hazardous Waste Research (Proc. Conf. Denver, 2000), Kansas State University, Kansas City (2000),
http://www.engg.ksu.edu/HSRC/abs34.doc

[209] ZIEMKIEWICZ, P., "Steel lag: Applications for AMD control", Hazardous Waste Research (Proc. Conf. Snowbird, 1998), Kansas State University, Kansas City (1998) 44–61,
www.engg.ksu.edu/HSRC/98Proceed/5Ziemkiewicz/5ziemkiewicz.pdf

[210] TRAN, T.D., FARMER, J.C., DE PRUNEDA, J.H., RICHARDSON, J.H., "Electrosorption on carbon aerogel electrodes as a means of treating low-level radioactive wastes and remediating contaminated groundwater", Radioactive Waste Management and Environmental Remediation (Proc. 6th Int. Conf. Singapore, 1997), American Society of Mechanical Engineers, New York (1997) 547–553.

[211] TAYLOR, R.M., ROBINS, R.G., "Treatment of Berkeley pitlake water using the green precipitate process", Hazardous Waste Research (Proc. Conf. Snowbird, 1998), Kansas State University, Kansas City (1998) 2–15,
www.engg.ksu.edu/HSRC/98Proceed/1Robins/1robins.pdf

[212] LAPIERRE, J., MANNSCHOTT, C., SAUTER, M., La contamination d'un captage d'eau potable par du tetrachloréthylène, Courants 17 (1992) 81–87.

[213] UNITED STATES DEPARTMENT OF ENERGY, Well Injection Depth Extraction (WIDE) Soil Flushing, Rep. DOE/EM-0577, USDOE, Washington, DC (2001),
http://apps.em.doe.gov/ost/pubs/itsrs/itsr2172.pdf

[214] ELLIS, W.D., et al., Treatment of Contaminated Soils with Aqueous Surfactants, Rep. EPA/600/2-85/129, United States Environmental Protection Agency, Washington, DC (1985).

[215] QUARANTA, J., GABR, M., SABODISH, M., GATES, K., "Well injection depth extraction (WIDE™) soil flushing for DNAPL and uranium remediation", Waste Management 2001 (Proc. Conf. Tucson, 2001),
www.wmsym.org/Abstracts/2001/43A/43A-2.pdf

[216] UNITED STATES ENVIRONMENTAL PROTECTION AGENCY, A Citizen's Guide to In Situ Soil Flushing, Rep. EPA/542/F-96/006, USEPA, Washington, DC (1996).

[217] JAMES, B.R., BARTLETT, R.J., Behavior of chromium in Soils: VII. Adsorption and reduction of hexavalent forms, J. Environ. Qual. 12 2 (1983) 177–181.

[218] ACAR, Y.B., et al., Electrokinetic Remediation: Basics and Technology Status, J. Hazardous Mater. 40 2 (1994) 117–137.

[219] KELSH, D.J., PARSONS, M.W., Department of Energy Sites Suitable for Electrokinetic Remediation, J. Hazardous Mater. 55 (1997) 109–116.

[220] ALSHAWABKEH, A.N., BRICKA, R.M., "Basics and applications of electrokinetic remediation", Remediation Engineering of Contaminated Soils (WISE, D., et al., Eds), Marcel Dekker, New York (2000) Ch. 4.

[221] ALSHAWABKEH, A.N., McGRATH, C.J., "Theoretical basis for the simulation of electrokinetic remediation", ibid., Ch. 6.

[222] POPOV, K., YACHMENEV, V., LOMASNEY, H., "The enhancement of electroosmotic flow in soils by organic reagents", Emerging Technologies in Hazardous Waste Management (Proc. 7th Symp. Birmingham, AL, 1996), American Chemical Society, Washington, DC (1996) 600–603.

[223] KOLOSOV, A., et al., Electrokinetic method of hazardous hydrophobic organic compounds removal from contaminated soil, Russ. J. Appl. Chem. **74** (2001) 613.

[224] POPOV, K.I., et al., A laboratory scale study of applied voltage and chelating agent on the electrokinetic separation of phenol from soil, Sep. Sci. Technol. **36** (2001) 2971.

[225] SENGUPTA, T., SENGUPTA, A., LOMASNEY, H.L., POPOV, K., YACHMENEV, V., Electrokinetically Enhanced Micellar Extraction of Radionuclides/Heavy Metals and Organics from Soil, Rep. DE-FG02-ER82007, ISOTRON Corp., New Orleans, LA (1996).

[226] LI, A., CHEUNG, K.A., REDDY, K.R., Co-solvent-enhanced electrokinetic remediation of soils contaminated with phenanthrene, J. Environ. Eng. (N.Y.) **126** (2000) 527–533.

[227] AL-ABED, S.R., CHEN, J.-L., "Transport of trichloroethylene (TCE) in natural soil by electroosmosis", Physicochemical Groundwater Remediation (SMITH, J.A., BURNS, S.E., Eds), Kluwer, New York (2001) 91.

[228] KIM, S.-O., MOON, S.-H., KIM, K.-W., Enhanced electrokinetic soil remediation for removal of organic contaminants, Environ. Technol. **21** 4 (2000) 417–426.

[229] GARDNER, K.H., ARIAS, M.S., Clay swelling and formation permeability reductions induced by a non-ionic surfactant, Environ. Sci. Technol. **34** 1 (2000) 160–166.

[230] REGENS, J.L., KELLEY, L., HODGES, D.G., WILKEY, P.L., An Integrated Framework for Environmental Technology Evaluation, Medical University of South Carolina Press, Charleston, SC (1998).

[231] SALE, T., GILBERT, D., BALLABAN, M., "Electrically induced redox barriers — Borden Field experiment", Geological Society of America Annu. Mtg Denver, 2002 (2002) Abstract 232-4,
http://gsa.confex.com/gsa/2002AM/finalprogram/ abstract_43654.htm

[232] FALTA, R.W., Using phase diagrams to predict the performance of co-solvent floods for NAPL remediation, Ground Water Monit. Rev. **18** 3 (1998) 227–232.

[233] ROSEN, M.J., Surfactants and Interfacial Phenomena, Wiley, New York (1978).

[234] LAKE, L.W., Enhanced Oil Recovery, Prentice Hall, Englewood Cliffs, NJ (1989).

[235] INTERA INC., NAVAL FACILITIES ENGINEERING SERVICE CENTER, Surfactant-Enhanced Aquifer Remediation (SEAR) Implementation Manual, Rep. TR-2219-ENV, NFESC, Washington, DC (2003).

[236] WINSOR, P.A., Solvent Properties of Amphophilic Compounds, Butterworth, London (1954).

[237] SABATINI, D.A., KNOX, R.C., HARWELL, J.H., "Emerging technologies for surfactant-enhanced subsurface remediation", Surfactant Enhanced Subsurface Remediation: Emerging Technologies (SABATINI, D.A., KNOX, R.C., HARWELL, J.H., Eds), ACS Symp. Ser. 594, American Chemical Society, Washington, DC (1995) 1.

[238] KO, S., SCHLAUTMAN, M.A., Partitioning of hydrophobic organic compounds to sorbed surfactants. 2. Model development/predictions for surfactant-enhanced remediation applications, Environ. Sci. Technol. **32** 18 (1997) 2776.

[239] SMITH, J.A., et al., Surfactant-enhanced remediation of a trichloroethene-contaminated aquifer. 1. Transport of Triton X-100, Environ. Sci. Technol. **31** 12 (1997) 3565.

[240] McKAY, D.M., CHERRY, J.A., Groundwater contamination: Limitations of pump-and-treat remediation, Environ. Sci. Technol. **23** (1989) 630–636.

[241] FOUNTAIN, J.C., KLIMEK, A., BEIDRICH, M.G., MIDDLETON, T.M., Use of surfactants for in situ extraction of organic pollutants from a contaminated aquifer, J. Hazard. Mater. **28** 3 (1991) 295–311.

[242] CHEN, Y., CHEN, L.Y., KNOX, R.C., Modeling the effectiveness of innovative measures for improving the hydraulic efficiency of surfactant injection and recovery systems", Surfactant Enhanced Subsurface Remediation: Emerging Technologies (SABATINI, D.A., KNOX, R.C., HARWELL, J.H., Eds), American Chemical Society, ACS Symp. Ser. 594, Washington, DC (1995) 249–264.

[243] UNITED STATES DEPARTMENT OF ENERGY, Remediation of DNAPLs in Low Permeability Soils: Subsurface Contaminants Focus Area, Rep. DOE/EM-0550, USDOE, Washington, DC (2000).

[244] FEDERAL REMEDIATION TECHNOLOGY ROUNDTABLE, Hydraulic and Pneumatic Fracturing at the US Department of Energy's Portsmouth Gaseous Diffusion Plant, Ohio, United States Department of Defense, Washington, DC (2000),
http://www.frtr.gov/matrix2/section4/4_7.html

[245] HERRLING, B., STAMM, J., "Numerical results of calculated 3D vertical circulation flows around wells with two screen sections for in situ or on-site remediation", Numerical Methods in Water Resources, Computational Methods in Water Resources IX, Vol. 1 (RUSSELL, T.F., et al., Eds), Elsevier Applied Science, New York (1992) 483–492.

[246] UNITED STATES ENVIRONMENTAL PROTECTION AGENCY, In Situ Remediation Technology Status Report: Thermal Enhancements, Rep. EPA542-K-94-009, USEPA, Washington, DC (1995),
http://www.gwrtac.org/html/topics/thermale.htm

[247] DAVIS, E.L., Steam Injection for Soil and Aquifer Remediation, Rep. EPA/540/S-97/505, United States Environmental Protection Agency, Washington, DC (1998).

[248] BROWN, N., PARKINSON, D., DABLOW, J., "Dynamic underground stripping and hydrous pyrolysis/oxidation of PCE and TCE at Savannah River Site", Waste Management 2001 (Proc. Conf. Tucson, 2001), WM Symposia, Inc., Tucson, AZ (2001) CD-ROM,
http://www.wmsym.org

[249] UNITED STATES DEPARTMENT OF ENERGY, Six Phase Soil Heating, Rep. Tech ID 5 SCFA, USDOE, Washington, DC (1995),
http://www.em.doe.gov/plumesfa/

[250] ENHANCED RECOVERY INC., Technology Overview for Microwave Remediation, ERI, Roanoke, TX (2001),
http://www.erinewave.com

[251] DROZD, J.M., Improved Method for In-Situ Soil Remediation: The Modified Lasagna™ Process, Rep. 68D98119, United States Environmental Protection Agency, Washington, DC (1999),
http://es.epa.gov/ncer/progress/sbir/hazard/68d98119.html

[252] NORRIS, R.D., et al. (Eds), Handbook of Bioremediation, Lewis Publishers, Boca Raton, FL (1994).

[253] UNITED STATES ENVIRONMENTAL PROTECTION AGENCY, Engineered Approaches to In Situ Bioremediation of Chlorinated Solvents: Fundamentals and Field Applications, Rep. EPA 542-R-00-008, USEPA, Washington, DC (2000),
http://clu-in.org/download/remed/engappinsitbio.pdf

[254] NATHANAIL, P., et al., "Risk based bioremediation — Experience from the UK", In Situ and On-Site Bioremediation (Proc. 7th Int. Symp. Orlando, 2003), Battelle Press, Columbus, OH (2003) CD-ROM, abstract.

[255] UNITED STATES DEPARTMENT OF ENERGY, In Situ Enhanced Soil Mixing, Rep. ID 54 SCFA, USDOE, Washington, DC (1996),
http://apps.em.doe.gov/ost/itsrscfa.html

[256] UNITED STATES DEPARTMENT OF ENERGY, In Situ Bioremediation Using Horizontal Wells, Rep. ID 1919 SCFA, USDOE, Washington, DC (1995),
http://apps.em.doe.gov/ost/itsrscfa.html

[257] FEDERAL REMEDIATION TECHNOLOGY ROUNDTABLE, Remediation Technologies Screening Matrix and Reference Guide Version 4.0, 3.4: Ex Situ Biological Treatment for Soil, Sediment, Bedrock and Sludge, FRTR (2000),
http://www.frtr.gov/matrix2/section3/3_4.html

[258] LAGNY, C., Cahier des charges et dimensionnement d'un pilote venting, Rep. 91NT016-4S/ENV, Bureau de recherches géologiques et minières, Orléans (1991).

[259] RAES, E.J., et al., "Quantification of microbial processes induced via injection of HRC at a CAH site", In Situ and On-Site Bioremediation (Proc. 7th Int. Symp. Orlando, 2003), Battelle Press, Columbus, OH (2003) CD-ROM.

[260] TING, Y.-P., et al., "Biodegradation on phenanthrene in a zinc co-contaminated soil", ibid., paper J-10.

[261] BALDRIAN, P., GABRIEL, J., NERUD, F., "Applicability of *Pleurous ostreatus* and *Trametes versicolor* for bioremediation of heavy metals-polluted soils", ibid., CD-ROM, paper G-03.

[262] BRIONES-GALLARDO, R., MUSTIN, C., LEYVAL, C., "Determination of metal tolerance mechanisms of arbuscular mycorrhizal fungi in contaminated soil by potentiometric titration", In Situ and On-Site Bioremediation (Proc. 7th Int. Symp. Orlando, 2003), Battelle Press, Columbus, OH (2003) CD-ROM, abstract.

[263] ADAMS, N., et al., Introduction to Phytoremediation, Rep. EPA/600/R-99/107, United States Environmental Protection Agency, Washington, DC (2000), www.clu-in.org

[264] YANG, R.T., Adsorbents: Fundamentals and Applications, Wiley, New York (2003).

[265] INTERNATIONAL ATOMIC ENERGY AGENCY, Application of Ion Exchange Processes for the Treatment of Radioactive Waste and Management of Spent Ion Exchangers, Technical Reports Series No. 408, IAEA, Vienna (2002).

[266] INTERNATIONAL ATOMIC ENERGY AGENCY, Chemical Precipitation Processes for the Treatment of Aqueous Radioactive Waste, Technical Reports Series No. 337, IAEA, Vienna (1992).

[267] UNITED STATES DEPARTMENT OF ENERGY, Flameless Thermal Oxidation, Rep. ID 52 SCFA, USDOE, Washington, DC (1995), http://apps.em.doe.gov/ost/itsrscfa.html

[268] WICKS, G.G., SCHULZ, R.L., CLARK, D.E., Hybrid Microwave Technology, Savannah River Site, Rep. WSRC-MS-2001-00131, National Technical Information Service, Springfield, VA (2001), http://www.srs.gov/general/pubs/fulltext/ms2001131/ms2001131.html

[269] WAGNER, J., New and Innovative Technologies for Mixed Waste Treatment, United States Environmental Protection Agency, Washington, DC (1997), http://www.epa.gov/radiation/docs/mixed-waste/innotech.pdf

[270] COWEN, M., et al., "Steam reforming technology for denitration and immobilization of DOE tank wastes", Waste Management 2004 (Proc. Conf. Tucson, 2004) CD-ROM.

[271] UNITED NATIONS ENVIRONMENT PROGRAMME, Solvated Electron Technology (SET™) — Annex to Pesticides Treatment Technology Fact Sheet, UNEP, Geneva (2003), http://www.unep.org/stapgef/documents/Wshop_docs/POPs%202003/Annex%209.pdf

[272] COMMODORE APPLIED TECHNOLOGIES INC., Solvated Electron Technology (SET™), CAT, New York, http://www.commodore.com/technologies/solvated_electron_tech.htm

[273] STRINGFELLOW, W.T., KOMADA, T., CHANG, L.-Y., "Feasibility of using biological degradation for on-site treatment of mixed wastes", In Situ and On-Site Bioremediation (Proc. 7th Int. Symp. Orlando, 2003), Battelle Press, Columbus, OH (2004) CD-ROM, paper P-09.

[274] UNITED STATES ENVIRONMENTAL PROTECTION AGENCY, How to Evaluate Alternative Cleanup Technologies for Underground Storage Tank Sites: A Guide for Corrective Action Plan Reviewers, Rep. EPA 510-B-95-007, Office of Underground Storage Tanks, USEPA, Washington, DC (1995), http://www.epa.gov/swerust1/pubs/tums.htm

[275] NAVAL FACILITIES ENGINEERING SERVICE CENTER, Biopile Design and Construction Manual, Technical Memorandum TM-2189-ENV, Port Hueneme, CA (1996), http://enviro.nfesc.navy.mil/erb/erb_a/restoration/technologies/remed/bio/tm-2189.pdf

[276] FEDERAL REMEDIATION TECHNOLOGY ROUNDTABLE, 4.14 Slurry Phase Biological Treatment, Remediation Technologies Screening Matrix and Reference Guide, Version 4.0, FRTR, Washington, DC (2000), http://www.frtr.gov/matrix2/section4/4-14.html

[277] TABAK, H.H., GOVIND, R., "Advances in biotreatment of acid mine drainage and biorecovery of metals", In Situ and On-Site Bioremediation (Proc. 7th Int. Symp. Orlando, 2003), Battelle Press, Columbus, OH (2003) Abstract.

[278] INTERNATIONAL ATOMIC ENERGY AGENCY, Advances in Technologies for the Treatment of Low and Intermediate Level Radioactive Liquid Wastes, Technical Reports Series No. 370, IAEA, Vienna (1994).

[279] INTERNATIONAL ATOMIC ENERGY AGENCY, Bituminization Processes to Condition Radioactive Wastes, Technical Reports Series No. 352, IAEA, Vienna (1993).

[280] KALB, P.D., et al., "Mercury bakeoff: Technology comparison for the treatment of mixed waste mercury contaminated soils at BNL", Waste Management 1999 (Proc. Conf. Tucson, 1999), WM Symposia, Inc., Tucson, AZ (1999), http://www.wmsym.org

[281] INTERNATIONAL ATOMIC ENERGY AGENCY, Improved Cement Solidification of Low and Intermediate Level Radioactive Wastes, Technical Reports Series No. 350, IAEA, Vienna (1993).

[282] UFA VENTURES INC., Phosphate Induced Metal Stabilization (PIMS), Summary of Apatite Remediation Results from Bunker Hill and Success Mine for Pb, Cd, Zn and Cu, Technical Brief, Richland, WA (1996), http://www.ufaventures.com/ufa_ventures/tech_briefs/apatite.html

[283] WRIGHT, J., CONCA, J.L., PIMS™: Remediation of Soil and Groundwater Contaminated with Metals, Rep. CU-0020, Environmental Security Technology Certification Program, Arlington, VA (2004), http://www.estcp.org/documents/techdocs/index.cfm

[284] KAROL, R.H., Chemical Grouting and Soil Stabilization, 3rd edn, Marcel Dekker, New York (2003).

[285] PQ CORPORATION, Soluble Silicates in Geotechnical Grouting Applications, Bull. 52-53, PQ Corporation, Valley Forge, PA (2003), http://www.pqcorp.com/technicalservice/..%5Cliterature%5Cbulletin_52-53.pdf

[286] PQ CORPORATION, PQ® Soluble Silicates in Waste Treatment, Bull. 52-52, PQ Corporation, Valley Forge, PA (2003),
http://www.pqcorp.com/technicalservice/..%5Cliterature%5Cbulletin_52-52.pdf

[287] MANCHESTER, K.R., NORTH-ABBOTT, M.A., ZALUSKI, M.H., TRUD-NOWSKI, J.M., BICKFORD, J.L., "Colloidal silica grout selection and characterization in support of the barrier deployment at Brookhaven National Laboratory", Waste Management 2001 (Proc. Conf. Tucson, 2001), WM Symposia, Inc., Tucson, AZ (2001),
www.wmsym.org/Abstracts/2001/43A/43A-1.pdf

[288] INTERNATIONAL ATOMIC ENERGY AGENCY, Immobilization of Low and Intermediate Level Radioactive Wastes with Polymers, Technical Reports Series No. 289, IAEA, Vienna (1988).

[289] BRUNKOW, W.G., CAMPBELL, D.R., KRAUSE, D.R., "PETRO BOND® oil solidification polymer: Helping to solve oil waste problems in the DOE Mound Facility complex", Waste Management 2001 (Proc. Conf. Tucson, 2001), WM Symposia, Inc., Tucson, AZ (2001),
http://www.wmsym.org

Annex I

CARBON TETRACHLORIDE CASE STUDY
(HANFORD, WA, USA)

I–1. CONTAMINATION HISTORY

Between 1944 and 1987 separation (finishing) plants at Hanford in Washington State were used to extract and purify plutonium. Between 1955 and 1973, during the finishing process, compounds such as carbon tetrachloride and other organic solvents were used to recover plutonium from aqueous streams, and the resulting liquid waste stream was discharged to the ground. It has been roughly estimated that 750 000 kg of carbon tetrachloride were discharged to the soil.

I–2. CONTAMINANT SETTING

As a result of this disposal practice, carbon tetrachloride has contaminated both the vadose zone and the groundwater [I–1]. On the basis of monitoring, it is thought that almost all of the plutonium has bound to the soil column and little has reached the groundwater, although elsewhere radionuclides have reached the groundwater. In general, plutonium is considered not to be very mobile. However, as the plutonium was complexed with the carbon tetrachloride, the radionuclides may have actually migrated deeper into the subsurface than would have been expected without organic complexation [I–2].

The areal extent of the dissolved carbon tetrachloride plume in the groundwater is approximately 10 km². The groundwater contamination is moving from the original disposal area towards the nearby Columbia River. The concentrations of dissolved carbon tetrachloride detected in the groundwater have been estimated to account for approximately 2% of the original carbon tetrachloride inventory [I–3]. However, the carbon tetrachloride probably exists locally as a separate phase liquid as it is a dense NAPL. On the basis of groundwater chemical analysis, the carbon tetrachloride appears to be degrading slowly to chloroform.

I-3. VADOSE ZONE REMEDIATION

In late 1990, the USEPA and the Washington State Department of Ecology (federal and state regulators, respectively) requested the current facility owner, the USDOE, to proceed with detailed planning, including non-intrusive field work to characterize the carbon tetrachloride contamination and identify likely remedial actions. In January 1991, site characterization investigation was initiated, and a pilot SVE was initiated. On the basis of the characterization investigation and the pilot test, the USEPA and the Washington State Department of Ecology in a 1992 action memorandum instigated an SVE system for the removal of carbon tetrachloride from the vadose zone in the original disposal areas. The primary goal of the SVE system was to remove the source of the carbon tetrachloride to prevent further contamination of the groundwater.

Three soil SVEs were operated from 1992 to 1997 [I–4]. The carbon tetrachloride was captured on granulated activated carbon that was sent away from the site for regeneration. Over time, the rate of contaminant removal dropped. In late 1997, on the basis of the observations of a rebound study, the USEPA and USDOE agreed to begin operating the systems in a cyclic mode. In 1998 and 1999, the vapour extraction system was run for six months [I–5]. Soil vapour extraction to remove carbon tetrachloride from the vadose zone resumed on 4 Apr. 2001. As of September 2001, 77 169 kg of carbon tetrachloride had been removed from the vadose zone since extraction operations started in 1991 [I–5]. The total mass of carbon tetrachloride removed represents just over an estimated 10% of the original carbon tetrachloride inventory discharge in the soil column.

The SVE systems were initially connected to several already existing wells that terminate above the groundwater table. These extraction wells were converted to vapour extraction wells by perforating the well casings at specific depth intervals and then isolating these intervals with down-hole inflatable packers. The use of existing wells avoided the need for drilling new wells in radioactively contaminated soils, a costly and lengthy endeavour due to safety considerations, thus expediting startup of remediation operations.

The SVE facility, including the associated extraction wells, was initially classified officially as a nuclear facility due to the radionuclides present in the subsurface. As a result a formal nuclear criticality analysis and safety programme was instituted that included assessment of the possibility of drawing plutonium particulates to the surface and exposing workers. The analysis of the findings was ultimately incorporated into the operations manual for the SVE system and into the site health and safety plan. Health and Safety specialists with expertise in working with radiological, industrial and hazardous contamination were employed. Site control barriers were emplaced around the operational facilities to limit accessibility in order to minimize potential contaminant exposures. Of special note was the fact that the granular activated carbon used to collect carbon tetrachloride also collected naturally occurring radon emanating from the underlying sediments (which subsequently decayed).

Another remediation technique demonstrated at the site was passive SVE, i.e. extraction using naturally induced pressure gradients between the subsurface and the surface to drive soil vapour to the surface. In general, falling atmospheric pressure causes soil gases to move to the atmosphere through wells, while rising atmospheric pressure causes surface air to move into the soil. Passive SVE systems are designed to use this phenomenon to remove carbon tetrachloride from the vadose zone [I–5]. The passive systems are fitted out with one-way check valves that only allow soil gases to flow out of the borehole and a canister holding granular activated carbon that adsorbs carbon tetrachloride vapour before it can be vented to the atmosphere. The check valve prohibits flow of surface air into the borehole during a reverse barometric pressure gradient, which would dilute and spread carbon tetrachloride vapours in the subsurface. Approximately 200 g of carbon tetrachloride were removed by the passive extraction system in 2001 [I–5].

I–4. GROUNDWATER REMEDIATION

A pump and treat system was implemented in a three phase approach. Phase I operations consisted of a pilot scale treatability test that ran from 29 Aug. 1994 to 19 Jul. 1996. During that period, contaminated groundwater was removed from a single extraction well at a rate of 150 L/min, treated using granular activated carbon, and returned to the aquifer through an injection well. In June 1995, a Record of Decision was issued by the USEPA and Washington State Department of Ecology [I–6], implementing a pump and treat system at the high concentration area of the plume to minimize further migration of carbon tetrachloride and co-contaminants, TCE and chloroform. The remedial measure was designed to "stabilize and reduce contaminant mass in the high concentration portion of the plume" [I–6].

Phase II operations ran from 5 Aug. 1996 until 8 Aug. 1997 and consisted of a well field configuration of three extraction wells pumping at a combined rate of 720 L/min, and five injection wells. In August 1997, Phase III operations began when the pump and treat system was upgraded to six extraction wells and five injection wells operating at rates greater than 800 L/min. The treatment system is the same as that of Phase I. The treated groundwater, which is discharged back into the aquifer, meets the carbon tetrachloride drinking water standard of 5 ppb.

As of 2002, well over 950 million litres of water have been treated and over 3300 kg of carbon tetrachloride have been removed. The high concentration areas of the plume are being contained by the pump and treat system that has helped reduce potential adverse impacts on human health and the environment [I–1].

I–5. FUTURE ACTIVITIES

Previous work [I–7] considered an order of magnitude estimate of the 1990 inventory of the carbon tetrachloride inventory remaining in the subsurface using available groundwater concentration data, soil gas concentration data and well venting data. Total atmospheric losses were estimated to be 21%; the unsaturated zone inventory (in soil gas, soil moisture and adsorbed phases) accounted for 12%; and the dissolved phase in the aquifer was estimated at 2%, leaving 65% of the original carbon tetrachloride volume unaccounted for. However, the estimates did not consider NAPL organic residual saturation in the unsaturated zone, perched organic liquid on low permeability lenses or separate organic liquid present within the unconfined aquifer. Any or all of these forms of carbon tetrachloride may be present within the subsurface, although none has been observed.

The SVE and pump and treat systems will continue to be operated. However, additional characterization of the subsurface is required to better understand and target the three dimensional distribution of the carbon tetrachloride plume and its behaviour. Regulators and the USDOE are now actively looking at alternative innovative technologies, establishing the vertical extent of contamination, presence of the carbon tetrachloride as DNAPL, uncertainty in the inventory, cleanup goals and effective remediation technologies [I–5].

REFERENCES TO ANNEX I

[I–1] HARTMAN, M.J., MORASCH, L.F., WEBBER, W.D. (Eds), Summary of Hanford Site Groundwater Monitoring for Fiscal Year 2002, Rep. PNNL-14187-SUM, Pacific Northwest Natl Lab., Richland, WA (2003).
[I–2] SMITH, R.M., 216-B-5 Reverse Well Characterization Study, Rep. RHO-ST-37, Rockwell Hanford Operations, Richland, WA (1980).

[I–3] TRUEX, M.J., et al., Assessment of Carbon Tetrachloride Groundwater Transport in Support of the Hanford Carbon Tetrachloride Innovative Technology Demonstration Program, Rep. PNNL-13560, Pacific Northwest Natl Lab., Richland, WA (2001).

[I–4] ROHAY, V.J., Performance Evaluation Report for Soil-Vapor Extraction Operations at the Carbon Tetrachloride Site, February 1992–September 1998, Rep. BHI-00720, Rev. 3, Bechtel Hanford Inc., Richland, WA (1998).

[I–5] ROHAY, V.J., "Carbon tetrachloride monitoring and remediation", Hanford Site Environmental Report for Calendar Year 2001 (POSTON, T.M., et al., Eds), Rep. PNNL-13910, Pacific Northwest Natl Lab., Richland, WA (2002) 7.17–7.20.

[I–6] UNITED STATES ENVIRONMENTAL PROTECTION AGENCY, EPA Superfund Record of Decision: Hanford 200-AREA (USDOE), OU 200-ZP-1, Benton County, WA, Rep. EPA/ROD/R10-95/114, Washington, DC (1995).

[I–7] SWANSON, L.C., ROHAY, V.J., FAUROTE, J.M., Hydrogeologic Conceptual Model for the Carbon Tetrachloride and Uranium/Technetium Plumes in the 200 West Area: 1994 Through 1999 Update, Rep. BHI-01311, Bechtel Hanford Inc., Richland, WA (1999).

WELDON SPRING SITE REMEDIAL ACTION PROJECT, (WELDON SPRING, MO, USA)

II-1. CONTAMINATION HISTORY

The Weldon Spring Site is located about 48 km west of St. Louis, Missouri. From 1941 to 1945 the US Department of the Army operated the Weldon Spring Ordnance Works on this site, producing explosives for use in World War II. The ordnance works produced dinitrotoluene (DNT) and trinitrotoluene (TNT). These operations resulted in nitroaromatic contamination of soil, sediments and some off-site springs.

A uranium feed materials plant, now called the Weldon Spring Chemical Plant, was constructed and operated on the site by the US Atomic Energy Commission (AEC) from 1957 to 1966 to process uranium and thorium ore concentrate. The plant consisted of 44 buildings, four settling basins totalling ten hectares termed raffinate pits, two ponds and two dumping areas. The plant converted processed ore concentrates to pure uranium trioxide, intermediate compounds and uranium metal. Processing operations resulted in radiological contamination of the same locations previously contaminated by the US Army operations.

The Weldon Spring quarry was mined for limestone aggregate used in the construction of the ordnance works, the US Army also used the quarry for burning wastes from explosives manufacturing and disposal of debris contaminated with TNT during operation of the ordnance works. From 1963 to 1969 the AEC used the quarry as a disposal area for uranium and thorium residues from the chemical plant (both drummed and uncontained) and for disposal of contaminated debris, process equipment and soils. These disposal activities resulted in nitroaromatic and radiological contamination of soil and groundwater at the quarry.

The AEC and subsequently the USDOE managed the Weldon Spring Site under caretaker status until 1985, at which time the USDOE designated remediation of the chemical plant, raffinate pits and quarry as a major project.

II-2. CONTAMINANT SETTING

The chemical plant, occupying an area of 89 ha, is located on the east–west Missouri–Mississippi River surface drainage divide. Elevations at the site range from 186 to 198 m above mean sea level. Although no natural drainage channels traverse the chemical plant area, drainage ways originate on the property and convey storm water off the site because the site is topographically higher than the surrounding areas.

The quarry, located about 6.4 km south-west of the chemical plant, was excavated into a limestone bluff that forms a valley wall at the edge of the Missouri River alluvial flood plain. Elevations in the quarry range from 140 to 174 m above mean sea level. The quarry is about 300 m long by 140 m wide and covers an area of approximately 3.6 ha. Most surface runoff discharges to two nearby streams that drain to the Missouri River.

Investigations of the extent of contamination at the chemical plant and quarry were conducted during the late 1980s and early 1990s. The buildings contained radioactive materials, process chemicals, asbestos and PCBs. Soils at the chemical plant site contained low levels of radionuclides, such as uranium, thorium and radium, some heavy metals, such as lead and arsenic, as well as inorganic ions, such as sulphate. Nitroaromatic compounds were present in the soil in discrete areas associated with the former ordnance works operations, and low levels of polycyclic aromatic hydrocarbons were present at some locations. Areas near transformers and around buildings were contaminated with PCBs.

Approximately 122 000 m^3 of wastes generated during uranium and thorium processing were stored in the raffinate pits. These pits contained several to several tens of Bq/g of radioactivity from uranium, radium and thorium isotopes. The wastes were relatively homogeneous in all but one pit, which also contained a large number of discarded drums, containers and debris. Other contaminants included arsenic, chromium, nitrate, fluoride and sulphate.

Wastes disposed of in the quarry included drummed radioactive materials, uncontained wastes and contaminated process equipment. On the basis of historical data and characterization results, it was estimated that 73 000 m^3 of contaminated materials were present in the quarry. These bulk wastes contained radiological and chemical contaminants including uranium, radium, thorium, metals, nitrates, PCBs, semivolatile organic compounds, nitroaromatic substances and asbestos. Wastes on the main floor of the quarry covered an area of almost 5600 m^2 and extended to depths of about 12 m; radioactive contamination in the entire quarry covered an area of about 15 900 m^2 and extended to an average depth of about 4 m.

II–3. SITE REMEDIATION

In 1986 the USDOE established an office at the Weldon Spring site after which the effort to clean up the former uranium and thorium processing plant was started. The scope of this work included dismantling the 44 chemical plant buildings and structures as well as disposal of both radiological and chemically contaminated structural materials and soils. It also included disposal of as much material as possible from the raffinate pits, quarry and nearby properties. The components that needed remediation and disposal included water, sludge, abandoned waste materials and structural materials. A specially designed disposal cell was constructed at the chemical plant site to provide long term containment and management of wastes from the Weldon Spring site.

The buildings were initially surveyed to determine the extent of radiological and chemical contamination. Asbestos, residual product and chemicals were removed first. The buildings and equipment were then vacuumed and washed before being dismantled and disposed of. The building foundations and contaminated soil beneath them were excavated and placed in the disposal cell.

Another important step in the cleanup of the site was the treatment of radiologically and chemically contaminated water. Water treatment began in 1992 with a mobile system that treated water generated during building decontamination and dismantling. The quarry water treatment plant became operational in the autumn of 1992 and began treatment of the water impounded at the quarry. In 1993, a site water treatment plant was constructed to increase treatment capacity. The plant was used for two separate operations. Train 1, a conventional chemical precipitation and media filtration system, treated contaminated water from dismantled buildings, storage areas and raffinate pit 4. Water from raffinate pits 1, 2 and 3 contained nitrates and selenium, which could not be treated with conventional wastewater systems. This water was treated through biological processes, reverse osmosis and site water treatment plant train 2. After treatment in the plants, water was tested to ensure compliance with water treatment standards, and then released to the Missouri River. Over 1.1 Mm^3 of water were treated, tested and released during water treatment operations.

Raffinate pit sludges were treated to provide a structurally stable waste form before they were placed in the on-site disposal cell. Chemical stabilization and solidification was determined to be the most effective technology for treatment of the contaminated sludge. In this process the sludge was screened for oversize materials, then thickened with a polymer before it was blended with cement and fly ash before being transferred as grout to the disposal cell. The chemical stabilization and solidification plant operated from June to

November 1998 for 24 hours a day and seven days a week. The plant produced approximately 142 200 m³ of grout.

Another step in the cleanup was removal of the bulk wastes in the quarry. These wastes were excavated and transported to the chemical plant site over a dedicated haulage road and initially placed in an engineered temporary storage area. No trucks were allowed to leave the quarry or storage area without first being thoroughly cleaned and inspected to ensure contamination-free transportation. As a result, no contaminants were released during transportation. In December 1995, the final load of bulk waste was removed from the quarry. Over 107 000 m³ of material were ultimately removed. Approximately 12 000 round trips totalling 155 000 km were made without incident due to a stringent and effective safety programme. The first load of waste was moved from the storage area to the disposal cell in March 1998 and by December 1998 all the quarry wastes were placed in the cell.

The disposal cell was constructed at the site of the chemical plant. It consists of four primary systems: the base liner with leachate collection and removal systems, the contaminated wastes, the clean-fill dyke and the cover systems.

The base liner is designed to prevent leachate from migrating from the bottom of the cell. It is composed of a primary composite liner, a secondary leachate collection and removal system, a secondary composite liner, and a primary leachate collection and removal system. The primary liner is a flexible membrane and geosynthetic clay liner with leak sealing capability. The secondary flexible membrane of the liner is paired with a clay liner that can adsorb the radionuclides and heavy metals that may be present in any leachate. The liners cover the bottom, side walls and interior slope of the perimeter clean-fill dyke.

The clean-fill dyke, constructed of compacted clay soil, surrounds the disposal facility and is designed to resist erosion, limit infiltration of moisture into the wastes, minimize radon emissions, reduce long term maintenance, discourage animal and human intrusions into the wastes, and reduce risk to human health and the environment.

The cover system serves to armour the clean-fill dyke, protecting it from storm water runoff, infiltration and biointrusion. It consists of multiple layers including (from bottom to top) an infiltration radon barrier of silty clay, a geomembrane and geosynthetic clay liner, clean sand bedding, and a mixture of cobbles and boulders designed to prevent intrusions by plant roots and burrowing animals.

II–4. POST-REMEDIATION LAND USE

The Weldon Spring site is among the most comprehensive cleanup projects in the USA. The site is about to complete a 17 year transformation from a contaminated site used to process uranium ores to a publicly accessible area for recreation and education. It is now a multiuse property, supporting both recreation and education, in a manner that is fully accessible by the public.

The site now includes:

— A local university that is permitted to use and to hold classes in the administration building;
— The largest prairie in the St. Louis, Missouri area;
— A hiking and biking trail through the site;
— An interpretive centre with programmes aimed at children and adults from the surrounding areas as well as tourists.

II–5. FUTURE ACTIVITIES

The USDOE is implementing a stewardship plan providing for long term monitoring, land use restrictions, disposal facility maintenance and continued public involvement at the Weldon Spring site. Institutional controls have been established to ensure that no wells are drilled at or near the site for any purpose other than monitoring.

BIBLIOGRAPHY TO ANNEX II

UNITED STATES DEPARTMENT OF ENERGY (Washington, DC)

Engineering Evaluation/Cost Analysis for the Proposed Management of Contaminated Water in the Weldon Spring Quarry, Rep. DOE/OR/21548-039 (1990).

Feasibility Study for Management of Bulk Wastes at the Weldon Spring Quarry, Weldon Spring, Missouri, Rev. 0, Rep. DOE/OR/21548-594 (1990).

Record of Decision for Remedial Action at the Chemical Plant Area of the Weldon Spring Site, Rep. DOE/OR/21548-376 (1993).

Chemical Plant Area Cleanup Attainment Confirmation Plan, Rev. 3, Rep. DOE/OR/21548-491 (1995).

Site Treatment Plan for the Weldon Spring Site, Rep. DOE/OR21548-473 (1995).

Chemical Plant Operable Unit Remedial Action Report, Rep. DOE/GJ/79491-909 (2004).

Long-Term Surveillance and Maintenance Plan for the Weldon Spring, Missouri, Site, Draft GJO-2004-592-TAC (2004).

UNITED STATES ENVIRONMENTAL PROTECTION AGENCY (Washington, DC)

Superfund Record of Decision: Weldon Spring Quarry/Plants/Pits, Rep. EPA/ROD/R07-90/043 (1990).

Record of Decision for Remedial Action for the Quarry Residuals Operable Unit at the Weldon Spring Site, Rep. EPA/541/R-98/166 (1998).

Annex III

TOXICITY OF SOME COMMON CONTAMINANTS

III–1. RADIONUCLIDES

III–1.1. Caesium

Regardless of the mode of exposure, ^{137}Cs is rapidly absorbed into the bloodstream and distributes throughout the active tissues of the body. Metabolically, ^{137}Cs behaves as an analogue of potassium. Distribution of caesium throughout the body and energetic β and χ radiation from the decay progeny, ^{137m}Ba, result in essentially whole body irradiation [III–1].

III–1.2. Radium

Radium, as a metabolic analogue of calcium, is readily absorbed through the gastrointestinal tract or the lungs into the bloodstream and subsequently is deposited in the bones. Values for fractional absorption through the gastrointestinal tract have been observed in the range from 0.15 to 0.21 [III–2]. During the first few days after intake, radium becomes heavily concentrated on bone surfaces, and then gradually shifts its primary deposition site to bone volume. A large percentage of subjects exposed to high doses of radium have developed bone cancer [III–3].

III–1.3. Strontium

Strontium, as a metabolic analogue of calcium, is readily absorbed into the bloodstream through the gastrointestinal tract or the lungs and subsequently is deposited in the bones. Observations indicate that a single brief oral, intravenous or inhalation intake generates a high incidence of tumours in bones and bone related tissues [III–4]. Inhalation is the major risk. Data from animal studies indicate that exposure to strontium results in lung and possibly liver damage [III–5].

III–1.4. Technetium

Technetium is readily absorbed through the gastrointestinal tract or the lungs into the bloodstream. Once in the body, technetium is subsequently deposited in the thyroid, gastrointestinal tract and liver [III–2].

III–1.5. Uranium

Uranium and its compounds are highly toxic. Studies have shown that fractions of the order of 0.005–0.05 of a uranium compound are likely to be absorbed into the blood through the gastrointestinal tract [III–2]. Soluble uranium compounds such as UF_6, UO_2F_2 and $UO_2(NO_3)_2$ are absorbed rapidly through the lungs [III–2]. Retention times for uranium in the body may range from 20 to 50 years [III–2]. Major target organs for uranium toxicity are the respiratory system, blood, liver, lymphatic system, kidneys, skin and bone marrow. Reports have confirmed that carcinogenicity is related to dose and exposure time. Soluble compounds have been reported to cause lung and bone cancers and cancer of the lymphatic tissues, whereas insoluble compounds have been reported to cause cancer of the lymphatic and blood forming tissues [III–5].

III–2. HEAVY METALS

III–2.1. Lead

Lead exposure in children and adults can cause a wide variety of health problems, ranging from convulsions, coma, renal failure and death at high doses to subtle effects on metabolism and brain function at low doses. Young children and developing fetuses are most vulnerable to the neurotoxic effects of lead. It has been demonstrated that low level exposure in children less than five years of age with blood lead levels of 50–250 μg/L retards intellectual development.

III–2.2. Mercury

Metallic mercury cannot be absorbed, therefore it is not very toxic if ingested, but if inhaled as vapour or fumes, it is readily absorbed through the lungs. On the other hand, mercurous (Hg^+) and mercuric (Hg^{2+}) mercury form inorganic or organic compounds with other chemicals that can be readily absorbed through ingestion.

High levels of mercury exposure can cause life threatening damage to the lungs and nervous system. For chronic low level exposures the following symptoms in humans have been observed, termed erethism: tremor of the hands, excitability, memory loss, insomnia, timidity and, sometimes, delirium. Of greatest concern on a global scale is the sensitivity of the fetal and infant nervous system to low level mercury toxicity.

III–2.3. Arsenic

The toxicity of an arsenic compound depends on the valence state of arsenic (zero valence, trivalent or pentavalent), the form (inorganic or organic) and factors that modify biological uptake and elimination. In general, inorganic compounds of arsenic are more toxic than pure arsenic, and trivalent arsenite is more toxic than pentavalent and zero valence arsenic. The major sites of accumulation in the body are skin, hair and nails, although arsenic also accumulates in soft tissue organs such as the liver, spleen, kidneys and lungs.

In acute arsenic poisoning, blood vessels and gastrointestinal tissues are destroyed and the heart and brain damaged. Chronic exposure to low levels of arsenic results in skin hyperpigmentation, nerve damage (numbness, tingling and weakness in hands and feet), diabetes and blood vessel damage that cause a gangrenous condition of the extremities. It also increases the risk for developing cancer of the skin, liver, lungs, bladder, kidneys and colon.

III–2.4. Cadmium

The effects of cadmium exposure are exacerbated by the relative inability of the human body to excrete cadmium. Acute high dose exposures can cause severe respiratory irritation. Chronic exposure to lower concentrations of cadmium increase the risk of chronic lung disease and cause testicular degeneration and irreversible kidney damage.

III–3. TOXIC ORGANIC COMPOUNDS

III–3.1. Carbon tetrachloride

The critical effect of carbon tetrachloride exposure in humans is liver lesions [III–6]. Exposure to high levels of carbon tetrachloride can be fatal. The most immediate harmful effects are to the central nervous system. Other effects include headaches, dizziness, nausea and vomiting. In severe cases, stupor, coma and permanent damage to nerve cells can occur [III–7].

The liver is sensitive to carbon tetrachloride. Liver damage can result from either acute or chronic exposure. Carbon tetrachloride can be absorbed through the skin in sufficient quantity to cause liver damage [III–7].

The kidneys are also sensitive to carbon tetrachloride. Kidney disease and inflammation leading to kidney failure and death are common effects in humans following inhalation exposure. Abnormally high serous fluid in the lungs (i.e. pulmonary oedema) commonly occurs in humans exposed to high levels of carbon tetrachloride in air. Ingestion of carbon tetrachloride has been associated with decreased function of the central nervous system, kidneys and lungs, and marked hepatoxicity.

The occurrence of liver cancer in individuals exposed, both acutely and for long periods, to carbon tetrachloride vapours has been noted in some reports. Though no studies have established that inhalation exposure to carbon tetrachloride poses a risk of cancer, the evidence for liver carcinogenicity has been shown by oral or parenteral exposure in animals. Because similar non-carcinogenic effects are observed in the liver following oral and inhalation exposures, it is likely that carcinogenic effects are similar for both types of exposure (i.e. inhalation exposure can lead to liver cancer) [III–7].

III–3.2. Methylene chloride

The critical effect of methylene chloride is liver toxicity [III–8]. Inhalation is the principal route of human exposure to methylene chloride. Evaluation of pulmonary uptake in humans indicates that 70–75% of inhaled methylene chloride vapour is absorbed. As for absorption of other lipophilic organic vapours, methylene chloride absorption appears to be influenced by factors other than the vapour concentration. Increased physical activity and higher body fat increases the amount of methylene absorbed by the body [III–8].

Effects from inhalation of methylene chloride include headaches, giddiness, stupors, irritability, numbness and tingling in the limbs. Irritation to the eyes and upper respiratory passages occurs at higher doses. In severe cases, toxic brain disease with hallucinations and effusion of fluid into the alveoli and interstitial spaces of the lungs; coma and death have been observed. Exposure to methylene chloride may cause elevated carboxyhaemoglobin levels that may be significant in smokers, workers with anaemia or heart disease, and those exposed to carbon monoxide [III–5].

The central nervous system is affected adversely in humans at exposure levels of 500 ppm or higher. Noted effects from these exposure levels are reduced visual and auditory functions; however, these effects are reversible once exposure has ceased. Similarly, psychomotoric performance (reaction time, hand precision and steadiness) was impaired and alterations in visually triggered responses have been observed in humans exposed to higher levels of methylene chloride [III–8].

III–3.3. Tetrachloroethylene (perchloroethylene)

Exposure to tetrachloroethylene may cause dysfunction of the central nervous system, hepatic injury and death. Signs and symptoms of exposure to tetrachloroethylene include malaise, dizziness, headaches, increased perspiration, fatigue, difficulty in walking and slowing of mental ability [III–5].

Other effects range from loss of muscular coordination at low concentrations to unconsciousness and respiratory paralysis at high concentrations. Tetrachloroethylene is of moderate to low toxicity by the oral route. Ingestion may cause bleeding and diarrhoea and irritate the gastrointestinal membranes. Chronic exposure to tetrachloroethylene most readily affects the central nervous system and liver [III–9].

III–3.4. PCB toxicity

Environmental processes alter PCB mixtures through partitioning, chemical transformation and preferential bioaccumulation; these processes can increase or reduce toxicity considerably. Chemical transformation occurs through biodegradation of PCB mixtures in the environment. The occurrence and extent of these dechlorinations can be limited by sediment PCB concentrations. It should be noted that dechlorination is not synonymous with detoxification, as congeners having carcinogenic activity can be formed through dechlorination.

Preferential bioaccumulation occurs in living organisms: PCBs are highly soluble in lipids and are absorbed by fish and other animals. Each species in the food chain retains persistent congeners that are resistant to metabolism and elimination. Bioaccumulation through the food chain tends to concentrate congeners of higher chlorine content. Congener distributions in animals and humans do not resemble those of any precursor [III–10]. Bioaccumulated PCBs are of greatest concern because they are more toxic than commercial PCBs and more persistent in the body.

A variety of serious health effects has been demonstrated to be caused by PCBs. They have been shown to cause cancer and to have other health effects in animals, including effects on the immune system, reproductive system and nervous system. Studies in humans provide supportive evidence for the potential carcinogenic and non-carcinogenic effects of PCBs. The International Agency for Research on Cancer has declared PCBs to be probable human carcinogens. Probable tumour sites include the liver, gall bladder, biliary tract, gastrointestinal tract, lungs and skin [III–11].

Studies have revealed a number of serious effects to the immune system following exposure to PCBs. Since PCBs suppress the immune system and immune system suppression has been demonstrated as a risk factor in non-Hodgkin's lymphoma, suppression of the immune system is a possible mechanism for PCB induced cancer.

Exposure to PCBs has been found to reduce the birth weights, conception rates and live birth rates of various animals. Studies of reproductive effects in human populations suggest that effects on the reproductive system may be important in humans following exposures to PCBs. Young animals exposed to PCBs showed persistent and significant deficits in neurological development, including visual recognition, short term memory and learning. Studies in humans show effects similar to those observed in animals, including learning deficits and changes in activity associated with exposure to PCBs. The similarity in effects observed in humans and animals provides additional support for the potential neurobehavioural effects of PCBs [III–12].

REFERENCES TO ANNEX III

[III–1] AMDUR, M.O., DOULL, J., KLASSEN, C.D., Casarett and Doull's Toxicology, The Basic Science of Poisons, 4th edn, Pergamon Press, Oxford (1991).

[III–2] INTERNATIONAL COMMISSION ON RADIATION PROTECTION, Limits for Intakes of Radionuclides by Workers, ICRP Publication 30, Pergamon Press, Oxford (1978).

[III–3] COMMITTEE ON THE BIOLOGICAL EFFECTS OF IONIZING RADIATIONS, Health Effects of Radon and Other Internally Deposited Alpha-Emitters, Rep. BEIR IV, National Academies Press, Washington, DC (1988).

[III–4] COMMITTEE ON THE BIOLOGICAL EFFECTS OF IONIZING RADIATIONS, Health Effects of Exposure to Low Levels of Ionizing Radiation, Rep. BEIR V, National Academies Press, Washington, DC (1990).

[III–5] SITTIG, M., Handbook of Toxic and Hazardous Chemicals and Carcinogens, 2nd edn, Noyes Publishing, Park Ridge, NJ (1985).

[III–6] UNITED STATES ENVIRONMENTAL PROTECTION AGENCY, Integrated Risk Information System (IRIS), Database for Risk Assessment, USEPA, Washington, DC (2004),
http://www.epa.gov/iris/

[III–7] AGENCY FOR TOXIC SUBSTANCES AND DISEASE REGISTRY, Toxicological Profile for Carbon Tetrachloride, Rep. PB90-168196, ATSDR, Atlanta, GA (1989).

[III–8] AGENCY FOR TOXIC SUBSTANCES AND DISEASE REGISTRY, Toxicological Profile for Methylene Chloride, Rep. PB93-182483, ATSDR, Atlanta, GA (1993).

[III–9] AGENCY FOR TOXIC SUBSTANCES AND DISEASE REGISTRY, Toxicological Profile for Tetrachloroethylene, Rep. PB90-247628, ATSDR, Atlanta, GA (1990).

[III–10] McFARLAND, V.A., CLARKE, J.U., Environmental occurrence, abundance, and potential toxicity of polychlorinated biphenyl congeners: Considerations for a congener-specific analysis, Environ. Health Perspect. **81** (1989) 225–239.

[III–11] INTERNATIONAL AGENCY FOR RESEARCH ON CANCER, Lists of IARC Evaluations, Overall Evaluations of Carcinogenicity to Humans, IARC, Lyon, France (2002),
http://www-cie.iarc.fr/monoeval/crthall.html

[III–12] EUROPEAN ENVIRONMENT AGENCY, Impact of Endocrine Disrupters on Human Health and Wildlife (Proc. Eur. Workshop Weybridge, 1996), Rep. EUR 17549, EEA, Copenhagen (1997).

GLOSSARY

Some of the definitions given below are broader than those given in the current IAEA Waste Safety and Waste Management Glossaries in order to accommodate this specific subject.

ADP. Adenosine diphosphate

AEA. Atomic Energy Act (USA)

ALARA. As low as reasonably achievable

ALARP. As low as reasonably practicable

ATP. Adenosine triphosphate

BOD. Biological oxygen demand

CA. Chloroethane

CAHs. Chlorinated aliphatic hydrocarbons

CERCLA. Comprehensive Environmental Response, Compensation, and Liability Act (USA)

CF. Chloroform

CM. Chloromethane

CT. Carbon tetrachloride

D&D. Decommissioning and decontamination

DCA. Dichloroethane

DCE. Dichloroethene

DNAPL. Dense non-aqueous phase liquid

ganglion. A globule of a substance

HEPA filtration. High efficiency particulate air filtration

HM. Heavy metal

HMX. High melting (point) explosive (also known as octogen and cyclotetra-methylene-tetranitramine)

industrial process. Term used very broadly in the present report to denote any human activity involving the application of technology, for example, mining, processing and drinking water treatment.

LCA. Life cycle analysis. A systematic set of procedures for compiling and examining the inputs and outputs of materials and energy and associated environmental impacts directly attributable to the functioning of a product or service system throughout its life cycle.

LNAPL. Light non-aqueous phase liquid.

MC. Methylene chloride

MFA. Material flow accounting or analysis, a method whereby the streams of material, chemical elements, energy, etc. are assessed and possibly balanced. It is centred on the material and chemical compound, rather than on the product or service in the case of LCA. MFA covers approaches such as substance flow analysis (SFA), product flow accounts, material balancing and overall material flow accounts.

NAD. Nicotinamide adenine dinucleotide

NAPL. Non-aqueous phase liquid

OPC. Ordinary Portland cement

PAH. Polycyclic aromatic hydrocarbon

PCB. Polychlorinated biphenyl

PCE. Tetrachloroethene

RCRA. Resources Control and Recovery Act (USA)

RDX. Cyclotrimethylenetrinitramine (explosive)

RN. Radionuclide

SVOC. Semivolatile organic compounds

TCA. Trichloroethane

TCE. Trichloroethylene (a solvent)

UXO. Unexploded ordnance

VC. Vinyl chloride

VOC. Volatile organic compound

CONTRIBUTORS TO DRAFTING AND REVIEW

Batandjieva, B.	International Atomic Energy Agency
Broomfield, B.	Westinghouse, United States of America
Falck, W.E.	International Atomic Energy Agency
Fellingham, L.	RWE NUKEM, United Kingdom
Hagood, M.	Consultant, United States of America
Pillette-Cousin, L.	Commissariat à l'Énergie Atomique, France
Rudneva, V.Y.	International Science and Technology Center, Russian Federation

IAEA
International Atomic Energy Agency

Where to order IAEA publications

In the following countries IAEA publications may be purchased from the sources listed below, or from major local booksellers. Payment may be made in local currency or with UNESCO coupons.

Australia
DA Information Services, 648 Whitehorse Road, MITCHAM 3132
Telephone: +61 3 9210 7777 • Fax: +61 3 9210 7788
Email: service@dadirect.com.au • Web site: http://www.dadirect.com.au

Belgium
Jean de Lannoy, avenue du Roi 202, B-1190 Brussels
Telephone: +32 2 538 43 08 • Fax: +32 2 538 08 41
Email: jean.de.lannoy@infoboard.be • Web site: http://www.jean-de-lannoy.be

Canada
Bernan Associates, 4611-F Assembly Drive, Lanham, MD 20706-4391, USA
Telephone: 1-800-865-3457 • Fax: 1-800-865-3450
Email: order@bernan.com • Web site: http://www.bernan.com

Renouf Publishing Company Ltd., 1-5369 Canotek Rd., Ottawa, Ontario, K1J 9J3
Telephone: +613 745 2665 • Fax: +613 745 7660
Email: order.dept@renoufbooks.com • Web site: http://www.renoufbooks.com

China
IAEA Publications in Chinese: China Nuclear Energy Industry Corporation, Translation Section, P.O. Box 2103, Beijing

Czech Republic
Suweco CZ, S.R.O. Klecakova 347, 180 21 Praha 9
Telephone: +420 26603 5364 • Fax: +420 28482 1646
Email: nakup@suweco.cz • Web site: http://www.suweco.cz

Finland
Akateeminen Kirjakauppa, PL 128 (Keskuskatu 1), FIN-00101 Helsinki
Telephone: +358 9 121 41 • Fax: +358 9 121 4450
Email: akatilaus@akateeminen.com • Web site: http://www.akateeminen.com

France
Form-Edit, 5, rue Janssen, P.O. Box 25, F-75921 Paris Cedex 19
Telephone: +33 1 42 01 49 49 • Fax: +33 1 42 01 90 90 • Email: formedit@formedit.fr

Lavoisier SAS, 145 rue de Provigny, 94236 Cachan Cedex
Telephone: + 33 1 47 40 67 02 • Fax +33 1 47 40 67 02
Email: romuald.verrier@lavoisier.fr • Web site: http://www.lavoisier.fr

Germany
UNO-Verlag, Vertriebs- und Verlags GmbH, Am Hofgarten 10, D-53113 Bonn
Telephone: + 49 228 94 90 20 • Fax: +49 228 94 90 20 or +49 228 94 90 222
Email: bestellung@uno-verlag.de • Web site: http://www.uno-verlag.de

Hungary
Librotrade Ltd., Book Import, P.O. Box 126, H-1656 Budapest
Telephone: +36 1 257 7777 • Fax: +36 1 257 7472 • Email: books@librotrade.hu

India
Allied Publishers Group, 1st Floor, Dubash House, 15, J. N. Heredia Marg, Ballard Estate, Mumbai 400 001,
Telephone: +91 22 22617926/27 • Fax: +91 22 22617928
Email: alliedpl@vsnl.com • Web site: http://www.alliedpublishers.com

Bookwell, 2/72, Nirankari Colony, Delhi 110009
Telephone: +91 11 23268786, +91 11 23257264 • Fax: +91 11 23281315
Email: bookwell@vsnl.net

Italy
Libreria Scientifica Dott. Lucio di Biasio "AEIOU", Via Coronelli 6, I-20146 Milan
Telephone: +39 02 48 95 45 52 or 48 95 45 62 • Fax: +39 02 48 95 45 48

Japan
Maruzen Company, Ltd., 13-6 Nihonbashi, 3 chome, Chuo-ku, Tokyo 103-0027
Telephone: +81 3 3275 8582 • Fax: +81 3 3275 9072
Email: journal@maruzen.co.jp • Web site: http://www.maruzen.co.jp

Korea, Republic of
KINS Inc., Information Business Dept. Samho Bldg. 2nd Floor, 275-1 Yang Jae-dong SeoCho-G, Seoul 137-130
Telephone: +02 589 1740 • Fax: +02 589 1746
Email: sj8142@kins.co.kr • Web site: http://www.kins.co.kr

Netherlands
De Lindeboom Internationale Publicaties B.V., M.A. de Ruyterstraat 20A, NL-7482 BZ Haaksbergen
Telephone: +31 (0) 53 5740004 • Fax: +31 (0) 53 5729296
Email: books@delindeboom.com • Web site: http://www.delindeboom.com

Martinus Nijhoff International, Koraalrood 50, P.O. Box 1853, 2700 CZ Zoetermeer
Telephone: +31 793 684 400 • Fax: +31 793 615 698 • Email: info@nijhoff.nl • Web site: http://www.nijhoff.nl

Swets and Zeitlinger b.v., P.O. Box 830, 2160 SZ Lisse
Telephone: +31 252 435 111 • Fax: +31 252 415 888 • Email: infoho@swets.nl • Web site: http://www.swets.nl

New Zealand
DA Information Services, 648 Whitehorse Road, MITCHAM 3132, Australia
Telephone: +61 3 9210 7777 • Fax: +61 3 9210 7788
Email: service@dadirect.com.au • Web site: http://www.dadirect.com.au

Slovenia
Cankarjeva Zalozba d.d., Kopitarjeva 2, SI-1512 Ljubljana
Telephone: +386 1 432 31 44 • Fax: +386 1 230 14 35
Email: import.books@cankarjeva-z.si • Web site: http://www.cankarjeva-z.si/uvoz

Spain
Díaz de Santos, S.A., c/ Juan Bravo, 3A, E-28006 Madrid
Telephone: +34 91 781 94 80 • Fax: +34 91 575 55 63 • Email: compras@diazdesantos.es
carmela@diazdesantos.es • barcelona@diazdesantos.es • julio@diazdesantos.es
Web site: http://www.diazdesantos.es

United Kingdom
The Stationery Office Ltd, International Sales Agency, PO Box 29, Norwich, NR3 1 GN
Telephone (orders): +44 870 600 5552 • (enquiries): +44 207 873 8372 • Fax: +44 207 873 8203
Email (orders): book.orders@tso.co.uk • (enquiries): book.enquiries@tso.co.uk • Web site: http://www.tso.co.uk

On-line orders:
DELTA Int. Book Wholesalers Ltd., 39 Alexandra Road, Addlestone, Surrey, KT15 2PQ
Email: info@profbooks.com • Web site: http://www.profbooks.com

Books on the Environment:
Earthprint Ltd., P.O. Box 119, Stevenage SG1 4TP
Telephone: +44 1438748111 • Fax: +44 1438748844
Email: orders@earthprint.com • Web site: http://www.earthprint.com

United Nations (UN)
Dept. I004, Room DC2-0853, First Avenue at 46th Street, New York, N.Y. 10017, USA
Telephone: +800 253-9646 or +212 963-8302 • Fax: +212 963-3489
Email: publications@un.org • Web site: http://www.un.org

United States of America
Bernan Associates, 4611-F Assembly Drive, Lanham, MD 20706-4391
Telephone: 1-800-865-3457 • Fax: 1-800-865-3450
Email: order@bernan.com • Web site: http://www.bernan.com

Renouf Publishing Company Ltd., 812 Proctor Ave., Ogdensburg, NY, 13669
Telephone: +888 551 7470 (toll-free) • Fax: +888 568 8546 (toll-free)
Email: order.dept@renoufbooks.com • Web site: http://www.renoufbooks.com

Orders and requests for information may also be addressed directly to:

Sales and Promotion Unit, International Atomic Energy Agency
Wagramer Strasse 5, P.O. Box 100, A-1400 Vienna, Austria
Telephone: +43 1 2600 22529 (or 22530) • Fax: +43 1 2600 29302
Email: sales.publications@iaea.org • Web site: http://www.iaea.org/books